ANALYTIC GEOMETRY

Analytic Geometry

ROSS R. MIDDLEMISS

Professor of Mathematics
Washington University

SECOND EDITION

McGRAW-HILL BOOK COMPANY, INC.

New York   Toronto   London

1955

ANALYTIC GEOMETRY

Library of Congress Catalog Card Number 55-6164

V

THE MAPLE PRESS COMPANY, YORK, PA.

PREFACE

The original edition of this text was written with the primary aim of giving students a better preparation for calculus and the sciences. To this end, less than the usual amount of space was devoted to the conic sections—and more than the average amount was devoted to the polynomials and rational fractional functions and to the graphs and properties of the exponential, logarithmic, and trigonometric functions. The chapter on exponential and logarithmic functions included a brief section on the hyperbolic functions. The material on trigonometric curves included a review of the basic definitions and formulas of trigonometry for the benefit of students who might have had only a very brief course or a high-school course in this subject. All these characteristics of the original text have been retained in this new edition. Some additional features are discussed in the following paragraphs.

A greater effort has been made, both in the text material and in the problems, to keep students from confusing theorems with their converses. Most students will readily see the difference between stating that if $x = 3$ and $y = 5$ then $x + y = 8$, and stating that if $x + y = 8$ then $x = 3$ and $y = 5$. Many of them will not as easily see the difference between proving that if the distance of a point in the xy-plane from the origin is 4 then its coordinates satisfy the equation $x^2 + y^2 = 16$, and proving the converse. It is of course not really necessary to prove the converse in each of the many cases that arise in analytic geometry— but if our main purpose is the training of students for work that requires clear thinking and careful analysis, we should strive for a minimum of confusion as to what has been proved and what has not been proved.

Experience has shown that most students enter courses in analytic geometry and calculus with a fair degree of competence in computational trigonometry but with almost no appreciation of the properties of the trigonometric functions that make them important in scientific work. If they are told that a certain quantity E varies with the time in accordance with the formula

$$E = 2 \sin \tfrac{1}{2}\pi t + 3 \cos \tfrac{2}{3}\pi t$$

where t is the number of seconds, they do not immediately observe that E is a periodic function of t that goes through a complete cycle of its values every 12 sec. In fact, even the better students seem to think in a very confused way about a function such as $\sin \tfrac{1}{2}\pi t$. They may ask whether t or $\tfrac{1}{2}\pi t$ is the "angle" that we are talking about, or how we get radians by multiplying the number of seconds by $\tfrac{1}{2}\pi$. Very good students may be puzzled if asked to find the value of $\sin \tfrac{1}{2}\pi t$ when $t = \tfrac{1}{2}\pi$—because radians simply do not come in packages involving π^2!

In the brief review that is given here, the author has defined the trigonometric functions of the *number* x and has tried to discuss the properties and graphs of the functions in such a way as to clear up some of this confusion. Instructors in several schools have indicated that they must treat trigonometry quite briefly in the first semester because they must also cover college algebra. It is hoped that the material given here will be useful as a supplement to a brief course of this kind.

In the chapter on polar coordinates recognition is given to the fact that there are really two distinct polar coordinate systems in common use—one in which ρ can be negative and one in which ρ is restricted to nonnegative values. Many modern mathematicians seem to feel that the latter system, which is used exclusively in advanced mathematical analysis, should be adhered to in elementary analytic geometry. The author has no strong opinion on the matter, but he believes that the student gains something if he is asked to examine both systems, decide whether or not certain things that are true for one system are true also for the other, and so on. For example, the average student might see immediately the truth of the relation $x = \rho \cos \theta$ for the system in which $\rho \geqq 0$, but he might be uncertain about it for the other system.

Nearly all the material on plane analytic geometry has been completely rewritten. The entire text was to be reset for a different page size, and it was considered worthwhile to rewrite every section on which it seemed, in the light of experience with the first edition, that some improvement could be made.   In some places more detailed explanations or different illustrative examples appeared to be indicated.   In several chapters a somewhat different way of organizing the material seemed to be desirable from the standpoint of improving teachability or saving a little time. Nearly all the problem sets have been replaced by new sets.

It is especially important in these days of crowded curricula that every credit unit devoted to mathematics should represent a sound investment of the student's time.   If he masters the fundamental methods of analytic geometry, he will have a powerful new tool to use in his future work in mathematics and the sciences. If the presentation is such that he emerges with a better understanding of the role of definitions, and with the habit of reasoning carefully from hypothesis to conclusion, then indeed his time will have been well spent.   The principal effort of the author has been toward a presentation that will make a substantial contribution of this kind to the general training of the student.

Thanks are again due to Professors C. A. Hutchinson and J. R. Britton of the University of Colorado and to Professors S. E. Warschawski of the University of Minnesota and G. C. Helme of Pratt Institute for their valuable contributions to the first edition. The author would like also to express his appreciation to Professors W. J. Thron of the University of Colorado and H. Margaret Elliott of Washington University for their suggestions regarding several sections of the new edition.   Finally, he would like to thank his wife for the many hours that she has devoted to the job of becoming an expert at typing mathematical manuscripts.

ROSS R. MIDDLEMISS

CONTENTS

CONTENTS

INTRODUCTION

REVIEW OF ESSENTIAL DEFINITIONS AND FORMULAS FROM ALGEBRA AND TRIGONOMETRY

1. *Equations.* An equation is a statement that two numbers are equal. For example, if x denotes a number, then $4x^2 - 7x + 13$ is a number and also $(x + 2)(2x - 5)$ is a number. The statement that these two numbers are equal is an equation. We write it as follows:

$$4x^2 - 7x + 13 = (x + 2)(2x - 5).$$

An equation is called a *rational integral equation* if it can be written in the form

$$a_0x^n + a_1x^{n-1} + a_2x^{n-2} + \cdots + a_{n-1}x + a_n = 0$$

where the a's are constants; and it is said to be of *degree n* if $a_0 \neq 0$. The first equation above can be reduced to the form

$$2x^2 - 6x + 23 = 0$$

so it is a rational integral of degree two.

Any value of x for which the equality stated by the equation is true is called a *root* of the equation. The student will recall that a rational integral equation of degree n has precisely n roots. Thus if it is of first degree (linear), it has one root, if it is of second degree (quadratic), it has two, and so on. It is shown in books on algebra that if the a's are real numbers then the roots consist only of real numbers and pairs of conjugate imaginary numbers. (These are numbers of the form $p \pm qi$, where p and q are real numbers and $i^2 = -1$.)

1

Examples

The equation $x^3 + 13x + 116 = 0$ has the three roots, -4, $2 + 5i$, and $2 - 5i$.

The equation $x^4 - 16 = 0$ has the four roots, 2, -2, $2i$, and $-2i$.

An important equation of the above type is the *quadratic equation*. It is usually written in the form

$$ax^2 + bx + c = 0,$$

and it is understood that $a \neq 0$. The two roots are given by the *quadratic formula:*

$$x = \frac{-b \pm \sqrt{b^2 - 4ac}}{2a}.$$

It is obvious that if a, b, and c are real numbers then these roots are

Real and unequal if $b^2 - 4ac > 0$;
Real and equal if $b^2 - 4ac = 0$;
Conjugate imaginary numbers if $b^2 - 4ac < 0$.

Examples

In the quadratic equation $3x^2 + x - 10 = 0$ we have $a = 3$, $b = 1$, and $c = -10$. The student may verify that the quadratic formula yields the two roots, $\frac{5}{3}$ and -2. In the equation $x^2 - 4x + 5 = 0$ we have $a = 1$, $b = -4$, and $c = 5$. In this case the roots are the conjugate imaginary numbers $2 + i$ and $2 - i$.

The problem of solving an equation that involves fractions or radicals or both frequently reduces to that of solving a rational integral equation. For example, the first step in solving the equation

$$(1) \qquad x + 2\sqrt{x - 1} = 25$$

is to subtract x from both members and then square both sides in order to remove the radical. We thus get in succession

$$(2) \qquad 2\sqrt{x - 1} = 25 - x$$
$$(3) \qquad 4(x - 1) = 625 - 50x + x^2$$
$$(4) \qquad x^2 - 54x + 629 = 0.$$

We can reason that if (1) is true for a certain (unknown) value of x then (4) must be true for this same value of x. Hence any roots that (1) may have must be contained in the roots of (4). We proceed to solve (4) and find that its roots are 17 and 37. We cannot be certain that either of these numbers is a root of **(1)** without further investigation—for although the truth of (1) implies that of (4), the converse is not valid. The difficulty arises from the operation of squaring both sides in getting from (2) to (3). If (2) is true, then (3) must be true, because if two numbers are equal their squares are equal. We cannot assert the converse—that if (3) is true then (2) must be true—because the squares of two numbers can be equal without the numbers being equal. (The numbers 4 and −4 are not equal, but their squares are equal.) The final step in solving the above equation is that of substituting 17 and 37 for x in (1) to determine whether or not they are roots. It turns out that 17 is a root and 37 is not. We can conclude that 17 is the only root of (1).

2. Determinants of second order. The symbol

$$\begin{vmatrix} a_1 & b_1 \\ a_2 & b_2 \end{vmatrix}$$

in which any four numbers are arranged in a square array consisting of two rows and two columns, and flanked on the sides by vertical bars, is called a *determinant of second order*. The symbol is defined to stand for the number $a_1b_2 - a_2b_1$; that is, by definition,

$$\begin{vmatrix} a_1 & b_1 \\ a_2 & b_2 \end{vmatrix} = a_1b_2 - a_2b_1.$$

The right member of this identity is called the *expansion* of the determinant on the left. The four individual numbers in the determinant are called its *elements*. The horizontal rows are numbered from top to bottom, and the vertical columns are numbered from left to right.

Example

$$\begin{vmatrix} 2 & -3 \\ 5 & 7 \end{vmatrix} = 2(7) - 5(-3) = 14 + 15 = 29.$$

In this determinant the elements 2 and −3 form the first row. The second row consists of the elements 5 and 7. The first column has the elements 2 and 5, and the second column is that containing the elements −3 and 7.

Consider now the system of equations

(1) $$a_1x + b_1y = k_1$$
(2) $$a_2x + b_2y = k_2.$$

By multiplying both sides of (1) by b_2 and both sides of (2) by b_1, and subtracting, we may eliminate y. In a similar fashion we may eliminate x. The results are

$$(3) \qquad (a_1b_2 - a_2b_1)x = k_1b_2 - k_2b_1$$
$$(4) \qquad (a_1b_2 - a_2b_1)y = a_1k_2 - a_2k_1.$$

It can now be seen that if $a_1b_2 - a_2b_1 \neq 0$ the original system has the unique solution

$$(5) \qquad x = \frac{k_1b_2 - k_2b_1}{a_1b_2 - a_2b_1}; \qquad y = \frac{a_1k_2 - a_2k_1}{a_1b_2 - a_2b_1}.$$

These results can be put into a convenient and easily remembered form by using determinants. Let D denote the determinant whose elements are the coefficients of x and y in the order in which they appear in (1) and (2); that is,

$$D = \begin{vmatrix} a_1 & b_1 \\ a_2 & b_2 \end{vmatrix}$$

This is called the *determinant of the coefficients*. Its value is the denominator in each of the solutions in (5). Furthermore, the numerator in the solution for x is this same determinant with each a replaced by the corresponding k; the numerator in the solution for y is this same determinant with each b replaced by the corresponding k. We may denote these determinants by D_x and D_y, respectively:

$$D_x = \begin{vmatrix} k_1 & b_1 \\ k_2 & b_2 \end{vmatrix} \qquad D_y = \begin{vmatrix} a_1 & k_1 \\ a_2 & k_2 \end{vmatrix}$$

The solution given by (5) can now be written in the form

$$x = \frac{D_x}{D}; \qquad y = \frac{D_y}{D}.$$

Example

Consider the system

$$2x - y = 4$$
$$x + 2y = 7.$$

In this case

$$D = \begin{vmatrix} 2 & -1 \\ 1 & 2 \end{vmatrix} = 4 - (-1) = 5$$

$$D_x = \begin{vmatrix} 4 & -1 \\ 7 & 2 \end{vmatrix} = 8 - (-7) = 15$$

$$D_y = \begin{vmatrix} 2 & 4 \\ 1 & 7 \end{vmatrix} = 14 - 4 = 10.$$

The solution of the system is

$$x = \tfrac{15}{5} = 3; \qquad y = \tfrac{10}{5} = 2.$$

3. Determinants of third order.   The symbol

$$\begin{vmatrix} a_1 & b_1 & c_1 \\ a_2 & b_2 & c_2 \\ a_3 & b_3 & c_3 \end{vmatrix}$$

in which any nine numbers are arranged in a square array consisting of three rows and three columns is called a *determinant of third order*.   The individual numbers are called *elements* of the determinant, and the rows and columns are numbered in the same way as in the determinant of second order.   The symbol is defined to denote the number that is obtained as follows:

$$\begin{vmatrix} a_1 & b_1 & c_1 \\ a_2 & b_2 & c_2 \\ a_3 & b_3 & c_3 \end{vmatrix} = a_1 \begin{vmatrix} b_2 & c_2 \\ b_3 & c_3 \end{vmatrix} - b_1 \begin{vmatrix} a_2 & c_2 \\ a_3 & c_3 \end{vmatrix} + c_1 \begin{vmatrix} a_2 & b_2 \\ a_3 & b_3 \end{vmatrix}$$

$$= a_1(b_2c_3 - b_3c_2) - b_1(a_2c_3 - a_3c_2) + c_1(a_2b_3 - a_3b_2)$$

$$= a_1b_2c_3 + a_2b_3c_1 + a_3b_1c_2 - a_1b_3c_2 - a_2b_1c_3 - a_3b_2c_1.$$

Any of the expressions on the right is called an *expansion* of the determinant on the left.

Example

$$\begin{vmatrix} 2 & 3 & -1 \\ 4 & 0 & 5 \\ 3 & -2 & 2 \end{vmatrix} = 2 \begin{vmatrix} 0 & 5 \\ -2 & 2 \end{vmatrix} - 3 \begin{vmatrix} 4 & 5 \\ 3 & 2 \end{vmatrix} + (-1) \begin{vmatrix} 4 & 0 \\ 3 & -2 \end{vmatrix}$$

$$= 2[0 - (-10)] - 3(8 - 15) - 1(-8 - 0)$$
$$= 2(10) - 3(-7) - 1(-8)$$
$$= 49.$$

By the *minor* of an element we mean the determinant that remains when the row and column in which that element appears are omitted.   For example, the minor of the element a_2 (below) is the determinant that remains when the first column and second row are omitted:

$$\begin{vmatrix} a_1 & b_1 & c_1 \\ a_2 & b_2 & c_2 \\ a_3 & b_3 & c_3 \end{vmatrix} \text{ minor of } a_2 \text{ is } A_2 \equiv \begin{vmatrix} b_1 & c_1 \\ b_3 & c_3 \end{vmatrix}$$

As indicated here, we often denote the minor of an element by the corresponding capital letter.   Thus the minor of a_1 is denoted by A_1, the minor of b_3 by B_3, etc.

Using this notation, we can write the above expansion of a determinant D of third order as follows:

$$D = \begin{vmatrix} a_1 & b_1 & c_1 \\ a_2 & b_2 & c_2 \\ a_3 & b_3 & c_3 \end{vmatrix} = a_1 A_1 - b_1 B_1 + c_1 C_1.$$

This is called the expansion of the determinant *using the minors of the elements of the first row*.   Precisely the same result is obtained if one writes either of the following expansions using the minors of the elements of the second or third row, respectively:

$$D = -a_2 A_2 + b_2 B_2 - c_2 C_2$$
$$D = a_3 A_3 - b_3 B_3 + c_3 C_3.$$

Finally, the expansion using the minors of the elements of any row can be replaced by a precisely similar expansion using the minors of the elements of the corresponding *column*.   Thus

$$D = a_1 A_1 - a_2 A_2 + a_3 A_3$$
$$D = -b_1 B_1 + b_2 B_2 - b_3 B_3$$
$$D = c_1 C_1 - c_2 C_2 + c_3 C_3.$$

Example

The determinant of the above illustrative example may be expanded using the minors of the elements of the third column as follows:

$$\begin{vmatrix} 2 & 3 & -1 \\ 4 & 0 & 5 \\ 3 & -2 & 2 \end{vmatrix} = -1 \begin{vmatrix} 4 & 0 \\ 3 & -2 \end{vmatrix} - 5 \begin{vmatrix} 2 & 3 \\ 3 & -2 \end{vmatrix} + 2 \begin{vmatrix} 2 & 3 \\ 4 & 0 \end{vmatrix}$$
$$= -1(-8) - 5(-13) + 2(-12)$$
$$= 8 + 65 - 24 = 49.$$

Consider now the system of linear equations,

$$a_1x + b_1y + c_1z = k_1$$
$$a_2x + b_2y + c_2z = k_2$$
$$a_3x + b_3y + c_3z = k_3.$$

Let D be the determinant of the coefficients:

$$D = \begin{vmatrix} a_1 & b_1 & c_1 \\ a_2 & b_2 & c_2 \\ a_3 & b_3 & c_3 \end{vmatrix}$$

Let D_x be the determinant that results when each of the a's in D is replaced by the corresponding k; let D_y be the determinant that results when each b in D is replaced by the corresponding k; and let D_z be the determinant that results when each c is replaced by the corresponding k.   It can be shown that if $D \neq 0$ the system of equations has the unique solution

$$x = \frac{D_x}{D}; \qquad y = \frac{D_y}{D}; \qquad z = \frac{D_z}{D}.$$

PROBLEMS

Find all solutions to each of the following equations:

1. $3(x^2 + 2) = (x - 1)(3x + 4)$.
2. $(x + 1)(x - 4) = x^2 + 5$.
3. $2x + x(4x - 5) = (2x - 3)(2x + 3)$.
4. $\frac{1}{3}(7x + 5) + \frac{1}{6} = 2x$.
5. $\frac{2x}{2x + 3} = 5 - \frac{3}{3 + 2x}$.
6. $\frac{4}{x} + \frac{3}{x + 4} = \frac{7x - 5}{x^2 + 4x}$.
7. $3\sqrt{x^2 - 8} = 3x - 2$.
8. $\sqrt{12 + 2x} = \sqrt{2x} + 3$.
9. $9x^2 = 6x + 4$.
10. $(5x)^2 = 6(5x - 1)$.
11. $\frac{x}{x - 2} + \frac{7}{3} = \frac{35}{x - 4}$.
12. $\frac{6x}{3x + 8} + 2x = 12$.
13. $\frac{x + 5}{x - 3} - \frac{x + 6}{2x} = \frac{1}{6}$.
14. $\frac{3x + 10}{x} + \frac{2x - 1}{3} = 8$.
15. $2\sqrt{4x + 7} = 7 + \sqrt{2x}$.
16. $\sqrt{3x + 8} + \sqrt{9x + 25} = 1$.
17. $\sqrt{2x + 1} - \sqrt{4x + 6} = 2$.
18. $\sqrt{2x - 3} - \sqrt{x + 2} = 1$.

19. Given that $-\frac{1}{2}$ is a root of the equation $2x^3 - 7x^2 + 6x + 5 = 0$, find the other roots.

20. Given that 4 is a root of the equation $2x^3 - 9x^2 - 2x + 24 = 0$, find the other roots.

21. Solve the equation $x^3 - 8 = 0$, and thus find the three cube roots of 8.

Evaluate each of the following determinants:

22. $\begin{vmatrix} 2 & 3 \\ 1 & -5 \end{vmatrix}.$ **23.** $\begin{vmatrix} 7 & \frac{3}{2} \\ 6 & 2 \end{vmatrix}.$ **24.** $\begin{vmatrix} \frac{3}{2} & -\frac{2}{3} \\ \frac{3}{4} & -\frac{4}{3} \end{vmatrix}.$

25. $\begin{vmatrix} 2 & 0 & 1 \\ 3 & 2 & 0 \\ -1 & 2 & 5 \end{vmatrix}.$ **26.** $\begin{vmatrix} 3 & -2 & 5 \\ 2 & 0 & 1 \\ 4 & -2 & 2 \end{vmatrix}.$ **27.** $\begin{vmatrix} 5 & -5 & 0 \\ 0 & 6 & 0 \\ 2 & -1 & 2 \end{vmatrix}.$

Solve each of the following systems of equations, using determinants:

28. $2x - y = 9,$
$\quad\;\; x - 3y = 7.$

29. $x - y = 1,$
$\quad\;\; 4x + 7y = 5.$

30. $x + 2y + z = 5,$
$\quad\;\; 3x - y + 2z = 3,$
$\quad\;\; x + 7y - z = 0.$

31. $3x - y - 5z = 5,$
$\quad\;\; 2x + y + z = 7,$
$\quad\;\; 4x + 5y + 3z = 7.$

32. $2x - 6y + z = 7,$
$\quad\;\; x - 2y + 2z = 6,$
$\quad\;\; 3x + y + 5z = 1.$

33. $3x - 2y - z = 8,$
$\quad\;\; x + y + z = \frac{5}{2},$
$\quad\;\; 2x + 4y + 3z = 6.$

4. Angles. In trigonometry a plane angle is usually thought of as being generated by rotation of a line in a plane about a point on the line. This point is called the *vertex* of the angle, and the rotating line is sometimes called the *generating line*. The initial position of the generating line is called the *initial side* of the angle, and the terminal position is called the *terminal side*, as indicated in Fig. 1. If the sense of rotation is counterclockwise, the angle is called positive, and if clockwise, it is called negative.

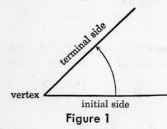

vertex   initial side

Figure 1

The most commonly used unit of angle measurement in trigonometry is the *degree*, which is one-ninetieth of a right angle. The degree is further subdivided as indicated below:

$$1 \text{ right angle } = 90 \text{ degrees},$$
$$1 \text{ degree } = 60 \text{ minutes},$$
$$1 \text{ minute } = 60 \text{ seconds}.$$

A unit of angular measurement that is used more commonly in advanced mathematics is the *radian*. A radian is defined as the angle subtended at the center of a circle by an arc whose length is equal to the radius of the circle (Fig. 2). It

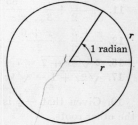

Figure 2

is a unit that is smaller than a right angle but of course much larger than a degree.   The relation between the two systems of units is obtained as follows:

The perimeter of a circle of radius r is $2\pi r$ so that r is contained in the perimeter 2π times.   This means that

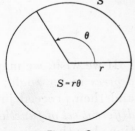

2π radians = 360 degrees;

$$1 \text{ radian} = \frac{360}{2\pi} = 57.296 \text{ degrees};$$

$$1 \text{ degree} = \frac{2\pi}{360} = 0.017453 \text{ radian.}$$

Figure 3

If θ is the number of radians in the angle subtended at the center of a circle of radius r by an arc whose length is S, then (Fig. 3)

$$\theta = \frac{S}{r} \quad \text{or} \quad S = r\theta.$$

5. *The trigonometric functions.*   It is assumed in the following paragraphs that the student is familiar with the rectangular coordinate system (see pages 24 to 26).

If θ is any real number, the trigonometric functions of θ are defined as follows: Construct an angle of θ radians with vertex at the origin and initial side along the positive x-axis.   This angle is to be generated by a counterclockwise rotation if θ is a positive

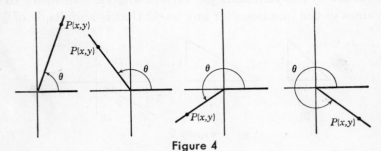

Figure 4

number and a clockwise rotation if θ is a negative number.   Choose any point $P(x,y)$ on the terminal side (not at origin), and denote the distance of P from the origin by r, it being understood that r is a positive number (Fig. 4).   The definitions are then

$$\sin \theta = \frac{y}{r} \qquad \csc \theta = \frac{r}{y}$$

$$\cos \theta = \frac{x}{r} \qquad \sec \theta = \frac{r}{x}$$

$$\tan \theta = \frac{y}{x} \qquad \cot \theta = \frac{x}{y}$$

If we wish, we may regard the given number θ as the number of *degrees* in an angle; i.e., we may construct an angle of θ *degrees* and then proceed just as we did above. The result is actually a *different set of functions* of the number θ. Each of these new functions has the value for $\theta = 180t/\pi$ that the corresponding function as defined above has for $\theta = t$, t being any real number. Thus the new function $\sin \theta$ has the value $\frac{1}{2}$ when $\theta = 30$, whereas the function $\sin \theta$ as defined above has the value $\frac{1}{2}$ when $\theta = \pi/6$.

6. The signs of the functions. The student is familiar with the fact that the x-coordinate of a point P is positive if P lies to the right of the y-axis and negative if to the left. The y-coordinate is positive if P lies above the x-axis and negative if below. These conventions regarding the signs of x and y, and the above agreement that r is positive, fix the signs of the trigonometric functions of θ for each quadrant. Thus if the terminal side of θ lies in the second quadrant, then $\cos \theta$ is a negative number; for $\cos \theta = x/r$ and the x-coordinate of a point P on the terminal side is negative while r is positive.

7. Values of the functions for certain angles. In order to find the values of the functions for any angle that is a multiple of $\frac{1}{6}\pi$ or

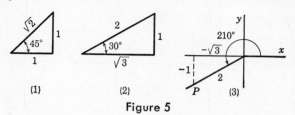

(1)   (2)   (3)

Figure 5

$\frac{1}{4}\pi$ (30° or 45°), one has only to remember that in the 45° right triangle the two legs are equal, and in the 30–60° right triangle the shortest leg is equal to one-half the hypotenuse [Fig. 5(1) and (2)]. Thus to find $\sin \frac{7}{6}\pi$ (or 210°), one draws Fig. 5(3) and writes down from it

$$\sin \frac{7\pi}{6} = -\frac{1}{2}.$$

The values of the functions for the quadrantal angles of 0, $\frac{1}{2}\pi$, π, and $\frac{3}{2}\pi$ can also be easily determined. For in each of these cases either x or y is zero, and the other is equal to $\pm r$. Thus for $\theta = \frac{3}{2}\pi$ (or 270°) we have $x = 0$ and $y = -r$; hence (Fig. 6)

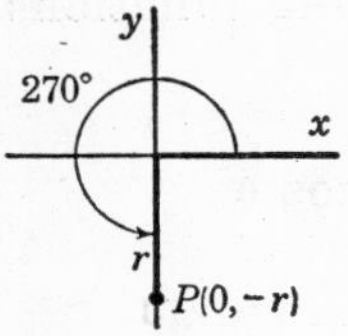

$$\sin \frac{3}{2}\pi = \frac{y}{r} = \frac{-r}{r} = -1;$$

$$\cos \frac{3}{2}\pi = \frac{x}{r} = \frac{0}{r} = 0.$$

Figure 6

In the study of analytic geometry, and particularly in connection with the sketching of curves in polar coordinates, it is necessary that the student be able to find quickly the values of the functions for these special angles.

8. The values of the functions when that of one is known. If, for a certain angle, the value of one of the six trigonometric functions, and the quadrant in which the terminal side lies, are known, the values of the other five functions can be found easily. Thus if it is known that $\sin \alpha = \frac{2}{3}$ and the terminal side of α is in the second quadrant, we may draw Fig. 7 and write down from it, $\cos \alpha = -\sqrt{5}/3$, $\tan \alpha = 2/-\sqrt{5}$, etc.

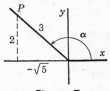

Figure 7

9. The fundamental identities. The following are the fundamental relations between the trigonometric functions. The proofs follow immediately from the definitions of the functions. The relations hold for all values of θ for which the functions are defined provided that no denominator is zero.

(a) $\sin^2 \theta + \cos^2 \theta = 1.$

(b) $1 + \tan^2 \theta = \sec^2 \theta.$

(c) $1 + \cot^2 \theta = \csc^2 \theta.$

(d) $\tan \theta = \dfrac{\sin \theta}{\cos \theta}.$

$$(e) \begin{cases} \csc \theta = \dfrac{1}{\sin \theta}. \\[2mm] \sec \theta = \dfrac{1}{\cos \theta}. \\[2mm] \cot \theta = \dfrac{1}{\tan \theta}. \end{cases}$$

10. Functions of −θ. It is easy to show, from the definitions of the trigonometric functions of θ, that

$$\sin(-\theta) = -\sin\theta;$$
$$\cos(-\theta) = \cos\theta;$$
$$\tan(-\theta) = -\tan\theta.$$

11. Reduction formulas. The following relations hold between the trigonometric functions of θ and the corresponding functions of $(\frac{1}{2}\pi \pm \theta)$ or $(\pi \pm \theta)$:

$$\sin\left(\frac{1}{2}\pi - \theta\right) = \cos\theta \qquad \sin\left(\frac{1}{2}\pi + \theta\right) = \cos\theta$$

$$\cos\left(\frac{1}{2}\pi - \theta\right) = \sin\theta \qquad \cos\left(\frac{1}{2}\pi + \theta\right) = -\sin\theta$$

$$\tan\left(\frac{1}{2}\pi - \theta\right) = \cot\theta \qquad \tan\left(\frac{1}{2}\pi + \theta\right) = -\cot\theta$$

$$\sin(\pi - \theta) = \sin\theta \qquad \sin(\pi + \theta) = -\sin\theta$$
$$\cos(\pi - \theta) = -\cos\theta \qquad \cos(\pi + \theta) = -\cos\theta$$
$$\tan(\pi - \theta) = -\tan\theta \qquad \tan(\pi + \theta) = \tan\theta$$

12. Addition formulas. Double and half-angle formulas. Let α and β be any two real numbers, and consider angles of $\alpha + \beta$ radians and $\alpha - \beta$ radians. The functions of these angles are given in terms of the functions of angles having α or β radians by the following formulas:

(*a*) $$\sin(\alpha + \beta) = \sin\alpha\cos\beta + \cos\alpha\sin\beta$$

(*b*) $$\cos(\alpha + \beta) = \cos\alpha\cos\beta - \sin\alpha\sin\beta$$

(*c*) $$\tan(\alpha + \beta) = \frac{\tan\alpha + \tan\beta}{1 - \tan\alpha\tan\beta}$$

(*d*) $$\sin(\alpha - \beta) = \sin\alpha\cos\beta - \cos\alpha\sin\beta$$

(*e*) $$\cos(\alpha - \beta) = \cos\alpha\cos\beta + \sin\alpha\sin\beta$$

(*f*) $$\tan(\alpha - \beta) = \frac{\tan\alpha - \tan\beta}{1 + \tan\alpha\tan\beta}$$

For the case in which $\beta = \alpha$, formulas (*a*), (*b*), and (*c*) reduce to

(*g*) $$\sin 2\alpha = 2\sin\alpha\cos\alpha$$

(*h*) $$\cos 2\alpha = \cos^2\alpha - \sin^2\alpha$$

(*i*) $$\tan 2\alpha = \frac{2\tan\alpha}{1 - \tan^2\alpha}.$$

From formula (h) it can readily be shown that

(j) $\sin \dfrac{1}{2}\alpha = \pm \sqrt{\dfrac{1 - \cos \alpha}{2}}$

(k) $\cos \dfrac{1}{2}\alpha = \pm \sqrt{\dfrac{1 + \cos \alpha}{2}}$

(l) $\tan \dfrac{1}{2}\alpha = \pm \sqrt{\dfrac{1 - \cos \alpha}{1 + \cos \alpha}} = \dfrac{1 - \cos \alpha}{\sin \alpha} = \dfrac{\sin \alpha}{1 + \cos \alpha}.$

It should be observed that the $\pm$ sign does not appear in the last two forms of the formula for $\tan \frac{1}{2}\alpha$. This is because $1 \pm \cos \alpha$ is never negative and $\tan \frac{1}{2}\alpha$ always has the same sign as $\sin \alpha$.

13. Sine and cosine laws. The *sine law* states that in any triangle the ratio of the lengths of any two sides is the same as the ratio of the sines of the opposite angles. Thus in Fig. 8, the ratio of a to b is the same as the ratio of $\sin \alpha$ to $\sin \beta$. The law can be written in the form

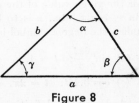

Figure 8

$$\frac{a}{\sin \alpha} = \frac{b}{\sin \beta} = \frac{c}{\sin \gamma}.$$

The *cosine law* states that the square of the length of any side of any triangle is equal to the sum of the squares of the lengths of the other two sides minus twice their product times the cosine of the included angle. Thus in Fig. 8

$$c^2 = a^2 + b^2 - 2ab \cos \gamma.$$

14. Greek alphabet.

LETTERS		NAMES	LETTERS		NAMES	LETTERS		NAMES
A	α	Alpha	I	ι	Iota	P	ρ	Rho
B	β	Beta	K	κ	Kappa	Σ	σ	Sigma
Γ	γ	Gamma	Λ	λ	Lambda	T	τ	Tau
Δ	δ	Delta	M	μ	Mu	Υ	υ	Upsilon
E	ϵ	Epsilon	N	ν	Nu	Φ	ϕ	Phi
Z	ζ	Zeta	Ξ	ξ	Xi	X	χ	Chi
H	η	Eta	O	o	Omicron	Ψ	ψ	Psi
Θ	θ	Theta	Π	π	Pi	Ω	ω	Omega

PROBLEMS

1. In each of the following cases the number of degrees in an angle is given. Find the corresponding number of radians.

(a) $315°$.   (b) $120°$.   (c) $750°$.   (d) $100°$.
(e) $68°$.   (f) $20°10'$.   (g) $250°$.   (h) $540°$.

2. In each of the following cases the number of radians in an angle is given. Find the corresponding number of degrees.

(a) $\frac{5}{4}\pi$.   (b) 1.6.   (c) 3.84.   (d) $\frac{5}{12}\pi$.
(e) 3π.   (f) 10.4.   (g) 7.62.   (h) 3.12.

3. In each of the following cases find the value of the trigonometric function for the given value of the number t. It is to be understood that in the symbols $\sin x$, $\cos x$, etc., x is to be interpreted as the number of radians in an angle unless the degree symbol is used.

(a) $\sin \dfrac{2\pi t}{3}$; $t = 1$.   (b) $\tan \dfrac{\pi}{2}(t + 1)$; $t = \dfrac{3}{2}$.

(c) $\cos 0.25t$; $t = 2\pi$.   (d) $\cot \frac{1}{2}\pi t$; $t = 2.5$.

4. Using the definition of a radian, find the number of radians subtended at the center of a circle of radius 4 ft. by an arc whose length is 9 ft.

Evaluate each of the following expressions without using tables:

5. $2(\cos 135° + \sin 330°) - 3 \tan 135°$.
6. $\sec 0° + 2 \cos 90° + 5 \sin 270° + 3 \cos 180°$.
7. $4 \tan 585° + \cot(-135°) + 2 \sin 450°$.
8. $3 \sin \frac{5}{6}\pi + 2 \cos \frac{4}{3}\pi - 7 \tan 2\pi$.

9. Using tables, find $\sin 384°$, $\cos(-200°)$, and $\tan 910°$.
10. Draw a figure showing an angle α whose terminal side lies in the third quadrant. Draw the angle $-\alpha$. Show that

$$\sin(-\alpha) = -\sin \alpha \quad \text{and} \quad \cos(-\alpha) = \cos \alpha.$$

11. Prove the fundamental identities of Sec. 9.
12. Prove the formulas for $\sin(\alpha + \beta)$ and $\cos(\alpha + \beta)$ for the case in which α and β are positive angles less than $\frac{1}{2}\pi$ and such that their sum is less than $\frac{1}{2}\pi$.
13. Derive the formulas for $\sin 2\alpha$, $\cos 2\alpha$, and $\tan 2\alpha$ from the formulas for $\sin(\alpha + \beta)$, $\cos(\alpha + \beta)$, and $\tan(\alpha + \beta)$.
14. If $\tan \theta = \frac{3}{4}$, θ being a positive angle less than $\frac{1}{2}\pi$, find $\sin 2\theta$, $\cos 2\theta$, and $\tan \frac{1}{2}\theta$.
15. If $\tan \theta = -\frac{5}{12}$ and the terminal side of θ lies in the fourth quadrant, find $\sin 2\theta$, $\cos 2\theta$, and $\tan 2\theta$.
16. If $\cos \alpha = \frac{5}{13}$ and $\tan \beta = \frac{3}{4}$, the terminal side of α being in the first quadrant and that of β being in the third, find $\sin(\alpha + \beta)$ and $\cos(\alpha - \beta)$.

17. If $\tan 2\alpha = \frac{24}{7}$ and 2α is a positive angle less than $\frac{1}{2}\pi$, find $\sin \alpha$ and $\cos \alpha$.

18. If $\tan 2\theta = -\frac{4}{3}$, 2θ being a positive angle between $\frac{1}{2}\pi$ and π, find $\sin \theta$ and $\cos \theta$.

Simplify each of the following expressions:

19. $\sec \theta - \sin \theta \tan \theta$.

20. $1 - \dfrac{\sin^2 \theta}{1 + \cos \theta}$.

21. $\dfrac{\sin \theta}{1 + \cos \theta} + \dfrac{1 + \cos \theta}{\sin \theta}$.

22. $\dfrac{\cos \theta + \cot \theta}{1 + \sin \theta}$.

In each of the following problems find all positive values of θ less than 2π that satisfy the given equation:

23. $\cos \theta - \sin 2\theta = 0$.

24. $2 \cos^2 \theta = 5 \cos \theta + 3$.

25. $3 \sin \theta = 2 \cos^2 \theta$.

26. $\sec^2 \theta = 2(\tan \theta + 2)$.

27. $\tan 2\theta = 2 \sin \theta$.

28. $\sin 3\theta = \sin 2\theta + \sin \theta$.

29. $3 \sin \theta + 4 \cos \theta = 5$.

30. $\sin 2\theta + 2 \cos^2 \frac{1}{2}\theta = \cos \theta$.

Prove each of the following identities:

31. $\cos^4 \theta - \sin^4 \theta = \cos 2\theta$.

32. $\sin 3\theta = 3 \sin \theta - 4 \sin^3 \theta$.

33. $\cos 3\theta = 4 \cos^3 \theta - 3 \cos \theta$.

34. $(\sin \frac{1}{2}\theta + \cos \frac{1}{2}\theta)^2 = 1 + \sin \theta$.

PLANE
ANALYTIC GEOMETRY

CHAPTER 1

RECTANGULAR COORDINATES. FUNDAMENTAL DEFINITIONS AND THEOREMS

1-1. *The system of real numbers.* The numbers that are called *natural numbers* or *positive integers* are the numbers 1, 2, 3, 4, and so on. These, together with the corresponding negative numbers -1, -2, -3, $\cdots$, and the number *zero*, constitute the *integers*. The integers may thus be indicated by writing

$$\cdots, \ -4, \ -3, \ -2, \ -1, \ 0, \ 1, \ 2, \ 3, \ 4, \ \cdots.$$

If p and q are two integers and $q \neq 0$, then the quotient p/q is called a *rational number*. The word rational comes from the idea of ratio—the *ratio of two integers*. The system of all rational numbers includes all the integers, these being the numbers p/q with $q = 1$.

Let us now take a straight line that extends indefinitely far in both directions and associate a definite point on it with each rational number as follows (Fig. 1-1):

Choose some point on the line, and associate with it the number *zero*. We shall call this point the *origin*. Now choose a unit of

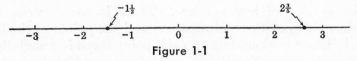

Figure 1-1

measurement and mark off this unit an indefinite number of times in both directions from the origin, and associate with the points so obtained the numbers 1, 2, 3, $\cdots$, and -1, -2, -3, $\cdots$. It is purely a matter of convention that we put the positive numbers on the right and the negative ones on the left. Now, in an

19

obvious way, associate a point of the line with every rational number p/q; for example, with $-1\frac{1}{2}$ or $-\frac{3}{2}$ associate the point that is halfway between -1 and -2; with $2\frac{3}{5}$ or $\frac{13}{5}$ associate the point that is three-fifths of the way from 2 to 3, etc.

When we have done this, the points of the line that have been associated with rational numbers are very close together—so close in fact that if we choose any two (as close together as we please but not coincident) then there are infinitely many others between them. This can be seen as follows: Think of the points associated with $\frac{43}{65}$ and $\frac{44}{65}$. They are quite close together, but the point associated with $\frac{1}{2}(\frac{43}{65} + \frac{44}{65})$ or $\frac{87}{130}$ lies midway between them. The point associated with $\frac{1}{2}(\frac{43}{65} + \frac{87}{130})$ also lies between them, and so on.

One would at first be inclined to think that all the points on the line have been "used up" when a point has been associated with each rational number in the above manner. This, however, is not the case. There are plenty of points on the line that have not yet been associated with any number—for example, the point whose distance from the origin is $\sqrt{2}$. It lies somewhere between the points associated with $\frac{141}{100}$ and $\frac{142}{100}$. (The student will recall from algebra that there is no rational number p/q which is equal to $\sqrt{2}$; so if there is a point on the line at a distance $\sqrt{2}$ from the origin, it must be distinct from all those associated with rational numbers.) The situation is similar for a point whose distance from the origin is $4\sqrt[3]{17}$ or $\frac{1}{2}(\sqrt[3]{5} - \sqrt{23})$ or $\sqrt{2}(1 + \sqrt[3]{7})$, etc. The numbers that are associated with all the remaining points of the line are called *irrational numbers*. It turns out that these points are also very close together, the "closeness" being like that described for the points associated with rational numbers.

The rational and irrational numbers together constitute what we call the system of *real numbers*. There is a one-to-one correspondence between the real numbers and the points of the line in Fig. 1-1; i.e., corresponding to each point there is a definite real number (rational or irrational), and corresponding to each real number there is a definite point.

Every real number can be expressed in decimal form. If the number is rational (for example, $\frac{3}{4}$ or $\frac{211}{330}$), its decimal representation is either terminating or periodic. If the number is irrational, its decimal representation is neither terminating nor periodic.

Examples

The terminating decimals 2.75 and 0.008 represent the rational numbers $\frac{275}{100}$ and $8/1,000$, respectively. The periodic decimal $0.6393939 \cdots$ (in which the block 39 is repeated indefinitely) represents the rational number $\frac{211}{330}$. On the other hand, the decimal representation of the irrational number $\frac{1}{2}(\sqrt{2} + 4\sqrt[3]{5})$ is 14.387 to three decimal places. No matter how far this decimal approximation is carried, it will not terminate or become periodic.

In speaking of two real numbers a and b we say that *a is greater than b* (written $a > b$) if $a - b$ is a *positive* number. The same thing is expressed by saying that *b is less than a* (written $b < a$). When the real numbers are associated with the points of a line as in Fig. 1-1, the statement $a > b$ always implies that the point associated with a lies to the right of that associated with b.

Examples

$$7 > 4; \quad 0 > -2; \quad -12 > -17; \quad -2 < 4.$$

1-2. Absolute value. By the *absolute value* of a real number a we mean the number a itself if a is positive, the positive number $-a$ if a is negative, and 0 if a is zero. We use the symbol $|a|$ to denote the absolute value of a. Thus $|-5| = 5$, $|4| = 4$, $\left|-\frac{2}{3}\right| = \frac{2}{3}$. Note also that $|3 - 12| = 12 - 3$, or 9 (*not* $3 - 12$), and

$$|x - 4| = \begin{cases} x - 4 & \text{if } x > 4, \\ 0 & \text{if } x = 4, \\ 4 - x & \text{if } x < 4. \end{cases}$$

It will be recalled that the symbol $\sqrt{a}$, where a is a positive number, is defined to stand for the *positive* number whose square is a. Thus $\sqrt{16} = 4$, *not* -4 or ± 4. Similarly, $\sqrt{9} = 3$, but $-\sqrt{9} = -3$, etc. *Observe now that $\sqrt{a^2} = a$ if a is positive, but $\sqrt{a^2} = -a$ if a is negative.* Thus if $a = -5$,

$$\sqrt{a^2} = \sqrt{(-5)^2} = \sqrt{25} = 5;$$

that is, if $a = -5$, then $\sqrt{a^2} = -(-5)$ or $-a$. Similarly,

$$\sqrt{(x - 4)^2} = \begin{cases} x - 4 & \text{if } x > 4, \\ 0 & \text{if } x = 4, \\ 4 - x & \text{if } x < 4. \end{cases}$$

All cases are covered by writing

$$\sqrt{(x - 4)^2} = |x - 4|.$$

PROBLEMS

1. What number describes the surface area of a cube whose volume is 54 cu in.? Is this a rational or an irrational number? Find its decimal approximation, correct to two decimal places. If carried sufficiently far, would this approximation be a periodic decimal?

2. What number describes the area of a regular octagon inscribed in a circle of radius 10 in.? Is this a rational or an irrational number? Find its decimal approximation, correct to two decimal places.

3. An equilateral triangle is inscribed in a circle of radius 12 in. What number describes the area that is inside the circle but outside the triangle? What is its decimal approximation, correct to two decimal places?

4. Prove that $\sqrt{2}$ is not a rational number by proving that there cannot exist two integers p and q such that $p/q = \sqrt{2}$.

5. Let A and B be the points of the line in Fig. 1-1 that are associated with $\frac{5}{7}$ and $\frac{6}{7}$, respectively. Find at least three rational numbers that are associated with points that lie between A and B. Would it be possible to find 5,000 such numbers?

6. Let P and Q be the points of the line in Fig. 1-1 that are associated with $\frac{13}{5}$ and $\frac{14}{5}$, respectively. Find at least three rational numbers that correspond to points that lie between P and Q.

7. Let A and B be the points of the line in Fig. 1-1 that are associated with $\frac{173}{100}$ and $\frac{174}{100}$, respectively. Find two rational numbers and an irrational number that correspond to points that lie between A and B.

8. Which lies farther to the right in Fig. 1-1, the point representing $\sqrt{73} + \sqrt{29}$ or that representing $\sqrt{194}$? (HINT: Show that $\sqrt{73} + \sqrt{29} > \sqrt{194}$. Do not use the decimal approximations to these numbers.)

9. Show by means of examples that the sum of two irrational numbers a and b may be a rational number. (HINT: Let $a = 3 + \sqrt{5}$, $b = 3 - \sqrt{5}$.) What about the sum of a rational and an irrational number?

10. In the quadratic equation $ax^2 + bx + c = 0$, let a, b, and c be rational numbers. Is it possible that one root may be rational and the other irrational?

11. Between what two real numbers does x lie if $|x| < 5$? If $|x - 3| < 5$?

12. Between what two real numbers does x lie if $|x| < 3$? If $|x + 2| < 3$?

13. Between what two real numbers does x lie if $|x| < 10$? If $|2x - 1| < 10$?

14. Write a statement involving absolute value that is equivalent to saying that $-3 < x < 5$.

15. Between what two real numbers does x lie if $5 < 2x - 3 < 10$?

16. For what values of x is $|x - 5| = x - 5$? For what values of x is it equal to $5 - x$?

17. For what values of x is $|2x - 7| = 2x - 7$? For what values of x is it equal to $7 - 2x$?

18. For what values of x is $|3 - 2x| = 3 - 2x$? For what values of x is it equal to $2x - 3$?

19. For what values of x is $|2x + 9| = 2x + 9$? For what values of x is it equal to $-2x - 9$?

20. Simplify the expression $3x + |x + y| + |x - y|$ given that x and y are positive numbers and $x < y$.

21. Simplify the expression $3x + |x - 1| + |2 - x|$ given that $1 < x < 2$.

22. Simplify the expression $3x + |x| + |3 - 2x|$ given that x is a negative number. What if x is a number between 0 and 1?

23. Show that if a is any real number other than 0, 1, or -1, then

$$\left(\frac{1}{1 + a} + \frac{1}{1 - a}\right) \div \left(\frac{1}{1 - a} - \frac{1}{1 + a}\right) = \frac{1}{a}.$$

Why are these restrictions on the value of a necessary?

24. Show that the result of dividing

$$\left(\frac{a}{a + b} + \frac{b}{a - b}\right) \quad \text{by} \quad \left(\frac{b}{a + b} - \frac{a}{a - b}\right)$$

is the same regardless of the values assigned to a and b, provided only that they are not both zero and $a^2 \neq b^2$.

25. Show that if one subtracts from 1 the number

$$\frac{1}{1 + a/(1 - a)},$$

where a is any real number different from 1, the result is equal to a.

1-3. *Directed distances.* Let A and B be two points on a line (Fig. 1-2), and let it be assumed that the distance between them is 2 units. If we wish, we may agree to say that the distance from A to B is $+2$ and that the distance from B to A is -2 (or vice versa). When we thus agree to regard segments measured in one direction along a line as positive and those measured in the opposite direction as negative, we call the line

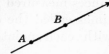

Figure 1-2

a *directed line*, and the distances *directed distances*. We may denote the distance from A to B by AB and that from B to A by BA. Then in the above case $AB = +2$ or 2, and $BA = -2$. The absolute value of AB or BA is called the *undirected distance* between the two points. It may be denoted by the symbol $|AB|$. When it is quite clear that we are concerned only with undirected distances, we may simplify the notation by omitting the vertical bars.

A fundamental property of a directed line is that if A, B, and C are any three points on it, then

$$AC = AB + BC,$$

regardless of the relative positions of these points (Fig. 1-3). Similarly, for any four points A, B, C, and D, it is always true that

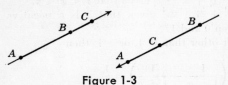

Figure 1-3

$$AD = AB + BC + CD,$$

and so on. This basic property has as a consequence the following important fact: *If A and B are any two points on a directed line, and if O is a reference point (or origin) on the line, then* (Fig. 1-4)

$$AB = OB - OA.$$

The proof follows immediately from the facts that $AB = AO + OB$ and $AO = -OA$.

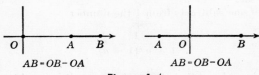

$AB = OB - OA$ $AB = OB - OA$

Figure 1-4

When we associate the real numbers with the points of a line as in Fig. 1-5, we may regard the line as a directed line on which distances measured from left to right are positive. The line is sometimes called the *axis of real numbers*, and the number associated with each point is called the *coordinate* of that point. *This*

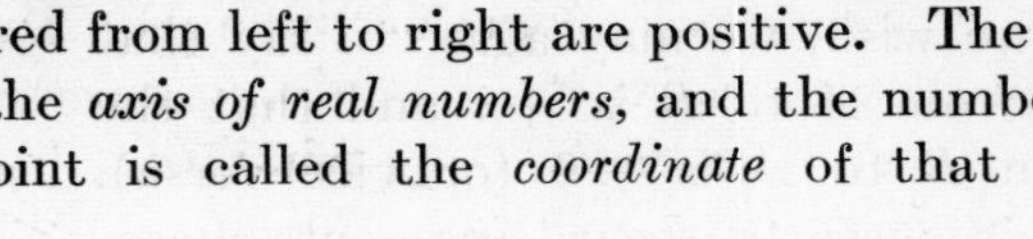

$$\begin{array}{c} D \qquad\qquad O \qquad\qquad L \\ \overline{\;-4\;\;-3\;\;-2\;\;-1\;\;\;0\;\;\;1\;\;\;2\;\;\;3\;\;\;4\;\;\;5\;} \end{array}$$

Figure 1-5

coordinate is the directed distance from the origin to the point. Thus D has the coordinate -3 ($OD = -3$), and L has the coordinate 4 ($OL = 4$). Observe that

$$DL = 4 - (-3) = 7;$$
$$LD = -3 - 4 = -7.$$

It is invariably true that if P_1 and P_2 are two points on the axis, with coordinates x_1 and x_2, respectively, then

$$P_1P_2 = x_2 - x_1.$$

1-4. *Rectangular coordinates.* Let $x'x$ and $y'y$ (Fig. 1-6) be two axes of the kind discussed in the preceding section and which intersect at right angles at a common origin. We call these lines *rectangular coordinate axes*, $x'x$ being the *x-axis* and $y'y$ the *y-axis*.

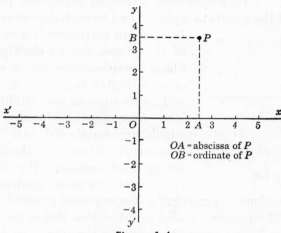

OA = abscissa of P
OB = ordinate of P

Figure 1-6

(It is purely a matter of convention that we take the positive direction on the x-axis to the right and that on the y-axis upward.)

Let P be any point in the plane of the axes. Its directed distance from the y-axis is called its *x-coordinate*, or *abscissa*. This is equal to the directed segment OA. Similarly, its directed distance from the x-axis is called its *y-coordinate*, or *ordinate*. This is equal to the directed segment OB. The abscissa and ordinate together are called the *rectangular coordinates* of P. When we write the coordinates of a point, we enclose them in parentheses, putting the x-coordinate first. Thus the coordinates of P and Q in Fig. 1-7 are written $P(3,4)$ and $Q(-2,-5)$.

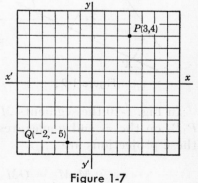

Figure 1-7

The process of locating and marking a point whose coordinates are given is called *plotting* the point. Plotting is facilitated by the use of paper that is ruled off into small squares as in Fig. 1-7. Such paper is called *rectangular coordinate paper*.

We have mentioned that there is a one-to-one correspondence between the real numbers and the points of a line. In two dimensions there is a corresponding situation regarding pairs of real numbers and the points of a plane; i.e., to each pair of real numbers

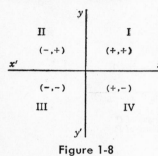

Figure 1-8

(x,y) there corresponds a definite point of the plane, and to each point of the plane there corresponds a unique pair of coordinates (x,y).

The coordinate axes divide the plane into four portions called *quadrants* which are numbered just as in trigonometry. Figure 1-8 shows the numbering and indicates the signs of the coordinates for each quadrant.

1-5. Projections. *Length of a line segment parallel to a coordinate axis.* The projection of a point onto a line is the foot of the perpendicular drawn from the point to the line. In Fig. 1-9 the projection of the point A onto the line l is the point A'; the projection of B is B'. The projection of the directed segment AB is the directed segment $A'B'$.

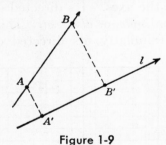

Figure 1-9   Figure 1-10

In Fig. 1-10 the segments M_1M_2 and N_1N_2 are the projections of P_1P_2 on the x- and y-axes, respectively. The directed lengths of these projections are

$$M_1M_2 = OM_2 - OM_1 = x_2 - x_1;$$
$$N_1N_2 = ON_2 - ON_1 = y_2 - y_1.$$

These formulas hold for all positions of P_1 and P_2. Thus in Fig.

1-11 the directed length of the projection of AB on the x-axis is $6 - (-3) = 9$.

It is convenient to take the positive direction on any segment that is parallel to a coordinate axis the same as that on the axis. The directed length of such a segment is then the same as that of its

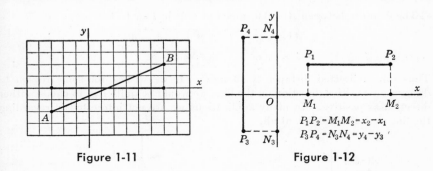

Figure 1-11   Figure 1-12

projection on the axis. Thus in Fig. 1-12 the directed length P_1P_2 is

$$P_1P_2 = M_1M_2 = OM_2 - OM_1 = x_2 - x_1.$$

Similarly, $\quad P_3P_4 = N_3N_4 = ON_4 - ON_3 = y_4 - y_3.$

Of course $P_2P_1 = x_1 - x_2$ and $P_4P_3 = y_3 - y_4$.

1-6. The distance formula. Let $P_1(x_1,y_1)$ and $P_2(x_2,y_2)$ be any two given points, and let it be re-
quired to find the distance between them (Fig. 1-13). Through P_1 draw P_1L parallel to the x-axis, and through P_2 draw P_2L parallel to the y-axis, thus forming the right triangle P_1LP_2. Then P_1P_2 is the

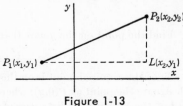

Figure 1-13

hypotenuse of a right triangle whose legs are $P_1L = x_2 - x_1$ and $LP_2 = y_2 - y_1$. Therefore

$$(P_1P_2)^2 = (x_2 - x_1)^2 + (y_2 - y_1)^2.$$

If we denote by d the *undirected distance* between the two points, we have

$$\boldsymbol{d} = \sqrt{(\boldsymbol{x}_2 - \boldsymbol{x}_1)^2 + (\boldsymbol{y}_2 - \boldsymbol{y}_1)^2}.$$

It may be observed that if $y_2 = y_1$ so that the line is parallel to the x-axis, the formula becomes

$$d = \sqrt{(x_2 - x_1)^2} = |x_2 - x_1|.$$

A similar situation results if the line is parallel to the y-axis.

Example 1

The distance between $A(-3,6)$ and $B(3,-2)$ in Fig. 1-14 is

$$d = \sqrt{[3 - (-3)]^2 + [-2 - 6]^2}$$
$$= \sqrt{6^2 + (-8)^2} = 10.$$

Thus the undirected distance is 10 units. If we wished for some reason to designate a positive direction on the line, we would be quite free to choose either direction as positive. In many applications we are not interested in regarding the line as a directed line at all.

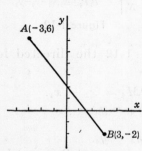

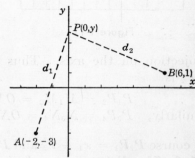

Figure 1-14   **Figure 1-15**

Example 2

Find the point on the y-axis that is equidistant from $A(-2,-3)$ and $B(6,1)$.

Solution (Fig. 1-15)

Since the required point is on the y-axis, its x-coordinate is zero. We may then designate the point as $P(0,y)$, where y is the unknown to be determined.

Let the undirected distances of P from A and B be d_1 and d_2, respectively. Then,

$$d_1 = \sqrt{[0 - (-2)]^2 + [y - (-3)]^2}; \qquad d_2 = \sqrt{(0 - 6)^2 + (y - 1)^2}.$$

The conditions of the problem require that we determine y so that $d_1 = d_2$. We therefore equate these and solve for y.

$$\sqrt{(0 + 2)^2 + (y + 3)^2} = \sqrt{(0 - 6)^2 + (y - 1)^2}$$
$$4 + y^2 + 6y + 9 = 36 + y^2 - 2y + 1$$
$$8y = 24$$
$$y = 3.$$

The required point is then $P(0,3)$.

PROBLEMS

1. In each of the following cases draw the given segments, and find the directed lengths of their projections on the coordinate axes:

   (a) $A(2,1)$ $B(4,3)$; $L(2,-5)$ $M(-4,-1)$; $P(-1,-6)$ $Q(3,1)$.

   (b) $A(-1,-5)$ $B(3,-7)$; $L(2,0)$ $M(-2,4)$; $P(0,-3)$ $Q(-3,-4)$.

   (c) $A(4,-3)$ $B(-2,-4)$; $L(0,-2)$ $M(3,0)$; $P(-6,-1)$ $Q(-4,0)$.

2. Each of the following segments is parallel to the x-axis. Draw each segment and find the directed distance from the first point to the second:

   (a) $A(2,3)$ $B(5,3)$; $L(0,-1)$ $M(-3,-1)$; $P(5,1)$ $Q(-3,1)$.

   (b) $A(4,4)$ $B(-2,4)$; $L(-2,0)$ $M(3,0)$; $P(-7,-4)$ $Q(-1,-4)$.

   (c) $A(-6,3)$ $B(0,3)$; $L(8,1)$ $M(2,1)$; $P(4,-3)$ $Q(-2,-3)$.

3. Each of the following segments is parallel to the y-axis. Draw each segment, and find the directed distance from the first point to the second.

   (a) $A(5,-2)$ $B(5,5)$; $L(0,1)$ $M(0,-5)$; $P(-3,-7)$ $Q(-3,-1)$.

   (b) $A(4,7)$ $B(4,-2)$; $L(1,-8)$ $M(1,-6)$; $P(-3,2)$ $Q(-3,0)$.

   (c) $A(5,-9)$ $B(5,-1)$; $L(2,-3)$ $M(2,1)$; $P(-2,6)$ $Q(-2,1)$.

4. Show that the directed distance from $A(2,3)$ to $B(x,3)$ is $x - 2$ for all values of x. What is the directed distance from B to A?

5. Plot the points $A(2,5)$ and $B(2,y)$, where y is negative, so that B is in the fourth quadrant. Is the directed distance BA equal to $5 + y$, $5 - y$, or $y - 5$?

6. Plot the points $P(4,3)$ and $Q(x,3)$, where x is negative, so that Q is in the second quadrant. Is the directed distance PQ equal to $4 - x$, $4 + x$, or $x - 4$?

7. Show that the triangle with vertices at $(1,3)$, $(3,-1)$, and $(-5,-5)$ is a right triangle.

8. Show that the triangle with vertices at $(-2,-3)$, $(5,-1)$, and $(3,6)$ is a right triangle.

9. A quadrilateral has vertices $A(-1,3)$, $B(5,7)$, $C(9,1)$, $D(3,-3)$. Prove that it is or that it is not a rectangle.

10. One vertex of a triangle is at the origin, and the other two are the points $(1,12)$ and $(11,-1)$. Prove that the triangle is or that it is not a right triangle.

11. Show that the triangle whose vertices are $(-1,0)$, $(7,-8)$, and $(-2,-9)$ is isosceles.

12. Show that $C(4,1)$ is the center of the circle that passes through $(0,-2)$, $(7,-3)$, and $(8,-2)$.

13. Show that $H(0,-3)$ is the center of the circle that passes through the points $(12,2)$, $(5,9)$, and $(0,10)$.

14. Find the center of the circle that is circumscribed about the triangle $A(2,2)$, $B(2,-8)$, $C(-1,6)$.

15. Two vertices of an equilateral triangle are $A(0,6)$ and $B(10,-4)$. Find the third vertex.

16. Find the point on the x-axis that is equidistant from $P(-4,6)$ and $Q(14,-2)$.

17. The two coordinates of a point are equal, and the point is equidistant from $A(-6,4)$ and $B(2,-8)$. What are its coordinates?

18. A point P lies on a line that is parallel to the x-axis and 5 units above it. P is equidistant from $A(4,1)$ and $B(-6,-4)$. What are its coordinates?

19. A point P lies on a line that is parallel to the x-axis and 2 units below it. P is twice as far from $A(6,2)$ as from the origin. Find its coordinates.

20. The ordinate of a certain point P is twice the abscissa. This point P is equidistant from $A(-3,1)$ and $B(8,-2)$. Find its coordinates.

21. The ordinate of a certain point P is greater than the abscissa by 4 units. This point P is equidistant from $A(-2,3)$ and $B(6,-3)$. Find its coordinates.

22. Which of the following expressions represent the undirected distance between the two points $A(2,3)$ and $B(x,3)$? $x - 2$; $|x - 2|$; $\sqrt{(x-2)^2}$; $2 - x$; $|2 - x|$.

23. Draw a line l parallel to the y-axis and 3 units to the left of it. Plot a point $P(x,y)$. Write down an expression which represents the undirected length of the perpendicular drawn from P to l. Write down also an expression which represents the directed length from the foot of the perpendicular to P.

24. A 50-lb. rectangular plate having the dimensions indicated in Fig. 1-16 is held in the position shown by a horizontal force P applied at A. In order to calculate the magnitude of the force P, it would be necessary to know the coordinates of A with respect to the axes shown. Find these coordinates.

25. The sum of the undirected distances from a point P to $A(8,0)$ and $B(-8,0)$ is 20. The abscissa of P is 6. Find its ordinate.

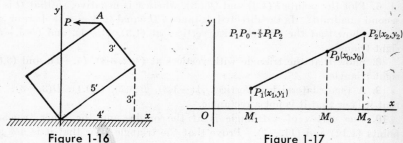

Figure 1-16   Figure 1-17

1-7. *Division of a line segment.* It is frequently necessary to find the coordinates of the point P_0 on a segment P_1P_2 such that P_1P_0 is some given fraction of the whole segment P_1P_2. As a preliminary example, let it be required to determine the point P_0 in Fig. 1-17 that is two-thirds of the way from P_1 to P_2; that is, such that $P_1P_0 = \frac{2}{3}P_1P_2$. If we let the required coordinates be (x_0,y_0), we have immediately,

$$x_0 = OM_0 = OM_1 + \tfrac{2}{3}(M_1M_2)$$
$$= OM_1 + \tfrac{2}{3}(OM_2 - OM_1)$$
$$= x_1 + \tfrac{2}{3}(x_2 - x_1).$$

Using the corresponding projections on the y-axis, one can simi-

larly show that
$$y_0 = y_1 + \tfrac{2}{3}(y_2 - y_1).$$

The more general situation, in which $\tfrac{2}{3}$ is replaced by any number k, is covered by the following:

Theorem. *If $P_0(x_0, y_0)$ is the point on the line $P_1(x_1, y_1)$ $P_2(x_2, y_2)$ such that $P_1P_0/P_1P_2 = k$, then*

$$x_0 = x_1 + k(x_2 - x_1);$$
$$y_0 = y_1 + k(y_2 - y_1).$$

The theorem is used most often where k is a fraction between 0 and 1; for a suitable value of k in this range, any point on the

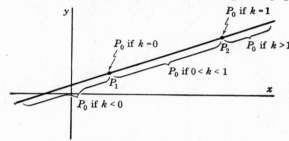

Figure 1-18

segment between P_1 and P_2 can be obtained. The theorem is valid, however, in a broader sense. In fact (see Fig. 1-18),

(a) *If $0 < k < 1$, P_0 lies between P_1 and P_2.*

(b) *If $k = 0$ or 1, P_0 coincides with P_1 or P_2, respectively.*

(c) *If $k > 1$, P_0 lies on P_1P_2 extended beyond P_2.*

(d) *If $k < 0$, P_0 lies on P_1P_2 extended in the opposite direction, beyond P_1.* In this case the directed segments P_1P_0 and P_1P_2 have opposite signs.

It can be proved that by a suitable choice of k one can obtain any point whatever on the line determined by P_1 and P_2.

Example

Find the coordinates of the point P_0 that is five-sixths of the way from $A(-2, 5)$ to $B(10, 1)$.

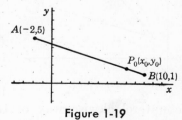

Solution (Fig. 1-19)

In this case $k = \tfrac{5}{6}$, and we have

$$x_0 = -2 + \tfrac{5}{6}[10 - (-2)] = 8;$$
$$y_0 = 5 + \tfrac{5}{6}[1 - 5] = \tfrac{5}{3}.$$

The required point is then $P_0(8, \tfrac{5}{3})$.

Figure 1-19

1-8. *The mid-point of a line segment.* As a special case of the preceding theorem we may find the coordinates of the mid-point of a given segment P_1P_2 by taking $k = \frac{1}{2}$. We get

$$x_0 = x_1 + \tfrac{1}{2}(x_2 - x_1) = \tfrac{1}{2}(x_1 + x_2);$$
$$y_0 = y_1 + \tfrac{1}{2}(y_2 - y_1) = \tfrac{1}{2}(y_1 + y_2).$$

We thus have the following special case of the above theorem: *If*

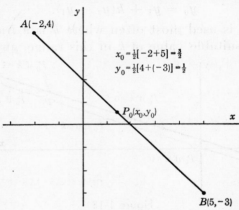

$A(-2,4)$

$x_0 = \frac{1}{2}[-2+5] = \frac{3}{2}$
$y_0 = \frac{1}{2}[4+(-3)] = \frac{1}{2}$

$P_0(x_0,y_0)$

$B(5,-3)$

Figure 1-20

$P_0(x_0,y_0)$ *is the mid-point of the segment* $P_1(x_1,y_1)$ $P_2(x_2,y_2)$, *then*

$$x_0 = \frac{x_1 + x_2}{2}; \qquad y_0 = \frac{y_1 + y_2}{2}.$$

Example

The coordinates of the mid-point of the segment $A(-2,4)$ $B(5,-3)$ are (Fig. 1-20)

$$x_0 = \frac{-2 + 5}{2} = \frac{3}{2}; \qquad y_0 = \frac{4 + (-3)}{2} = \frac{1}{2}.$$

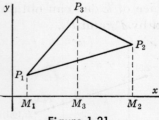

Figure 1-21

1-9. *Area of a triangle.* In Fig. 1-21, P_1, P_2, and P_3 are the vertices of a triangle lettered so that if one traverses the perimeter from P_1 to P_2 to P_3 to P_1 the area lies always to his left. This counterclockwise way of traversing the perimeter is sometimes called positive because the formula that we shall now develop for the area gives a positive result only if the points are taken in this order—otherwise it gives a negative number whose absolute value is equal to the area.

For the case shown it is obvious that the area of the triangle $P_1P_2P_3$ can be obtained by adding the trapezoids $M_1M_3P_3P_1$ and $M_3M_2P_2P_3$, and subtracting the trapezoid $M_1M_2P_2P_1$. Now, since the area of a trapezoid is equal to one-half the sum of the parallel sides times the altitude, we have

$$M_1M_3P_3P_1 = \tfrac{1}{2}(y_1 + y_3)(x_3 - x_1);$$
$$M_3M_2P_2P_3 = \tfrac{1}{2}(y_3 + y_2)(x_2 - x_3);$$
$$M_1M_2P_2P_1 = \tfrac{1}{2}(y_1 + y_2)(x_2 - x_1).$$

If we denote the area of the triangle by $P_1P_2P_3$, we have

$$
\begin{aligned}
P_1P_2P_3 &= \tfrac{1}{2}(y_1 + y_3)(x_3 - x_1) + \tfrac{1}{2}(y_3 + y_2)(x_2 - x_3) \\
&\qquad\qquad\qquad - \tfrac{1}{2}(y_1 + y_2)(x_2 - x_1) \\
&= \tfrac{1}{2}[y_1x_3 - y_3x_1 + y_3x_2 - y_2x_3 + y_2x_1 - y_1x_2].
\end{aligned}
$$

The expression in the brackets is precisely the expansion of the determinant

$$
\begin{vmatrix}
x_1 & y_1 & 1 \\
x_2 & y_2 & 1 \\
x_3 & y_3 & 1
\end{vmatrix}
$$

Therefore, at least for the case shown in the figure, the area of the triangle is equal to one-half the value of this determinant. For other positions of the vertices relative to the coordinate axes the proof may differ somewhat in the details, but the result turns out to be the same. In fact we have the following:

Theorem. *Let $P_1(x_1,y_1)$, $P_2(x_2,y_2)$, $P_3(x_3,y_3)$ be the vertices of a triangle, lettered so that in traversing the perimeter from P_1 to P_2 to P_3 to P_1 one would have the area always on his left. Then the area is given by the formula*

$$
\text{Area} = \frac{1}{2}\begin{vmatrix}
x_1 & y_1 & 1 \\
x_2 & y_2 & 1 \\
x_3 & y_3 & 1
\end{vmatrix}
$$

If the order of the points is such that the above traverse of the perimeter has the opposite sense, then the formula yields a negative number whose absolute value is equal to the area.

Example

The area of the triangle ABC in Fig. 1-22 is

$$\frac{1}{2} \begin{vmatrix} -2 & 2 & 1 \\ 0 & -4 & 1 \\ 5 & 6 & 1 \end{vmatrix} = 25 \text{ square units.}$$

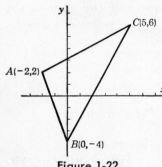

Figure 1-22

PROBLEMS

1. In each of the following cases find the coordinates of the point P on AB such that AP is the given fractional part of AB. Draw the given line segment, and show the required point.

(a) $A(2,-4)$ $B(8,12)$; $\frac{3}{4}$.
(b) $A(-3,6)$ $B(7,-8)$; $\frac{1}{3}$.
(c) $A(-9,-6)$ $B(1,4)$; $\frac{1}{5}$.
(d) $A(8,6)$ $B(0,-2)$; $\frac{5}{6}$.
(e) $A(-4,6)$ $B(11,1)$; $\frac{2}{5}$.
(f) $A(0,7)$ $B(7,-2)$; $\frac{3}{7}$.

2. In each of the following cases find the coordinates of the mid-point of AB. Draw the given line segment, and show the required point.

(a) $A(4,-8)$ $B(-2,0)$.   (b) $A(-5,2)$ $B(-1,5)$.
(c) $A(6,-1)$ $B(12,5)$.   (d) $A(3,0)$ $B(-4,6)$.
(e) $A(-8,-3)$ $B(-1,3)$.   (f) $A(-2,-6)$ $B(5,8)$.

3. In each of the following cases find the coordinates of the point P so that $AP/AB = k$. Draw AB, and extend it as required to show P.

(a) $A(-1,-1)$; $B(2,3)$; $k = 2$.   (b) $A(6,-2)$ $B(-2,4)$; $k = \frac{3}{2}$.
(c) $A(1,-2)$ $B(6,3)$; $k = -\frac{3}{2}$.   (d) $A(3,-6)$ $B(0,0)$; $k = -\frac{2}{3}$.
(e) $A(2,-6)$ $B(4,3)$; $k = -\frac{4}{3}$.   (f) $A(6,0)$ $B(0,-3)$; $k = \frac{4}{3}$.

4. Find the coordinates of the points that divide the segment $A(-6,-3)$ $B(3,1)$ into three equal parts.

5. Find the coordinates of the points that divide the segment $P(8,-3)$ $Q(-2,6)$ into four equal parts.

6. Draw the triangle $A(-3,-4)$ $B(6,-2)$ $C(3,8)$. Find the coordinates of the point on each median* that is two-thirds of the way from the vertex to the mid-point of the opposite side.

7. Draw the triangle $P(-6,2)$ $Q(0,-8)$ $R(2,6)$. Find the coordinates of the point on each median that is two-thirds of the way from the vertex to the mid-point of the opposite side.

* The medians are the lines drawn from the vertices to the mid-points of the opposite sides.

8. Draw the triangle $A(x_1,y_1)$ $B(x_2,y_2)$ $C(x_3,y_3)$.   Show that the point on each median which is at a distance from the vertex equal to two-thirds the length of the median has the coordinates

$$\left(\frac{x_1 + x_2 + x_3}{3}, \frac{y_1 + y_2 + y_3}{3}\right).$$

9. In Fig. 1-23, L and M are the mid-points of BC and CD, respectively; the distance $AP = \frac{2}{3}AL$, and $AQ = \frac{2}{3}AM$.   Show that P and Q lie on the diagonal BD and that they divide it into three equal parts. $ABCD$ is any parallelogram.   HINT: Take the origin at A and the x-axis along AD.   Thus let the vertices of the parallelogram be $A(0,0), D(x_1,0),$ $B(x_2,y_2), C(x_1 + x_2,y_2).$

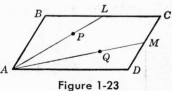

Figure 1-23

10. In each of the following cases draw the triangle whose vertices are the three given points, and compute its area:

(a) $(-4,1)$, $(0,-5)$, $(3,2)$. 　　　　(b) $(1,-6)$, $(6,1)$, $(-2,5)$.
(c) $(0,3)$, $(8,-1)$, $(0,-7)$. 　　　　(d) $(1,-1)$, $(6,-2)$, $(3,-5)$.
(e) $(-6,-7)$, $(2,-1)$, $(-1,4)$. 　　(f) $(-6,3)$, $(1,-3)$, $(-2,7)$.

11. Draw each of the following parallelograms, and find its area:

(a) $A(-2,-3)$ $B(6,-1)$ $C(-1,2)$ $D(7,4)$.
(b) $A(-3,1)$ $B(1,-2)$ $C(7,1)$ $D(3,4)$.
(c) $A(0,-2)$ $B(6,-4)$ $C(2,-5)$ $D(8,-7)$.

12. Find the area of each of the following polygons by breaking it up into triangles:

(a) $A(-2,-3)$ $B(1,7)$ $C(8,5)$ $D(6,-1)$.
(b) $A(-4,0)$ $B(0,-6)$ $C(8,-2)$ $D(1,5)$.
(c) $A(0,0)$ $B(5,1)$ $C(7,6)$ $D(2,8)$ $E(0,3)$.

13. The triangle OAB in Fig. 1-24 has one vertex at the origin.   Show that its area is given by the absolute value of $\dfrac{1}{2}\begin{vmatrix} x_1 & y_1 \\ x_2 & y_2 \end{vmatrix}$.

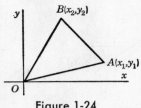

Figure 1-24

14. Show that the points $(-3,-4)$, $(0,-2)$, and $(9,4)$ all lie on the same straight line.   HINT: Find the area of the triangle.

15. In the triangle $A(-2,-6)$ $B(10,-1)$ $C(2,8)$, find the length of the altitude drawn from C.   HINT: Find the area, and use the fact that area $= \frac{1}{2}$ base times altitude.

16. In the triangle $A(-4,-3)$, $B(2,8)$, $C(8,0)$, find the length of the altitude drawn from A (see hint in Prob. 15).

17. A line crosses the x-axis at 12 and the y-axis at -5.   Find the length of the perpendicular drawn from the origin to this line (see hint in Prob. 15).

18. Find the shortest distance from the origin to the line that passes through (3,5) and (6,9).   IF you are reading this, I feel empathy. If you also have Kaelin, Make out your will.

19. Consider the line determined by the points $A(2,3)$ and $B(6,5)$. For what value of k, in the theorem of Sec. 1-7, does one obtain the point on the line that has 7.5 as its abscissa?

20. Let the coordinates of P_1 and P_2 in the theorem of Sec. 1-7 be rational numbers. What points on the line determined by P_1 and P_2 does one get by using for k all rational numbers satisfying the condition $0 \leqq k \leqq 1$?

1-10. *Inclination. Slope.* A line l, not parallel to the x-axis, intersects this axis at some point Q (Fig. 1-25). The direction of

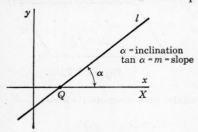

Figure 1-25

the line, relative to the coordinate axes, is specified by giving the counter-clockwise angle $\alpha < 180°$ through which QX would have to be rotated to bring it into coincidence with l. *This angle is called the inclination of l.* The inclination of a line parallel to the x-axis is defined to be zero.

The *slope* of a line, usually denoted by the letter m, is defined as the *tangent of the angle α of inclination:*

If $0 < \alpha < 90°$, m is a positive number;

If $90° < \alpha < 180°$, m is a negative number;

If $\alpha = 0$, $m = 0$;

If $\alpha = 90°$, the line has no slope. Why?

1-11. *Slope in terms of coordinates*. We wish now to express the slope of a line l in terms of the coordinates of two points

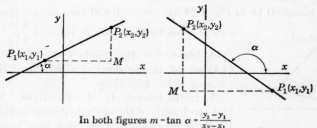

In both figures $m = \tan \alpha = \dfrac{y_2 - y_1}{x_2 - x_1}$

Figure 1-26

$P_1(x_1,y_1)$ and $P_2(x_2,y_2)$ on it. The student can readily see that for either of the cases shown in Fig. 1-26

$$\tan \alpha = \frac{MP_2}{P_1M} = \frac{y_2 - y_1}{x_2 - x_1}.$$

This formula holds for all positions of P_1 and P_2 provided $x_1 \neq x_2$. We may therefore state the following:

Theorem. *If $P_1(x_1,y_1)$ and $P_2(x_2,y_2)$ are any two points on a line l not perpendicular to the x-axis, then the slope of l is*

$$m = \frac{y_2 - y_1}{x_2 - x_1}.$$

It of course makes no difference which of two given points is called P_1. The slope of the line through $(1,-3)$ and $(5,7)$ is (Fig. 1-27)

$$\frac{7 - (-3)}{5 - 1} = \frac{5}{2} \quad \text{or} \quad \frac{-3 - 7}{1 - 5} = \frac{5}{2}.$$

If a point moves along the line, it will move 5 units in the y-direction for every 2 units in the x-direction—or $2\frac{1}{2}$ units in the y-direction for each unit in the x-direction. The slope is thus a measure of the steepness of the line.

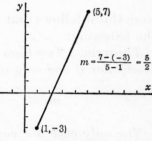

Figure 1-27

The slope of a road is called its *grade*, a 10 per cent grade meaning a slope of 0.10; this indicates a rise of 10 ft. for each 100 ft. of horizontal distance (Fig. 1-28).

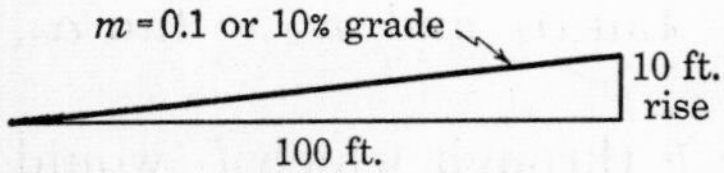

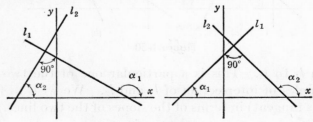

Figure 1-28

1-12. Parallel and perpendicular lines. Two lines l_1 and l_2 are parallel if and only if their inclinations are equal. If the lines have slopes m_1 and m_2, the condition for parallelism is that

$$m_1 = m_2.$$

If the lines l_1 and l_2 are mutually perpendicular, the inclination of one of them exceeds that of the other by 90°; that is, either $\alpha_1 = \alpha_2 + 90°$, or $\alpha_2 = \alpha_1 + 90°$ (Fig. 1-29).

Figure 1-29

In either case $\quad \tan \alpha_1 = - \cot \alpha_2 = - \dfrac{1}{\tan \alpha_2};$

or since $\tan \alpha_1 = m_1$ and $\tan \alpha_2 = m_2,$

$$m_1 = - \frac{1}{m_2}, \quad \text{or} \quad m_1 m_2 = -1.$$

Conversely, if $m_1 = -1/m_2,$

$$\tan \alpha_1 = - \cot \alpha_2 \quad \text{and} \quad \alpha_1 = \alpha_2 \pm 90°;$$

from this it follows that the lines are perpendicular. We have then the following:

Theorem. *Two lines having slopes m_1 and m_2 are mutually perpendicular if and only if*

$$m_1 = - \frac{1}{m_2} \quad \text{or} \quad m_1 m_2 = -1.$$

The only case not covered by the theorem is that of two lines parallel to the x- and y-axes, respectively. They are of course mutually perpendicular; the slope of one of them is zero, and the other has no slope.

1-13. *Angle between two lines.* Let l_1 and l_2 be two lines intersecting at P and having slopes $m_1 = \tan \alpha_1$ and $m_2 = \tan \alpha_2,$ respectively.

The smallest counterclockwise angle θ through which l_1 would have to be rotated about P to make it coincide with l_2 is called the

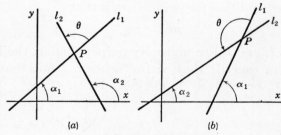

(a)   (b)

Figure 1-30

angle from l_1 to l_2. This is a particular one of the two supplementary angles of intersection of l_1 and l_2. We wish to find this angle (or its tangent) in terms of the slopes of the two lines. There are two cases:

CASE I. $\alpha_1 < \alpha_2$ (Fig. 1-30a).   Since the exterior angle α_2 is equal to $\alpha_1 + \theta$, we have

$$\theta = \alpha_2 - \alpha_1.$$

Then, $$\tan \theta = \tan (\alpha_2 - \alpha_1)$$
$$= \frac{\tan \alpha_2 - \tan \alpha_1}{1 + \tan \alpha_2 \tan \alpha_1}$$
$$= \frac{m_2 - m_1}{1 + m_2 m_1}.$$

CASE II. $\alpha_1 > \alpha_2$ (Fig. 1-30b).   In this case,

$$180° - \theta = \alpha_1 - \alpha_2;$$
$$\tan (180° - \theta) = \frac{\tan \alpha_1 - \tan \alpha_2}{1 + \tan \alpha_1 \tan \alpha_2}$$
$$\tan \theta = \frac{\tan \alpha_2 - \tan \alpha_1}{1 + \tan \alpha_1 \tan \alpha_2}$$
$$= \frac{m_2 - m_1}{1 + m_1 m_2}.$$

The result is the same in both cases, and we therefore state the following:

Theorem.   *If two lines l_1 and l_2 have slopes m_1 and m_2, respectively, and if θ is the angle from l_1 to l_2, then*

$$\tan \theta = \frac{m_2 - m_1}{1 + m_1 m_2}.$$

Example

Find the tangent of angle A of the triangle $A(-3,-4)$ $B(6,-1)$ $C(5,6)$.

Solution (Fig. 1-31)

If we think of the line determined by A and B as l_1, and that determined by A and C as l_2, then the required angle is the angle from l_1 to l_2.   The slopes are

$$m_1 = \frac{-1 - (-4)}{6 - (-3)} = \frac{1}{3}; \qquad m_2 = \frac{6 - (-4)}{5 - (-3)} = \frac{5}{4}.$$

We have then

$$\tan A = \frac{m_2 - m_1}{1 + m_1 m_2} = \frac{\frac{5}{4} - \frac{1}{3}}{1 + \frac{5}{4} \cdot \frac{1}{3}} = \frac{\frac{11}{12}}{\frac{17}{12}} = \frac{11}{17}.$$

If we wish, we may use tables to find that the angle whose tangent is $\frac{11}{17}$, or 0.6471, is approximately 32°54′.

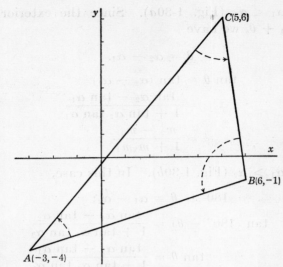

Figure 1-31

The other angles could be similarly computed. Observe that angle B is the angle from BC to BA so that BC would be taken as l_1 and BA as l_2 in using the formula. Similarly, the angle at C is the angle from CA to CB.

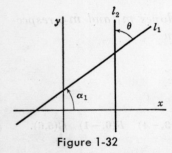

Figure 1-32

In deriving our formula for $\tan \theta$ we assumed that neither line is parallel to the y-axis. A case in which l_2 is parallel to the y-axis is shown in Fig. 1-32. It is left for the student to show that in this case $\tan \theta = \cot \alpha_1 = 1/m_1$.

It will be observed that if the angle between two lines having slopes m_1 and m_2 is $90°$ then $m_1 m_2 = -1$, and the denominator in the formula for $\tan \theta$ becomes zero.

PROBLEMS

1. The inclination of a line is $120°$. What is its slope?

2. The slope of a line is -1. What is its inclination?

3. Draw a line through $P(3,4)$ with inclination $60°$. What is its slope? What is the slope of a line through P which is perpendicular to this line?

4. Find the slope of side BC in the triangle $A(1,6)$ $B(-2,-8)$ $C(7,-2)$. What is the slope of the altitude drawn from A perpendicular to BC?

5. Find the slope of the shortest line that can be drawn from the origin to the line $P(-4,1)$ $Q(6,5)$.

6. A line is drawn from $A(-4,5)$ perpendicular to a line connecting the origin and $P(6,-2)$. What is its slope?

7. Draw the triangle $A(-3,6)$ $B(2,8)$ $C(4,-7)$. Show that the line joining the mid-points of AC and BC is parallel to AB and half as long as AB.

8. Draw the triangle $A(-2,7)$ $B(13,1)$ $C(0,-3)$. Find the slope of each of its altitudes and of each of its medians. NOTE: An *altitude* is a line drawn from a vertex perpendicular to the opposite side. A *median* is a line drawn from a vertex to the mid-point of the opposite side.

9. Show that the triangle $P(-10,4)$ $Q(7,3)$ $R(4,-3)$ is a right triangle.

10. Show that the quadrilateral with vertices at $(7,9)$, $(8,-4)$, $(-5,-5)$, and $(-6,8)$ is a square.

11. Show that the points $A(-2,6)$, $B(1,1)$, and $C(7,-9)$ lie on the same straight line.

12. Show that the points $(-5,-2)$, $(1,7)$, $(2,2)$, and $(0,-1)$ are the vertices of an isosceles trapezoid.

13. A wedge ABC rests on an inclined plane as shown in Fig. 1-33. Find the slopes (to the horizontal) of faces AB and BC.

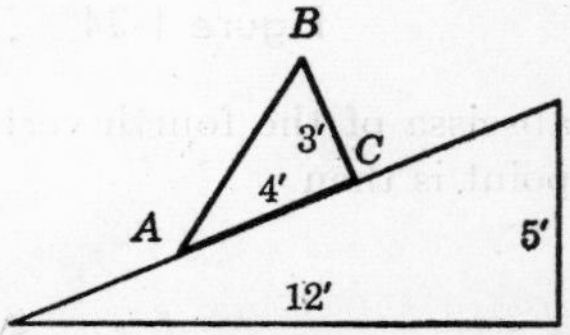

14. In each of the following cases find the tangent of the angle from the line AB to the line PQ. Then, using tables, find the angle.

Figure 1-33

   (a) $A(-2,-6)$ $B(8,2)$; $P(2,8)$ $Q(4,-2)$.
   (b) $A(0,-3)$ $B(6,1)$; $P(2,0)$ $Q(5,-2)$.
   (c) $A(-4,-1)$ $B(8,2)$; $P(0,-4)$ $Q(2,2)$.
   (d) $A(-8,-2)$ $B(0,0)$; $P(-3,-5)$ $Q(0,3)$.

15. Find the tangents of the angles at B and D in the quadrilateral $A(-2,-2)$ $B(-4,-7)$ $C(3,-5)$ $D(5,2)$.

16. In each of the following cases find the tangent of each angle of the given triangle:

   (a) $A(3,6)$ $B(8,1)$ $C(5,-2)$.   (b) $P(-5,2)$ $Q(0,6)$ $R(-4,-4)$.
   (c) $L(-4,0)$ $M(0,6)$ $N(4,1)$.   (d) $A(-8,-6)$ $B(-4,2)$ $C(-1,-4)$.

17. A line is drawn from A perpendicular to side BC in the triangle $A(2,6)$ $B(8,2)$ $C(-2,-8)$. Find the tangent of the angle from this line to side AB.

18. In the triangle of Prob. 17, a line is drawn from A to the mid-point of BC, and another line is drawn from A perpendicular to BC. Find the tangent of the acute angle between these lines.

19. A line l_1 is drawn from $P(4,3)$ to the origin, and another line l_2 is drawn from P perpendicular to the line $A(-2,1)$ $B(3,7)$. Find the tangent of the acute angle between l_1 and l_2.

20. A line l_1 is drawn from A to the mid-point of BC in triangle $A(6,-2)$ $B(8,7)$ $C(0,3)$. Another line l_2 is drawn from A to the origin. Find the tangent of the acute angle between l_1 and l_2.

1-14. *Applications to elementary geometry.* The methods of analytic geometry can frequently be used to obtain simple proofs of theorems of elementary geometry. The procedure will be illustrated by two examples.

Example 1

Prove that the diagonals of a parallelogram bisect each other.

Solution (Fig. 1-34)

After drawing the parallelogram we may choose the coordinate system relative to it in such a manner as to make the coordinates to be used as simple as possible. Thus we may choose one vertex as the origin and let the x-axis coincide with one side. The coordinates of three vertices are then obviously

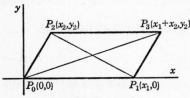

Figure 1-34

$$P_0(0,0); \quad P_1(x_1,0); \quad P_2(x_2,y_2).$$

Since the figure is a parallelogram, the abscissa of the fourth vertex must be $x_1 + x_2$ and its ordinate must be y_2. This point is then

$$P_3(x_1 + x_2, y_2).$$

The mid-point of P_0P_3 is $\left(\dfrac{x_1 + x_2}{2}, \dfrac{y_2}{2} \right)$;

The mid-point of P_1P_2 is $\left(\dfrac{x_1 + x_2}{2}, \dfrac{y_2}{2} \right)$.

These mid-points therefore coincide, and the theorem is proved.

Example 2

Prove that the mid-point of the hypotenuse of a right triangle is equidistant from the vertices.

Solution (Fig. 1-35)

After drawing any right triangle we may again choose the coordinate system in the most convenient way as shown in the figure. Then if M is the mid-point of P_1P_2, its coordinates are $(\frac{1}{2}x_1,\frac{1}{2}y_2)$. The distance of M from P_1 or P_2 is of course $\frac{1}{2}P_1P_2$ or $\frac{1}{2}\sqrt{x_1{}^2 + y_2{}^2}$.

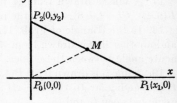

Figure 1-35

Its distance from P_0 is also $\frac{1}{2}\sqrt{x_1{}^2 + y_2{}^2}$. Hence the theorem is proved.

It should be evident to the student that our special choice of axes does not result in a loss in generality in the theorem. The theorems concern properties of the geometrical figures themselves and are independent of the coordinate system to which they are referred. In each case we have drawn the figure first and then added the coordinate system in a convenient position.

It must be emphasized that in using this analytical method we carry out the proof *algebraically*, using the *coordinates* of the points. We do not use the figure that we have drawn except as an aid in visualizing the problem. The coordinates then, rather than the figure, must express the given data. If in Example 1 we had used (x_3,y_3) as the coordinates of P_3, we would not have been dealing with a parallelogram—*even though we had drawn a figure that looked like one*. It is the use of $(x_1 + x_2,y_2)$ as the coordinates of P_3 that makes the figure a parallelogram.

A suitable choice of axes and coordinates for proving theorems concerning any triangle, trapezoid, or general quadrilateral is shown in Fig. 1-36.

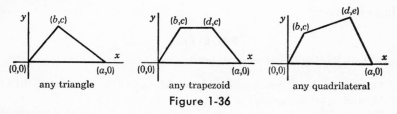

any triangle   any trapezoid   any quadrilateral

Figure 1-36

1-15. Summary. In this chapter we first discussed the correspondence between the real numbers and the points of a directed line—noting that to every real number there corresponds a definite point of the line, and conversely. We defined the absolute value of a real number, and we agreed upon meanings for "greater than" and "less than" as applied to real numbers.

We next defined directed distances. We found that if P_1 and P_2 are any two points on a directed line, and if the coordinate of

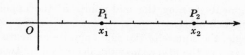

Figure 1-37

P_1 is x_1 and that of P_2 is x_2, with respect to some origin on the line, then the directed distance P_1P_2 is always equal to $x_2 - x_1$ (Fig. 1-37).

We were then ready to study the details of the rectangular

coordinate system and develop the basic formulas and theorems which we shall use over and over again throughout our work in this subject. The formula for the directed length of a line segment parallel to a coordinate axis, and the general distance formula, were the first of these. The formula for division of a line segment, and its special case for finding the mid-point of a line, were next. We developed a general formula, in the form of a determinant, for computing the area of the triangle determined by three given points. Finally, we defined inclination and slope of a line, discovered the conditions for parallelism and perpendicularity of two lines, and developed a formula for finding the angle between two lines whose slopes are known.

These are the fundamental things upon which a great deal of our future work will rest. The student should make certain that he has a thorough grasp of them before he proceeds with the following chapters.

PROBLEMS

Prove the following theorems analytically:

1. The line joining the mid-points of two sides of a triangle is parallel to the third side and equal to one-half of it.

2. The line joining the mid-points of the nonparallel sides of a trapezoid is equal to one-half the sum of the parallel sides.

3. The diagonals of a square are perpendicular to each other.

4. The diagonals of an isosceles trapezoid are equal.

5. The line segments that join the mid-points of the successive sides of any rectangle form a rhombus.

6. The line segments that join the mid-points of the successive sides of any quadrilateral form a parallelogram.

7. If two medians of a triangle are equal, the triangle is isosceles.

8. The sum of the squares of the four sides of any parallelogram equals the sum of the squares of the diagonals.

9. The line segments joining the mid-points of the opposite sides of any quadrilateral bisect each other.

10. In any triangle, the square of the side opposite an acute angle is equal to the sum of the squares of the other two sides decreased by twice the product of one of those sides by the projection of the other upon it.

11. In any triangle, the sum of the squares of the medians is equal to three-fourths the sum of the squares of the three sides.

12. In any triangle, the sum of the squares of two sides is equal to twice the square of one-half the third side plus twice the square of the median drawn to that side.

13. In any quadrilateral, the sum of the squares of the four sides is equal to the sum of the squares of the diagonals plus four times the square of the line segment joining the mid-points of the diagonals.

REVIEW PROBLEMS

14. Prove in two ways that $(-5,0)$, $(8,6)$, and $(3,-4)$ are the vertices of a right triangle.   Find the acute angles.

15. A line l_1 is drawn from $(-2,-3)$ to $(7,0)$.   Another line l_2 is drawn from $(-2,-3)$ to $(2,y)$.   What must be the value of y if the angle from l_1 to l_2 is to be $45°$?   What if the angle from l_2 to l_1 is to be $45°$?

16. The line $A(9,8)$ $B(1,2)$ is extended to cut the x-axis at C.   From C another line is drawn, this line being perpendicular to AB.   At what point does this line cut the y-axis?

17. For what value or values of y will the triangle $A(-3,4)$ $B(6,1)$ $C(4,y)$ have an area of 24 square units?

18. Find the center and radius of the circle that passes through $(-6,4)$, $(-2,0)$, and $(8,0)$.

19. A line l_1 has slope m_1.   What must be the slope of a second line, l_2, if the angle from l_1 to l_2 is to be $135°$?

20. Find the length of the perpendicular drawn from the point $(3,-2)$ to the line through the points $(2,5)$ and $(10,-3)$.   Hint: Use the area of the triangle.

21. The sum of the abscissa and ordinate of a certain point P is zero.   The point is equidistant from $A(-8,-10)$ and $B(2,-2)$.   Find its coordinates.

22. A line is drawn from $P(-3,4)$ perpendicular to $A(-6,1)$ $B(-2,-8)$.   A second line is drawn from P to the mid-point of segment AB.   Find the tangent of the acute angle between these lines.

23. A point P lies on the line that is parallel to the x-axis and 8 units above it.   The slope of the line drawn from P to $(2,0)$ is twice that of the line drawn from P to $(-2,2)$.   What is the abscissa of P?

24. A point P lies on the line that is parallel to the y-axis and 4 units to the right of it.   The sum of the undirected distances of P from $(4,0)$ and $(16,0)$ is 20.   What are the coordinates of P?

25. Plot the points $A(2,12)$ and $B(10,3)$.   Find the coordinates of a point P on the y-axis such that the slopes of AP and BP are equal in absolute value but opposite in sign.

CHAPTER 2

FUNCTIONS AND GRAPHS. EQUATION OF A LOCUS

2-1. Constants and variables. As mentioned in Chap. 1, we shall be concerned almost entirely with *real numbers*. When we use a letter to denote a number, it will be understood that we mean a *real number* unless the contrary is specifically stated. We shall use the word *constant* to signify a particular number or a letter that is understood to stand for some particular number, even though the number has not been specified. The word *variable* will signify a letter that denotes any one of some specified set of numbers. This set is called the *range* of the variable.

Example

The total surface area of a right-circular cylinder of radius x in. and height y in. is

$$2\pi x^2 + 2\pi xy \quad \text{sq. in.}$$

The number 2 and the Greek letter π are *constants*. The letters x and y may denote *any* positive numbers, and hence may be regarded as variables in the above sense. If we wish to think of y as having some *fixed* value, then x is the only variable in the expression, and it then gives the surface areas of cylinders having various radii but having this fixed height.

We shall frequently employ the later letters of the alphabet such as x, y, z, u, v, for variables, and the early letters such as a, b, c, d, for constants. We shall also use symbols such as a_0, a_1, a_2, $\cdots$, to denote constants.

2-2. Functions. Let x denote a variable with some specified range. (The range might be all real numbers, all negative numbers, all positive integers, all numbers between -2 and $+2$, etc.) Suppose now that some relation has been established between the value of x and the value of a second variable y, such that to each value of x in its range there corresponds one or more values of y.

46

We say then that **y** *is a function of* **x** over this range.   If there is just one value of y corresponding to each admissible value of x, then y is said to be a *single-valued* function of x.

For example, if we let x denote any real number and specify that y shall depend upon x in accordance with the relation

$$y = \frac{6x}{x^2 + 3},$$

then we have defined y as a function of x.   It is a single-valued function because to each value of x there corresponds just one value of y.

The student is familiar with many examples of dependence of one variable upon another.   Thus the volume of a sphere depends upon its radius, or is a function of its radius.   The relation in this case is $V = \frac{4}{3}\pi r^3$.   To every (positive) value of r there corresponds a definite value of V.   The equation $3x - 4y = 12$ yields a definite value of y for each value assigned to x, and we may therefore say that it defines y as a function of x.   It also, of course, defines x as a function of y; that is, we may assign values to y, and the equation determines corresponding values of x.   The variable to which we assign values is called the *independent variable;* the other is called the *dependent variable.*

The statement "y is a function of x" is abbreviated by writing $y = f(x)$, which is read "y equals f of x."   We also use symbols such as $f(x)$, $g(x)$, and $\phi(x)$ to denote specific functions of x.   Thus if we are concerned in a particular problem with the functions $x^3 + 14x^2 - 5$ and $3x^2 - 7x + 2$, we may find it convenient to let $f(x)$ denote the first and $g(x)$ the second of these functions. We can then refer to the first function, for example, as "the function f," or "the function $f(x)$."   This will be simpler than saying "the function $x^3 + 14x^2 - 5$."

If $f(x)$ denotes a certain function of x, then $f(a)$ denotes the value of $f(x)$ when x has the value a; it is found by substituting a for x in the expression defining $f(x)$.   Thus if

$$
\begin{aligned}
f(x) &= x^2 - 4x + 2,\\
f(0) &= 0^2 - 4(0) + 2 = 2,\\
f(1) &= 1^2 - 4(1) + 2 = -1,\\
f(-2) &= (-2)^2 - 4(-2) + 2 = \mathbf{14},\\
f(h) &= h^2 - 4h + 2.
\end{aligned}
$$

The corresponding definitions and notation concerning the case in which one variable is a function of two or more other variables are obvious.   Thus the volume of a right-circular cylinder is a function of its radius and height.   The distance D between the point $(3, -5)$ and $P(x,y)$ is a function of x and y; that is, when x and y are specified, the value of D is fixed.   In this case the relation is $D = \sqrt{(x - 3)^2 + (y + 5)^2}$.

2-3. Graph of an equation.   The coordinate system that we have discussed enables us to associate a point in the xy-plane with a pair of real numbers (x,y).   We may now associate a line or curve or other geometrical configuration with an equation in the variables x and y as follows:

Let each pair of values of x and y (real numbers only) that satisfy the equation be regarded as the coordinates (x,y) of a point, and let all such points be plotted.   The totality of these is called the *graph* of the equation.

Example 1

The equation $2y = x + 2$ is satisfied by the pairs of values of x and y given in the following table:

x	-4	-3	-2	-1	0	1	2	3	4	5
y	-1	$-\frac{1}{2}$	0	$\frac{1}{2}$	1	$1\frac{1}{2}$	2	$2\frac{1}{2}$	3	$3\frac{1}{2}$

When these points are plotted, they appear to lie on a straight line (Fig. 2-1). We may suspect that the coordinates of every point on this line satisfy the

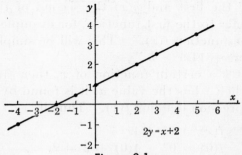

Figure 2-1

equation and that the equation is not satisfied by the coordinates of any point not on the line.   This is true, but we shall not give the proof here.

Example 2

The equation $x^2 + y^2 = 25$ is satisfied by the pairs of values of x and y given in the following table:

x	-5	-4	-3	-2	-1	0	1	2	3	4	5
y	0	± 3	± 4	$\pm \sqrt{21}$	$\pm \sqrt{24}$	± 5	$\pm \sqrt{24}$	$\pm \sqrt{21}$	± 4	± 3	0

When these points are plotted, they appear to lie on a circle with center at the origin and radius 5 (Fig. 2-2). It is easy to prove that the equation is satisfied

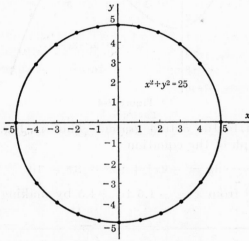

Figure 2-2

by the coordinates of every point on this circle and that it is not satisfied by the coordinates of any point not on the circle. The proof is as follows:

The distance from the origin to any point (x,y) in the plane is equal to $\sqrt{x^2 + y^2}$, as is apparent from Fig. 2-3. Hence for any point on the circle we have $\sqrt{x^2 + y^2} = 5$, or $x^2 + y^2 = 25$. If (x,y) is a point of the plane that does not lie on this circle, the value of $\sqrt{x^2 + y^2}$ is more or less than 5, and hence $x^2 + y^2$ is not equal to 25.

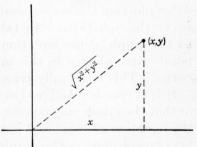

Figure 2-3

In making the graph of a given equation, we of course cannot actually plot all the points whose coordinates satisfy the equation.

We actually plot as many as are deemed necessary to indicate the graph with sufficient accuracy for the purpose at hand, and then draw a curve through these points.   This curve is in general an

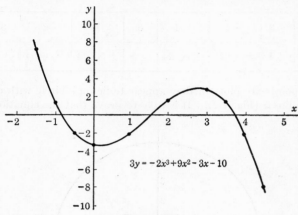

$$3y = -2x^3 + 9x^2 - 3x - 10$$

Figure 2-4

approximation to the actual graph.   Thus in Fig. 2-4 we have drawn the graph of the equation

$$3y = -2x^3 + 9x^2 - 3x - 10$$

in the interval from $x = -1.5$ to $+4.5$ by making the following table:

x	-2	-1.5	-1	-0.5	0	1	2	3	3.5	4	4.5
y	16	7.2	1.3	-2	-3.3	-2	1.3	2.7	1.3	-2	-7.8

After plotting the corresponding points, we have drawn a smooth curve through them.   In taking this curve as an approximation to the graph of the equation, we are assuming that if additional points were plotted in this interval they would lie on or near this curve.   This is actually true, but we cannot give the proof here.

It is of course possible that a given equation may have no graph, or that the graph may consist of one or more isolated points.   Thus the equation $x^2 + y^2 = 0$ is not satisfied by any pair of real numbers except $(0,0)$.   The graph then consists of this one point.   The equation $2x^2 + 3y^2 + 4 = 0$ has no graph because it is not satisfied by any pair of real numbers.

2-4. *Graph of a function.* By the graph of a function $f(x)$ we
mean the graph of the equation $y = f(x)$. Thus we may speak of
the graph of the function $x^2 + 5$ and the graph of the equation
$y = x^2 + 5$ interchangeably. Figure 2-1 may be regarded as the
graph of the function $\frac{1}{2}(x + 2)$. The top half of the circle in
Fig. 2-2 is the graph of the function $\sqrt{25 - x^2}$, and the bottom
half is the graph of the function $-\sqrt{25 - x^2}$.

PROBLEMS

1. For what points is the abscissa equal to the ordinate? Write down an
equation that has these points for its graph.

2. For what points is the abscissa equal to -3? Write down an equation
that has these points for its graph.

3. For what points is the ordinate equal to 5? Write down an equation that
has these points for its graph.

4. For what points is the sum of the abscissa and ordinate equal to zero?
Write down an equation that has these points as its graph.

5. Using the definition of the graph of an equation, prove that the graph of
the equation $xy = 0$ consists of all points on the x-axis and all points on the
y-axis.

6. Show that the equations $xy = 0$ and $xy(x^2 + y^2) = 0$ have the same graph.
(Recall that a product is zero if and only if at least one of the factors is zero.)

In each of the following cases make a table of corresponding values of the two
variables, plot the points, and draw a smooth curve through them. Use the
specified interval on the x-axis.

7. $y = x^2 + 4x$; $x = -6$ to $+2$.

8. $3y = 2x + 3$; $x = -3$ to $+4$.

9. $x - 3y = 6$; $x = -2$ to $+8$.

10. $2y = 2x^2 + 3x - 14$; $x = -4$ to $+3$.

11. $4y = 8x - x^2$; $x = -1$ to $+9$.

12. $y^2 = 4x$; $x = 0$ to $+6$.

13. $2y = x^3 - 4x^2$; $x = -1$ to $+5$.

14. $x^2 + y^2 = 36$; $x = -6$ to $+6$.

15. $y + 2x^2 = 5x + 12$; $x = -3$ to $+6$.

16. $y = \frac{1}{4}x^2(6 - x)$; $x = -2$ to $+7$.

17. $6y = x(x + 4)^2$; $x = -6$ to $+2$.

18. $8y = x^3 - 6x^2 + 4x - 24$; $x = -3$ to $+7$.

19. $6y = x^2(x^2 - 16)$; $x = -4.5$ to 4.5.

20. $y = \frac{1}{8}x^2(x - 6)^2$; $x = -1$ to $+7$.

21. $y = \dfrac{24}{x^2 + 4}$; $x = -5$ to $+5$.   **22.** $y = \dfrac{16x}{x^2 + 4}$; $x = -6$ to $+6$.

In each of the following cases make the graph of the given function over the specified interval:

23. $6 - \frac{1}{4}x^2$; $x = 0$ to 6.   **24.** $\sqrt{x - 4}$; $x = 4$ to 13.

25. $3 + 2x - x^2$; $x = -3$ to $+5$.   **26.** $\dfrac{4}{1 + x^2}$; $x = -3$ to $+3$.

27. $\dfrac{2x^2}{x^2 + 4}$; $x = -6$ to $+6$.   **28.** $\sqrt[3]{2x}$; $x = -10$ to $+10$.

29. $\dfrac{x^3}{x^3 + 8}$; $x = -5$ to $+5$.   **30.** $\dfrac{8}{x^3 - 8}$; $x = -5$ to $+5$.

31. $-\frac{2}{3}\sqrt{36 - x^2}$; $x = -6$ to $+6$.

32. $\frac{1}{3}x\sqrt{36 - x^2}$; $x = -6$ to $+6$.

33. Express the volume of a cube as a function of its surface area.   HINT: If the edge is x in., then $V = x^3$ and $S = 6x^2$.   From these relations derive an expression for V in terms of S.

34. Express the volume of a sphere as a function of its surface area (see hint in Prob. 33).

35. The period T of a pendulum is expressed as a function of its length by the formula $T = 2\pi\sqrt{L/g}$, where g is a constant.   Express L as a function of T.

36. Express the length of a chord of a circle of diameter 24 in. as a function of its distance from the center of the circle.

37. Express the undirected distance between the points $A(2,-3)$ and $P(x,5)$ as a function of x.

38. A line is drawn parallel to the y-axis and 3 units to the left of it.   Express the directed distance from the line to the point $P(x,y)$ as a function of x.   HINT: Observe that this is the same as the directed segment AP, where A has the coordinates $(-3,y)$.

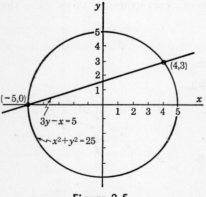

Figure 2-5

2-5. Intersections of graphs. In Fig. 2-5 the graphs of the equations $3y - x = 5$ and $x^2 + y^2 = 25$ are drawn on the same coordinate axes.   The first is a straight line,* and the second is a circle.

From our definition of the graph of an equation it is clear that the equation $3y - x = 5$ is satisfied by the coordinates of every point on the line, and is not satisfied by the coordinates of any

* It will be proved in Chap. 3 that the graph of any equation of first degree in x and y is a straight line.

other point.   Similarly, the equation $x^2 + y^2 = 25$ is satisfied by
the coordinates of every point on the circle, and is not satisfied
by the coordinates of any other point.   It is thus clear that the
two equations

$$3y - x = 5,$$
$$x^2 + y^2 = 25,$$

are *both* satisfied by the coordinates of those points that lie on both
the line and the circle, and are not *both* satisfied by any other pair
of real numbers.   Thus the coordinates of the points of intersection of the graphs are the pairs of real numbers that satisfy the
system of equations.

   These coordinates can be found in simple cases by methods discussed in books on algebra.   In this case we would proceed as
follows:

(1) $$3y - x = 5,$$
(2) $$x^2 + y^2 = 25.$$

Solve (1) for x in terms of y: $x = 3y - 5$.   Now, substitute this
for x in (2), and then solve the resulting quadratic equation for y.

$$(3y - 5)^2 + y^2 = 25;$$
$$9y^2 - 30y + 25 + y^2 = 25;$$
$$y^2 - 3y = 0.$$
$$y = 0 \text{ or } 3.$$

Substituting these values for y in (1), we find that the corresponding values of x are -5, and 4, respectively.   The coordinates of
the points of intersection are then
$(-5,0)$ and $(4,3)$.

   If the graphs of the equations have
no point in common, it can be con-
cluded that the corresponding equations have no common solutions in the
field of real numbers.   Figure 2-6
shows the graphs of the equations

$$y^2 - x = 2;$$
$$2x - 3y + 6 = 0.$$

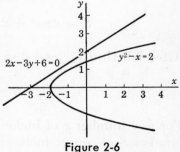

Figure 2-6

The student may prove analytically that the two equations are
not both satisfied by any pair of real numbers (x,y).

2-6. *Applications of graphs.* One frequently wishes to study the way in which some physical or geometrical quantity Q, which is known to be a function of a certain variable x, changes as the value of x changes. One procedure is to express the relation between Q and x in the form of an equation, $Q = f(x)$, and make the corresponding graph. This graph may be regarded as a picture which shows the value of Q for each value of x within a certain range; it shows pictorially the way in which the value of Q increases and decreases as x increases. The following example should make the idea clear:

A manufacturer of an antifreeze compound packages his product in 1-gal. cylindrical tin cans. He recognizes that such a can may be relatively small in radius and rather tall, or larger in radius and shorter. He knows that different combinations of radius and height yield cans requiring different amounts of tin, and he suspects that there should be a particular radius that would result in a can having the smallest amount of surface area and therefore requiring the smallest amount of tin. He knows that when the radius is specified the height is fixed by the requirement that the volume must be 1 gal. (231 cu. in.). Consequently, the surface area S is determined if the radius x is specified; in other words, S is a function of x.

In order to get the relation between S and x, we observe that for any radius x (inches) there will be a bottom and a top each having an area of πx^2 sq. in. In addition there is a lateral area of $2\pi x h$ sq. in., where the height h is related to x by the requirement that $\pi x^2 h = 231$ cu. in. Thus we have

$$S = 2\pi x^2 + 2\pi x h, \qquad \text{where } h = \frac{231}{\pi x^2}.$$

After substituting for h its value in terms of x, we have the relation

$$S = 2\pi x^2 + \frac{462}{x}.$$

For any number x of inches in the radius, this equation gives the number S of square inches in the surface area of the 1-gal. can.

The graph of this equation is shown in Fig. 2-7. It shows pictorially that S is large if x is small, and that S decreases as x increases, until x reaches a value around $3\frac{1}{4}$ in. where S appears

19. A rectangular box is made from a sheet of tin that is 18 in. long and 12 in. wide, by cutting a square from each corner and turning up the sides as in the example on page 55. Express the volume of the box obtained as a function of the edge x of the square cut out, and make a graph of the function. For about what size square would the largest box be obtained?

20. A can in the form of a right-circular cylinder is to contain 600 cu. in. The material used for the top costs 3 cents per square inch, and that for the rest of the can costs 1 cent per square inch. Express the cost C of material as a function of the radius x of the can. Make a graph of this function. Estimate the value of x for which the cost is least.

21. A rectangle is inscribed in an isosceles triangle as shown in Fig. 2-10. Express the area of the rectangle as a function of its height y. Draw the graph of this function. What value of y appears to give the largest rectangle? HINT: Find the other dimension of the rectangle in terms of y by using similar triangles.

22. A chord is drawn in a circle of radius 6 in. Express the length L of the chord as a function of its distance x from the center of the circle. Make a graph of the function.

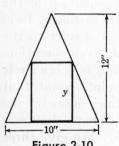

Figure 2-10

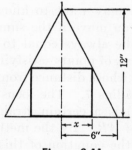

Figure 2-11

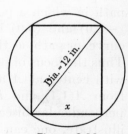

Figure 2-12

23. A right-circular cylinder of radius x is inscribed in a right circular cone of radius 6 in. and height 12 in., as indicated in Fig. 2-11. Express the volume of the cylinder as a function of x, and make a graph of the function. What value of x appears to give the largest cylinder? In making the graph it is convenient to let a unit on the "volume" axis represent π cu. in.

24. A rectangle is inscribed in a circle of radius 6 in. Express the area A of the rectangle as a function of the length x of its base (Fig. 2-12). Make a graph of this function, and estimate the value of x for which A is largest.

25. The following experimentally determined data give the length L of a certain spring (inches) when subjected to a pull of x lb. Make the corresponding graph showing how the length varies with the load.

x	0	1	2	3	4	5	6	7	8
L	13.10	14.32	15.56	16.82	18.04	19.30	20.58	21.88	23.18

26. The following data give the period T (seconds) of a simple pendulum of length L (feet). Make the corresponding graph showing how the period varies with the length. The period is the time required for the pendulum to make one complete swing (over and back).

L	0.50	1.0	1.5	2.0	2.5	3.0	3.5	4.0
T	0.78	1.11	1.35	1.56	1.75	1.92	2.07	2.21

2-7. Equation of a locus.

One of the principal problems of analytic geometry is that of finding the equation of a curve which is defined by some geometrical condition or other property. For example, we may want the equation of the path of a point which moves in the xy-plane in such a way as to be always equidistant from two given points. Or we may want the equation of the curve every point of which is the same distance from the y-axis as from the point $(4,0)$. Or we may want to know the equation of the path in which a point can move if the sum of its distances from $(-3,0)$ and $(3,0)$ is to be always equal to 10. We refer to the curve, or path, as the *locus* of points satisfying the given condition. Thus the locus of points whose distance from $A(2,3)$ is 7, is a circle with center at A and radius 7. The locus of points equidistant from $A(1,1)$ and $B(6,3)$ is a certain straight line—namely, the perpendicular bisector of AB. By the methods that we shall now illustrate, one can find the equation of this line. We give three examples, which the reader should study carefully.

Example 1

Find the equation of the locus of points equidistant from $A(1,1)$ and $B(6,3)$.

Solution (Fig. 2-13)

Let (x,y) be the coordinates of a point in the xy-plane. Let d_1 and d_2 be its (undirected) distances from A and B, respectively. Then

$$d_1 = \sqrt{(x - 1)^2 + (y - 1)^2}; \qquad d_2 = \sqrt{(x - 6)^2 + (y - 3)^2}.$$

If we are to have $d_1 = d_2$, then we must have

$$(1) \qquad \sqrt{(x - 1)^2 + (y - 1)^2} = \sqrt{(x - 6)^2 + (y - 3)^2}.$$

Squaring both sides and simplifying the result, we get

$$(2) \qquad x^2 - 2x + 1 + y^2 - 2y + 1 = x^2 - 12x + 36 + y^2 - 6y + 9,$$
$$(3) \qquad -2x - 2y + 2 = -12x - 6y + 45,$$

and finally,

(4) $10x + 4y = 43.$

If (1) is to be true, then (4) must be true—so we know that if a point (x,y) has $d_1 = d_2$ its coordinates must satisfy (4). Conversely, (4) implies (3), (2), and

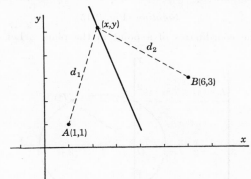

Figure 2-13

finally (1)—so that *every* point whose coordinates satisfy (4) has $d_1 = d_2$. We are thus assured that the points (x,y) whose coordinates satisfy (4) are those, and only those, for which $d_1 = d_2$.

Example 2

Find the equation of the locus of points whose (undirected) distance from $(3,2)$ is 5.

Solution (Fig. 2-14)

Let (x,y) be the coordinates of a point in the xy-plane. Let d be its (undirected) distance from $(3,2)$. Then

$$d = \sqrt{(x-3)^2 + (y-2)^2}.$$

If we are to have $d = 5$, then we must have

(1) $\sqrt{(x-3)^2 + (y-2)^2} = 5.$

Squaring both sides and simplifying the result, we get

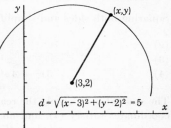

Figure 2-14

(2) $(x-3)^2 + (y-2)^2 = 25$

or

(3) $x^2 + y^2 - 6x - 4y - 12 = 0.$

From the fact that (1) implies (3) we can conclude that if a point (x,y) has $d = 5$ then its coordinates must satisfy (3). From the fact that (3) implies (1) we can conclude that every point whose coordinates satisfy (3) has $d = 5$. Thus the graph of (3) contains all points that are 5 units from $(3,2)$, and no other points. The locus is of course a circle.

Example 3

A line *l* is drawn parallel to the *y*-axis and 3 units to the left of it.   A point moves so that it is always twice as far from this line as from the origin.   Find the equation of its path.

Solution (Fig. 2-15)

Let (x,y) be the coordinates of a point in the plane.   Let d_1 and d_2 be its

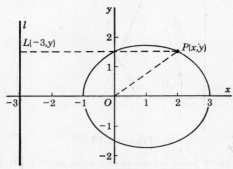

Figure 2-15

undirected distances from *l* and from the origin, respectively.   Then

$$d_1 = \sqrt{(x+3)^2} \text{ (or } |x+3|); \qquad d_2 = \sqrt{x^2 + y^2}.$$

If we are to have $d_1 = 2d_2$, then we must have

$$(1) \qquad \sqrt{(x+3)^2} = 2\sqrt{x^2 + y^2}.$$

Squaring both sides and simplifying the result, we have

$$(2) \qquad (x+3)^2 = 4(x^2 + y^2),$$
$$(3) \qquad x^2 + 6x + 9 = 4x^2 + 4y^2,$$
$$(4) \qquad 3x^2 + 4y^2 - 6x - 9 = 0.$$

The student may supply the reasoning that assures us that the points (x,y) whose coordinates satisfy (4), and no other points, have $d_1 = 2d_2$.   The graph of the equation is a curve called an *ellipse*.   Its properties will be studied later.

It is perhaps worthwhile to return briefly to Example 1 and reemphasize the following point:

Before we can conclude that $10x + 4y = 43$ is the solution to the problem, we must be certain that the following two conditions are satisfied:

1. The coordinates of *every* point (x,y) having $d_1 = d_2$ satisfies the equation; briefly, *if $d_1 = d_2$, then $10x + 4y = 43$.*

2. Every point (x,y) such that $10x + 4y = 43$ has $d_1 = d_2$; briefly, *if $10x + 4y = 43$, then $d_1 = d_2$.*

The reasoning underlying the steps by which we obtained (4) from (1) in Example 1 takes care of the first part: If (1) is true, then (2) must be true, because if two numbers are equal their squares are equal. If (2) is true, then (3) and (4) must be true because of the axioms about adding equals to equals. We can thus conclude that

if　　　　$\sqrt{(x-1)^2 + (y-1)^2} = \sqrt{(x-6)^2 + (y-3)^2},$

then　　　　　　　　　$10x + 4y = 43.$

This means that if a point (x,y) in the plane is such that $d_1 = d_2$ then it lies on the graph of the equation $10x + 4y = 43$. It does not assure us that *every point* on this graph has $d_1 = d_2$. (The fact that every person with two quarters has at least 50 cents does not assure us that everyone with 50 cents has two quarters.) We must be certain of the truth of the assertion,

if　　　　　　　　　$10x + 4y = 43,$

then　　$\sqrt{(x-1)^2 + (y-1)^2} = \sqrt{(x-6)^2 + (y-3)^2}.$

This involves reversing the above steps—starting with (4) as our hypothesis and showing that (1) is a logical consequence. In this connection it is important to observe that if (2) is true then (1) is true because the *positive* square roots of two equal positive numbers are equal.

PROBLEMS

1. Find the equation of the locus of all points whose undirected distance from $A(-3,-1)$ is 3.

2. Find the equation of the circle with center at $(6, -2)$ and radius 4.

3. Find the equation of the circle whose center is at $(-5,5)$, and which passes through the origin.

4. A point moves in the xy-plane so as to be always equidistant from $A(-2,-6)$ and $B(4,-1)$. Find the equation of its path.

5. Find the equation of the perpendicular bisector of the segment $P(-2,3)$ $Q(4,-5)$.

6. A point moves so as to be always equidistant from the two given points A and B. Find the equation of its path, and draw the graph.

(a) $A(6,2)$ $B(-1,5)$.   (b) $A(-4,0)$ $B(0,-6)$.
(c) $A(-1,-3)$ $B(6,1)$.   (d) $A(-2,4)$ $B(4,0)$.

7. Find the equation of the locus of points equidistant from the y-axis and the point $(4,0)$.

8. Find the equation of the locus of points equidistant from the x-axis and the point $(3,4)$.

9. A point moves so as to be always equidistant from the origin and a line drawn parallel to the x-axis 4 units above it. Find the equation of its path.

10. A point moves so as to be always equidistant from the point $(4,0)$ and a line parallel to the y-axis and 4 units to the left of it. Find the equation of its path, and sketch the graph.

11. Find the equation of the curve each of whose points is twice as far from the point $(12,0)$ as from the origin.

12. A point moves in the xy-plane in such a way as to be always twice as far from $A(-8,0)$ as from $B(4,0)$. Find the equation of its path.

13. A point moves in the xy-plane in such a way that the sum of the slopes of the lines joining it to $(1,4)$ and $(1,-2)$ is always equal to 2. Find the equation of its path, and plot it.

14. A certain curve has the following property: The slope of the line joining any point P on it to $A(6,0)$ is equal to twice the slope of the line joining P to the origin. Find the equation of this curve, and plot it.

15. The slope of the line joining any point P of a certain curve to the origin is equal to one-third the slope of the line joining P to $(1,1)$. What is the equation of this curve?

16. A point moves in the xy-plane in such a way that its distance from the x-axis is always equal to twice its distance from the point $(0,4)$. Find the equation of its path.

17. A point moves in the xy-plane so that the sum of the squares of its distances from the points A and B is equal to the square of the distance AB. Find the equation of its path, and identify the curve.

(a) $A(-6,0)$ $B(6,0)$.   (b) $A(0,2)$ $B(8,2)$.
(c) $A(-2,0)$ $B(4,4)$.   (d) $A(-3,-4)$ $B(3,0)$.

18. From any point on a certain curve the sum of the undirected distances to $(-3,0)$ and $(3,0)$ is equal to 10. Find the equation of this curve.

19. From any point of a certain curve the undirected distance to $(-5,0)$ minus the undirected distance to $(5,0)$ is equal to 8. Find the equation of this curve.

20. A point moves in the xy-plane in such a way that the sum of its distances from the origin and the point $(8,0)$ is equal to 12. Find the equation of its path.

In each of the following cases state whether or not the given assertion is valid. Write down the converse, and state whether or not it is valid.

21. If $x = -4$, then $x^2 = 16$.

22. If $(x + 3)^2 = 1$, then $|x + 3| = 1$.

23. If $\sqrt{(x + 1)^2} = 5$, then $(x + 1)^2 = 25$.

24. If $|x + 3| = 5$, then $(x + 3)^2 = 25$.

25. If $\sqrt{(x - 4)^2 + (y + 1)^2} = 4 - x$, then
$$(x - 4)^2 + (y + 1)^2 = (4 - x)^2.$$

26. If $\sqrt{(x - 4)^2 + (y + 1)^2} = |6 - x|$, then
$$(x - 4)^2 + (y + 1)^2 = (6 - x)^2.$$

27. If $\sqrt{(x - 1)^2 + (y - 2)^2} = 2\sqrt{(x + 4)^2 + (y + 2)^2}$, then
$$(x - 1)^2 + (y - 2)^2 = 4[(x + 4)^2 + (y + 2)^2].$$

28. Prove each of the following propositions:

(a) If a point $P(x,y)$ is equidistant from $A(1,6)$ and $B(4,-3)$, then its coordinates satisfy the equation $3y - x = 2$.

(b) Every point whose coordinates satisfy the equation $3y - x = 2$ is equidistant from $A(1,6)$ and $B(4,-3)$.

CHAPTER 3

THE LINE

3-1. *Introduction.* A line is completely determined if the coordinates of two points on it are specified. It may also be determined by specifying one point and the slope, or by giving certain other data—such as the length and direction of the shortest segment that can be drawn from the origin to the line.

We proceed now to derive formulas for writing down the equation of a line in terms of the various data that may be given to determine it. We shall see that in each case we are led to an equation of first degree in x and y, and we shall then prove that every equation of first degree in x and y represents a straight line.

3-2. *The point-slope form.* Let a line be determined by specifying its slope m and the coordinates (x_1,y_1) of one point on it.

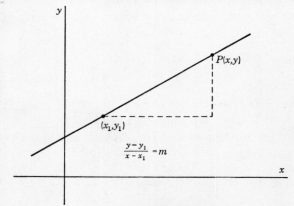

Figure 3-1

We wish to find the equation of the line; i.e., we wish to find an equation in x and y which is satisfied by the coordinates (x,y) of *every* point on the line—and which is not satisfied by any other pair of real numbers. We proceed as follows (Fig. 3-1):

If $P(x,y)$ is any point in the plane, then the slope of the segment joining P to the given point (x_1,y_1) is $(y - y_1)/(x - x_1)$. This is equal to the given number m if and only if $P(x,y)$ lies on the specified line. The desired equation is then

$$\frac{y - y_1}{x - x_1} = m$$

or

$$y - y_1 = m(x - x_1).$$

This is called the *point-slope* form of the equation of a line. It may be used as a formula for writing down the equation of a line when its slope, and one point on it, are known.

Example

The equation of the line through $(-4,2)$ with slope $\frac{3}{2}$ is

$$y - 2 = \tfrac{3}{2}[x - (-4)]$$

or

$$3x - 2y + 16 = 0.$$

3-3. *The slope-intercept form.* If a line intersects the y-axis at $(0,b)$ as in Fig. 3-2, then b is called the *y-intercept* of the line. The equation of the line in terms of its slope m and its y-intercept b is found by using $(0,b)$ in place of (x_1,y_1) in the point-slope formula. The result is

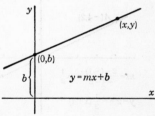

$$y - b = m(x - 0)$$

or

$$y = mx + b.$$

Figure 3-2

This is called the *slope-intercept form* of the equation of a line. It may be used conveniently for writing down the equation when the slope and y-intercept are known.

Example

The equation of the line with slope $\frac{1}{2}$ and y-intercept -3 is

$$y = \tfrac{1}{2}x + (-3)$$

or

$$x - 2y - 6 = 0.$$

3-4. *Given two points.* If a line is determined by specifying the coordinates (x_1,y_1) and (x_2,y_2) of two points on it, one may find its slope (if $x_1 \neq x_2$) from the formula

$$m = \frac{y_2 - y_1}{x_2 - x_1}.$$

The equation may then be written down by using one of the given points (either will do) and the slope.

Example

Find the equation of the line through $A(-4,2)$ and $B(2,-1)$.

Solution (Fig. 3-3)

The slope of the line is $\dfrac{2 - (-1)}{-4 - 2} = -\dfrac{1}{2}.$

The equation, obtained by using point A and the slope, is

$$y - 2 = -\tfrac{1}{2}[x - (-4)]$$

or $x + 2y = 0.$

3-5. *The intercept form.* Figure 3-4 shows a line intersecting the x-axis at $(a,0)$ and the y-axis at $(0,b)$. The numbers a and b

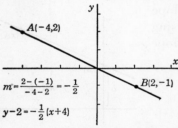

Figure 3-3

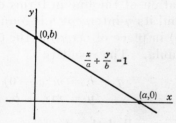

Figure 3-4

are called the *intercepts* of the line. If neither of them is zero, we may obtain the equation of the line as follows: Its slope is

$$m = \frac{b - 0}{0 - a} = -\frac{b}{a}.$$

Using the point $(a,0)$ and the slope, we find its equation to be

$$y - 0 = -\frac{b}{a}(x - a)$$

or $bx + ay = ab.$

This can be put into a somewhat more convenient form by dividing both sides by ab. The result is

$$\frac{x}{a} + \frac{y}{b} = 1.$$

This is called the *intercept form* of the equation of a line. It can be used conveniently for writing down the equation of a line when its intercepts are known, provided that neither of them is zero.

Example

The equation of the line that crosses the x-axis at $x = 4$ and the y-axis at $y = -1$ is

$$\frac{x}{4} + \frac{y}{-1} = 1$$

or

$$x - 4y - 4 = 0.$$

3-6. *Lines parallel to the coordinate axes.* Figure 3-5 shows a line parallel to the x-axis and with y-intercept b. It is evident that every point on this line satisfies the equation $y = b$, and, conversely, every point with ordinate equal to b is on the line. The equation of the line is therefore

$$y = b.$$

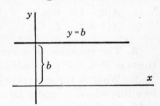

Figure 3-5

Similarly, the equation of a line parallel to the y-axis, and crossing the x-axis at $x = a$, is

$$x = a.$$

PROBLEMS

1. In each of the following cases, find the equation of the line through the given point A with the given slope m:

(a) $A(-5,3)$; $m = \frac{2}{3}$.

(b) $A(3,-4)$; $m = -\frac{1}{2}$.

(c) $A(6,1)$; $m = -2$.

(d) $A(-2,7)$; $m = \frac{1}{3}$.

(e) $A(-3,-5)$; $m = 0.3$.

(f) $A(-4,0)$; $m = -\frac{3}{4}$.

2. Find the equation of the line determined by the given points A and B.

(a) $A(2,3)$ $B(6,-2)$.

(b) $A(-5,-2)$ $B(0,-1)$.

(c) $A(-3,4)$ $B(3,-2)$.

(d) $A(5,2)$ $B(0,3)$.

(e) $A(\frac{4}{3},0)$ $B(\frac{5}{2},-\frac{3}{2})$.

(f) $A(-2,-\frac{5}{3})$ $B(0,\frac{2}{3})$.

3. Write down the equation of the line with given y-intercept b and slope m, or with given intercepts a and b.

(a) $b = -4$, $m = \frac{2}{3}$. (b) $b = 6$, $m = -\frac{1}{2}$.
(c) $b = -8$, $m = -\frac{5}{2}$. (d) $a = \frac{3}{2}$, $b = -2$.
(e) $a = -5$, $b = -\frac{7}{2}$. (f) $a = \frac{1}{2}$, $b = -\frac{2}{3}$.

4. The vertices of a rectangle are $A(0,0)$, $B(-8,0)$, $C(-8,-6)$, and $D(0,-6)$. Write equations for the lines which form its sides and diagonals.

5. The vertices of a triangle are $A(2,6)$, $B(8,-4)$, and $C(-3,-5)$. Two lines are drawn from A, one parallel to and the other perpendicular to BC. Find the equation of each of these lines.

6. Write the equation of the line that is the perpendicular bisector of the given segment AB.

(a) $A(-2,4)$ $B(4,0)$. (b) $A(-5,-3)$ $B(2,1)$.
(c) $A(0,-4)$ $B(6,0)$. (d) $A(8,-3)$ $B(3,2)$.

7. In the triangle ABC, find the equation of the altitude drawn from A perpendicular to side BC.

(a) $A(0,-4)$ $B(6,2)$ $C(-3,8)$. (b) $A(-4,-2)$ $B(0,-6)$ $C(6,4)$.
(c) $A(-8,3)$ $B(-2,5)$ $C(1,-4)$.

8. The equation of a certain straight line is $y = \frac{2}{3}x + 2$. A line is drawn through $P(8,-3)$ perpendicular to this line. What is its equation?

9. What is the equation of the line drawn through the origin perpendicular to a line whose x- and y-intercepts are 5 and $-\frac{3}{2}$, respectively?

10. Find the equation of the line that goes through the point $P(0,6)$ and is parallel to the line whose equation is $y = -3x + 2$.

11. In each of the following cases, find the equation of the median drawn from B to the mid-point of AC in triangle ABC:

(a) $A(0,6)$ $B(8,0)$ $C(3,-4)$. (b) $A(-7,5)$ $B(1,6)$ $C(5,-6)$.
(c) $A(-2,-8)$ $B(3,-1)$ $C(-5,4)$.

12. The equation of a line is $2x - 3y = 30$. What point on it is equidistant from $A(1,3)$ and $B(7,9)$? HINT: Find the point where the perpendicular bisector of AB intersects the given line.

13. A line passes through $P(-4,5)$ and $Q(2,1)$. What point on it is equidistant from $A(-2,0)$ and $B(2,-1)$ (see hint in Prob. 12)?

14. A line passes through $L(8,1)$ and $M(4,-2)$. What point on it is equidistant from $A(-3,0)$ and $B(0,6)$ (see hint in Prob. 12)?

15. Find the coordinates of the center of the circle that passes through $A(8,7)$, $B(6,-7)$ and $C(-8,-5)$. HINT: Find the point of intersection of the perpendicular bisectors of segments AB and BC.

16. Find the coordinates of the center of the circle that passes through the points $A(1,0)$, $B(8,1)$, and $C(2,-7)$ (see hint in Prob. 15).

17. Show that the equation of the line determined by the points (x_1, y_1) and (x_2, y_2) can be written in the form

$$\begin{vmatrix} x & y & 1 \\ x_1 & y_1 & 1 \\ x_2 & y_2 & 1 \end{vmatrix} = 0.$$

18. Use the determinant of Prob. 17 to find the equation of the line determined by the given points A and B.

(a) $A(-6,2)$ $B(0,4)$. (b) $A(4,0)$ $B(-2,2)$.
(c) $A(8,-6)$ $B(0,0)$. (d) $A(-3,-7)$ $B(5,3)$.

19. Find the area of the triangle $A(-3,5)$ $B(-2,-2)$ $C(6,2)$ by multiplying $\frac{1}{2}BC$ by the altitude drawn from A. Check by using the determinant.

20. Find the area of the triangle $A(-2,-1)$ $B(10,8)$ $C(12,-3)$ by multiplying $\frac{1}{2}BC$ by the altitude drawn from A. Check by using the determinant.

3-7. *The general equation of first degree.* Any equation that is of the first degree in the variables x and y can be written in the form

$$Ax + By + C = 0$$

where A, B, and C are constants and A and B are not both zero. We wish now to prove that the graph is in all cases a straight line. (It is for this reason that the equation is called a *linear* equation.)

If $B = 0$, then the graph is a straight line because the equation becomes $Ax + C = 0$ or $x = -C/A$—and we know that the locus of any equation of the form $x = a$ *constant* is a straight line parallel to the y-axis. If $B \neq 0$, then we can solve the equation for y in terms of x. Thus we know that in this case the graph is the same as that of the equation

$$y = -\frac{Ax}{B} - \frac{C}{B}.$$

But this is an equation of the form $y = mx + b$, and we know that its graph is a straight line having slope $-A/B$ and y-intercept $-C/B$. Since B either is zero or is not zero, and since the graph is a straight line in both of these cases, the proof is complete.

It is evident from the above discussion that a general linear equation $Ax + By + C = 0$ in which $B \neq 0$ can be put into the slope-intercept form simply by solving it for y in terms of x. The coefficient of x in the resulting equation will be the slope, and the constant term will be the y-intercept.

Example

If we solve the equation $3x - 4y = 8$ for y, we get

$$y = \tfrac{3}{4}x - 2.$$

The graph is then a line with slope $\tfrac{3}{4}$ and y-intercept -2.

If it is desired to change a general linear equation into the intercept form, one may first find the intercepts and then rewrite the equation in this form.

3-8. *Conditions for parallelism and perpendicularity.* The condition for parallelism of two lines having slopes m_1 and m_2 is that $m_1 = m_2$. Let the equations of the lines be

$$A_1x + B_1y + C_1 = 0$$
$$A_2x + B_2y + C_2 = 0.$$

The slope of the first is $m_1 = -A_1/B_1$, and that of the second is $m_2 = -A_2/B_2$. If the A's and B's are different from zero, the condition for parallelism is

$$-\frac{A_1}{B_1} = -\frac{A_2}{B_2} \quad \text{or} \quad \frac{A_1}{A_2} = \frac{B_1}{B_2}.$$

Example

The lines $\begin{cases} 2x + 3y - 6 = 0 \\ 4x + 6y + 5 = 0 \end{cases}$ are parallel because

$$\frac{A_1}{A_2} = \frac{2}{4} \quad \text{and} \quad \frac{B_1}{B_2} = \frac{3}{6} \quad \text{so that} \quad \frac{A_1}{A_2} = \frac{B_1}{B_2}.$$

The corresponding condition for perpendicularity is that $m_1 = -1/m_2$; this means that

$$-\frac{A_1}{B_1} = +\frac{B_2}{A_2} \quad \text{or} \quad A_1A_2 + B_1B_2 = 0.$$

Example

The lines $\begin{cases} 2x + 3y - 6 = 0 \\ 9x - 6y + 1 = 0 \end{cases}$ are mutually perpendicular because
$$A_1A_2 + B_1B_2 = 2(9) + 3(-6) = 18 - 18 = 0.$$

In the proof of the theorem of Sec. 3-10 we shall have use for the following consequence of the above condition for parallelism: If a line l has the equation $Ax + By + C = 0$, then the equation of any line l' that is parallel to l is $Ax + By + k = 0$, where k is a suitable constant.

Example

Find the equation of the line that passes through the point $A(4,-7)$ and is parallel to the line $5x - 3y + 10 = 0$.

Solution

The required line has the equation $5x - 3y + k = 0$, where k is to be determined from the fact that the line goes through the point $A(4,-7)$. Thus the value of k must be such that

$$5(4) - 3(-7) + k = 0.$$

We conclude that $k = -41$; so the required equation is $5x - 3y - 41 = 0$.

3-9. Length of the perpendicular from the origin to the line $Ax + By + C = 0$. We wish to prove the following:

Theorem. *The undirected length p of the perpendicular drawn from the origin to the line $Ax + By + C = 0$ is equal to the absolute value of C divided by $\sqrt{A^2 + B^2}$; that is*

$$p = \frac{|C|}{\sqrt{A^2 + B^2}}.$$

Proof. Let the line l in Fig. 3-6 be the graph of the equation $Ax + By + C = 0$, it being assumed at first that A, B, and C are

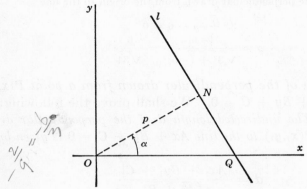

Figure 3-6

all different from zero. Let α be the inclination of the perpendicular drawn from the origin to l, and let $p = |ON|$ be the required length. Then

$$(1) \qquad\qquad p = |OQ| \cdot |\cos \alpha|.$$

Now OQ is the x-intercept of l; hence $OQ = -C/A$, and $|OQ| = |C/A|$. To find $|\cos \alpha|$, we observe that the slope of l is $-A/B$, and since $ON \perp l$, the slope of ON is $+B/A$; thus

$$\tan \alpha = \frac{B}{A},$$

so that

$$|\cos \alpha| = \frac{|A|}{\sqrt{A^2 + B^2}}.$$

Returning to (1), we have

$$p = |OQ| \cdot |\cos \alpha| = \frac{|C|}{|A|} \cdot \frac{|A|}{\sqrt{A^2 + B^2}} = \frac{|C|}{\sqrt{A^2 + B^2}}.$$

This completes the proof for the case in which A, B, and C are all different from zero. Suppose now that $C = 0$. In this case the line l goes through the origin so that $p = 0$. The above formula then gives the correct result. It is left for the student to show that if either $A = 0$ or $B = 0$, with $C \neq 0$, the formula again gives the correct result.

Example

The length of the perpendicular drawn from the origin to the line

$$3x - 5y - 6 = 0$$

is

$$p = \frac{|-6|}{\sqrt{3^2 + (-5)^2}} = \frac{6}{\sqrt{34}}.$$

3-10. Length of the perpendicular drawn from a point $P(x_1,y_1)$ to the line $Ax + By + C = 0$. We shall prove the following:

Theorem. *The undirected length d of the perpendicular drawn from a point $P(x_1,y_1)$ to the line $Ax + By + C = 0$ is given by the formula*

$$d = \frac{|Ax_1 + By_1 + C|}{\sqrt{A^2 + B^2}}.$$

Proof. Let the line l in Fig. 3-7 have the equation

$$Ax + By + C = 0.$$

Let $P(x_1,y_1)$ be the given point, and let $d = |MP|$ be the required length.

Draw a line l' through P parallel to l, and let OQ_1 and OQ_2 be the x-intercepts of l and l', respectively (it being assumed that $A \neq 0$). Then

(1) $$d = |MP| = |MN| \cdot |\cos \alpha| = |Q_1Q_2| \cdot |\cos \alpha|$$
$$= |OQ_2 - OQ_1| \cdot |\cos \alpha|$$

Now $OQ_1 = -C/A$. In order to find OQ_2, we first observe that the equation of l', since it is parallel to l, is $Ax + By + k = 0$,

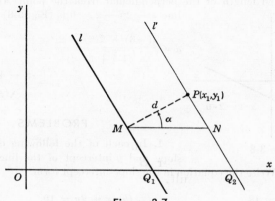

Figure 3-7

where k is determined by the fact that (x_1,y_1) is a point on the line. Thus $Ax_1 + By_1 + k = 0$; so $k = -Ax_1 - By_1$. Then

$$OQ_2 = -k/A = (Ax_1 + By_1)/A.$$

We then have

$$OQ_2 - OQ_1 = \left(\frac{Ax_1 + By_1}{A}\right) - \left(-\frac{C}{A}\right)$$
$$= \frac{Ax_1 + By_1 + C}{A}.$$

As in the corresponding derivation of the preceding section,

$$|\cos \alpha| = \frac{|A|}{\sqrt{A^2 + B^2}}.$$

Returning to equation (1), we have

$$d = |OQ_2 - OQ_1| \cdot |\cos \alpha|$$
$$= \frac{|Ax_1 + By_1 + C|}{|A|} \cdot \frac{|A|}{\sqrt{A^2 + B^2}}$$
$$= \frac{|Ax_1 + By_1 + C|}{\sqrt{A^2 + B^2}}.$$

This completes the proof for the case in which $A \neq 0$. The student may show that the formula is also correct if $A = 0$.

Example

The undirected length of the perpendicular from the point $A(-3,2)$ to the line $x - 2y - 2 = 0$ is (Fig. 3-8)

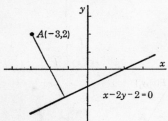

$$d = \frac{|(-3) - 2(2) - 2|}{\sqrt{(1)^2 + (-2)^2}}$$
$$= \frac{|-3 - 4 - 2|}{\sqrt{5}} = \frac{9}{\sqrt{5}}.$$

Figure 3-8

PROBLEMS

1. In each of the following cases, find the slope and y-intercept of the line whose equation is given. Write the equation in the slope-intercept form.

(a) $3x - 4y = 18$.   (b) $x + 2y = 10$.
(c) $2x - 3y + 4 = 0$.   (d) $0.4x - 2y = 6.4$.
(e) $\dfrac{2x}{3} + \dfrac{y}{2} = 1$.   (f) $\dfrac{x}{5} - \dfrac{y}{3} = 1$.

2. In each of the following cases, find the intercepts of the line determined by the given equation or by the given points. Write the equation of the line in the intercept form.

(a) $3x + 4y = 24$.   (b) $x - 3y = 6$.
(c) $y = \frac{2}{3}x - 6$.   (d) $3x = y - 12$.
(e) $A(-3,4)$ $B(1,-6)$.   (f) $A(2.6,1.4)$ $B(3.8,2)$.

3. In each of the following cases, find the value that must be assigned to A or B in order that the two lines may be (1) parallel, (2) perpendicular:

(a) $Ax - 2y = 4$
     $x + 3y = 7$.   (b) $4x + 5y = 20$
                         $Ax - 6y = 4$.
(c) $x + 3y + 7 = 0$
     $5x + By + 4 = 0$.   (d) $1.2x - 3.6y = 5$
                           $x + By = 2$.

4. In each of the following cases, find the equations of two lines through the point A, one parallel to and the other perpendicular to the given line:

(a) $A(3,-5)$; $3x + 2y = 10$. (b) $A(-2,-1)$; $x - 7y = 16$.
(c) $A(6,4)$; $3x - 5y = 20$.

5. Find the equation of a line that goes through the point $(6,-3)$ and has the sum of its intercepts equal to 10.

6. In each of the following cases, draw the two lines whose equations are given, and find the tangent of the angle from the first line to the second:

(a) $3x - 4y = 12$,

$\dfrac{x}{2} + \dfrac{y}{-6} = 1$.

(b) $x + y = 5$,

$y = \tfrac{1}{2}x - 3$.

(c) $\dfrac{x}{-4} + \dfrac{y}{3} = 1$,

$6x + 3y + 5 = 0$.

(d) $3y = 2x + 5$,

$x - 4y + 8 = 0$.

7. Find the angle from the line $2x - 3y + 6 = 0$ to the line $x = 4$.

8. In triangle $A(-2,4)$ $B(6,2)$ $C(4,-3)$, the median is drawn from A to the mid-point of BC. Find the tangent of the acute angle between this median and the line $y = 2x$.

9. In the triangle of Prob. 8, a line is drawn from B perpendicular to AC. Find the tangent of the acute angle between this line and the line $x + y = 0$.

10. In each of the following cases, find the length of the perpendicular drawn from the origin to the line whose equation is given:

(a) $3x + y = 10$.

(b) $\dfrac{x}{2} - \dfrac{y}{6} = 1$.

(c) $y = \tfrac{3}{4}x + 5$.

(d) $y - 4 = \tfrac{3}{4}(x + 2)$.

11. In each of the following cases, find the length of the perpendicular drawn from the given point A to the given line:

(a) $6x - 8y - 20 = 0$; $A(1,2)$.

(b) $x + y = 4$; $A(-1,-1)$.

(c) $5x + 12y = 30$; $A(-3,1)$.

(d) $\dfrac{x}{3} + \dfrac{y}{5} = 1$; $A(2,1)$.

12. A line is parallel to the line $3x - 4y = 6$, and the undirected length of the perpendicular drawn from the origin to it is 3. Find its equation.

13. A line is parallel to the line $A(-6,2)$ $B(6,7)$ and tangent to the circle with center at the origin and radius 5. Find its equation.

14. Find the area of triangle $A(-2,6)$ $B(5,3)$ $C(2,-3)$ by multiplying $\tfrac{1}{2}BC$ by the altitude. Check by using the determinant.

15. Find the area of triangle $A(-4,6)$ $B(-3,-1)$ $C(5,3)$ by multiplying $\tfrac{1}{2}BC$ by the altitude. Check by using the determinant.

16. Find the distance between the parallel lines

$$x - 2y = 9 \quad \text{and} \quad 2x - 4y + 12 = 0.$$

17. Show that the equation of the line that passes through a given point $P(x_1,y_1)$ and is parallel to a given line $Ax + By + C = 0$ can be written in the form

$$Ax + By = Ax_1 + By_1.$$

Example. The line through $(2,3)$ parallel to the line $7x + 5y = 10$ has the equation $7x + 5y = 7(2) + 5(3)$, or $7x + 5y = 29$.

18. Show that the equation of the line that passes through a given point $P(x_1,y_1)$ and is perpendicular to a given line $Ax + By + C = 0$, can be written in the form

$$Bx - Ay = Bx_1 - Ay_1.$$

Example. The line through $(2,3)$ perpendicular to the line $7x + 5y = 10$ has the equation $5x - 7y = 5(2) - 7(3)$, or $5x - 7y = -11$.

19. For what value or values of A is the acute angle between the lines

$$3x + 2y = 10 \quad \text{and} \quad Ax - 2y = 3$$

equal to 45°?

20. The intercept form of the equation of a line is $\dfrac{x}{4} + \dfrac{y}{(-2)} = 1$. That of a second line is $\dfrac{x}{a} + \dfrac{y}{(-2)} = 1$. For what value or values of a is the acute angle between them equal to 45°?

21. A line l is completely determined if the length and direction of the perpendicular from the origin to l are specified. In Fig. 3-9 let the directed segment $OP = p$ be positive, and let the direction of OP be given by specifying the counterclockwise angle $\omega < 360°$ from Ox to OP. Show that the coordinates of P are

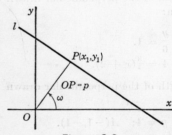

Figure 3-9

$$x_1 = p \cos \omega \quad \text{and} \quad y_1 = p \sin \omega,$$

and that the slope of l is $-\cot \omega$. Then, using the point-slope formula, show that the equation of l, in terms of p and ω, is

$$x \cos \omega + y \sin \omega = p.$$

This is called the *normal form* of the equation of the line.

In each of the following cases, write the equation of the line in the normal form, using the result of Prob. 21:

22. $\omega = 135°$; $p = 8$.   **23.** $\omega = 90°$; $p = 3$.
24. $\omega = 240°$; $p = 6$.   **25.** $\omega = 180°$; $p = 5$.

3-11. *Number of essential constants.* Two of the forms in which the equation of a line can be written are

$$y = mx + b; \qquad \frac{x}{a} + \frac{y}{b} = 1.$$

Each of these equations contains two constants such that the line is completely determined when their values have been specified. Thus if m is to be 2 and b is to be 4, in the first of the above forms, we have the line $y = 2x + 4$.

When the equation of a line is written in the form

$$Ax + By + C = 0,$$

there are *three* constants. We can, however, divide through by any one of them whose value is not zero, thus reducing the number to two. Thus if $A \neq 0$, the equation $Ax + By + C = 0$ is equivalent to

$$x + dy + e = 0,$$

where $d = B/A$ and $e = C/A$. The number of *essential* constants in this equation is therefore also two. This is of course connected with the fact that two conditions—such as two points, or one point and the slope—suffice to determine a line. Each such condition will, in general, yield an equation in the constants to be determined. For example, the condition that the line $y = mx + b$ shall pass through the point $(6,2)$ means that m and b must satisfy the equation

$$6m + b = 2;$$

the additional condition that the x-intercept shall be 5 means that

$$5m + b = 0;$$

This system of two equations in m and b has the unique solution $m = 2$, $b = -10$. The equation of the line satisfying the conditions is then

$$y = 2x - 10.$$

3-12. *Systems of lines.* In the equation $y = mx + b$, let us fix the value of m, say let $m = 2$, but leave the value of b unspecified. We have then the equation

$$y = 2x + b.$$

It defines a line with slope 2 for each value assigned to b. Furthermore, any line with slope 2 can be obtained from it by a proper choice of b. It is therefore said to represent the *family of lines*, or *system of lines*, with slope 2. Several are shown in Fig. 3-10.

If one wishes to find the equation of the line with slope 2 which also satisfies one other condition, he may start with the above equation and determine the proper value of b.

Example

Find the equation of the line with slope 2 which passes through (8,3).

Solution (Fig. 3-10)

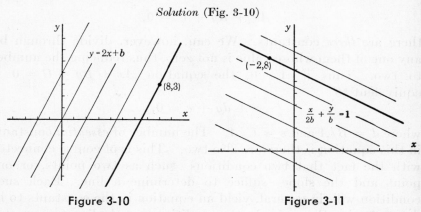

Figure 3-10   Figure 3-11

Since the slope is 2, the equation is

$$y = 2x + b,$$

where b is to be determined. Now, if the line goes through (8,3), these coordinates must satisfy the equation; i.e.,

$$3 = 2(8) + b \qquad \text{or} \qquad b = -13.$$

The required equation is then

$$y = 2x - 13.$$

In general, one may wish to find the equation of the line that satisfies two given conditions. He may start by writing down the equation that defines the system of lines all of which satisfy one of these conditions. This equation will contain one arbitrary constant called the *parameter* of the system. He may then proceed to determine the value of this parameter in order that the second condition may be satisfied.

Example

Find the equation of the line which has its x-intercept equal to twice its y-intercept, and which passes through the point $(-2,8)$.

Solution (Fig. 3-11)

An obvious solution is of course the line through $(-2,8)$ and the origin. Both intercepts are zero. Aside from this case, we can say that all lines having the

x-intercept equal to twice the y-intercept are defined by the equation

$$\frac{x}{2b} + \frac{y}{b} = 1.$$

We want the member of this family for which $y = 8$ when $x = -2$; this means that

$$\frac{-2}{2b} + \frac{8}{b} = 1 \qquad \text{or} \qquad b = 7.$$

The desired equation is then $\dfrac{x}{14} + \dfrac{y}{7} = 1$.

3-13. *Equations representing two or more lines.* The graphs of the equations

$$x - y = 0,$$
$$x + 6y - 6 = 0$$

are, respectively, the lines l_1 and l_2 in Fig. 3-12. If we multiply the left-hand members of the equations, and set the product equal to zero, we have the equation

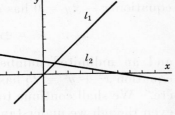

(1) $\qquad (x - y)(x + 6y - 6) = 0$

or

(2) $\quad x^2 + 5xy - 6y^2 - 6x + 6y = 0.$

Figure 3-12

The product in (1) is equal to zero for all pairs of values of x and y that make either factor zero, and for no other values.   Consequently, the graph of (1), which is the same as (2), consists of the two lines l_1 and l_2.

More generally, if the graph of an equation $g(x,y) = 0$ is a curve C_1 and the graph of an equation $h(x,y) = 0$ is a curve C_2, then the graph of the equation

$$g(x,y) \cdot h(x,y) = 0$$

consists of the curves C_1 and C_2.   The extension to any number of factors is obvious.   It follows that if the left-hand member of an equation of the form

$$f(x,y) = 0$$

can be factored into real linear factors, the graph consists of the corresponding lines.

Example 1

The equation $x^3 - xy^2 = 0$ can be written in the form

$$x(x - y)(x + y) = 0.$$

The graph then consists of the lines $x = 0$, $x - y = 0$, and $x + y = 0$.

Example 2

The equation $x^3 - 2x^2y + xy^2 - 2y^3 = 0$ can be written in the form

$$(x^2 + y^2)(x - 2y) = 0.$$

Its graph, therefore, is precisely that of the linear equation $x - 2y = 0$. Why?

Some remark should perhaps be made at this point regarding the fact that while we usually speak of *the* equation of a certain line or curve, it would perhaps be more appropriate to speak of *an* equation. As indicated in Example 2, the line which has the equation $x - 2y = 0$ has also the equation

$$x^3 - 2x^2y + xy^2 - 2y^3 = 0,$$

and an unlimited number of others. The circle that has the equation $x^2 + y^2 = 25$ has also the equation $(x^2 + y^2 - 25)^3 = 0$, etc. We shall continue to speak of *the* equation of a given curve, even though we understand that other equations could be devised that would have precisely the same locus.

PROBLEMS

1. Draw several members of each of the following systems of lines, and determine what property is possessed by all members of the system:

(a) $2y = 3x + b.$

(b) $4x + by = 12.$

(c) $(y - 3) = a(x + 2).$

(d) $y = k(x - 3).$

(e) $\dfrac{x}{a} + \dfrac{y}{2a} = 1.$

(f) $\dfrac{x}{b + 4} + \dfrac{y}{b} = 1.$

2. Write down the equation of the family of lines perpendicular to the line that passes through $A(-2, -3)$ and $B(6, 3)$. Then find the member of this system that has its y-intercept equal to 4.

3. Write down the equation of the family of lines passing through $P(6,4)$. Then find the member of this system that goes through the point $(2,-5)$.

4. Write down the equation of the system of lines through the point $P(-3,6)$. Then find the member of this system that has its x-intercept equal to 9.

5. Write down the equation of the system of lines each of which has its y-intercept equal to the negative of its x-intercept. Then find the members of this system for which the length of the perpendicular drawn from the origin is equal to $\sqrt{50}$.

6. Write down the equation of the system of lines with x-intercept equal to -6. Then find the member of the system that is perpendicular to the line $2x + 3y = 6$.

7. Write down the equation of the system of lines through the point $P(6,-5)$. Find the two members of the system that form with the coordinate axes a triangle of area 20 square units.

8. Write the equation of the system of lines through $P(6,4)$. Find the member (or members) of the system having the sum of its two intercepts equal to 20.

9. Write the equation of the system of lines with y-intercept equal to -4. Sketch the curve $y = x^2$, and find the members of the above system that are tangent to the curve. HINT: Solving $y = mx - 4$ and $y = x^2$ simultaneously leads to the equation $x^2 - mx + 4 = 0$. The two roots of this quadratic equation must be equal for tangency.

10. Write the equation of the system of lines with slope -2. Sketch the curve $y = x^2 - 8x + 18$, and find the members of this system that are tangent to the curve (see hint in Prob. 9).

11. Show that if the lines $A_1x + B_1y + C_1 = 0$ and $A_2x + B_2y + C_2 = 0$ intersect at a point P, then the equation

$$(A_1x + B_1y + C_1) + k(A_2x + B_2y + C_2) = 0,$$

where k is any real number, represents a line through P. HINT: Observe that the equation is of first degree in x and y and is satisfied by the coordinates of P.

12. Write the equation of the system of lines through the point of intersection of the lines $3x + 4y - 6 = 0$ and $x - 2y + 10 = 0$. Find the member of the system that passes through the point $A(-2,1)$. (Use the result of Prob. 11.)

13. A line goes through the point of intersection of the lines $2x + 3y = 1$ and $x + y = 3$ and is perpendicular to the line $y - 2x = 4$. Find its equation, using the result of Prob. 11.

14. Show that the graphs of the two equations

$$x + y = 0 \qquad \text{and} \qquad x^2 + 2xy + y^2 = 0$$

are identical. HINT: Prove that the second equation is satisfied by every pair of real numbers (x,y) that satisfies the first and is not satisfied by any other pair.

15. Show that the graphs of the two equations $x^2 - y^2 = 0$ and $x^4 - y^4 = 0$ are identical (see hint in Prob. 14).

16. In what way does the graph of the equation $(x^2 + y^2) \cdot (x^2 + y^2 - 25) = 0$ differ from that of the equation $x^2 + y^2 = 25$?

In each of the following cases, make the graph of the given equation after factoring the left-hand member:

17. $x^2 - 6x = 0$.
18. $y^2 - 9 = 0$.
19. $x^3 - 9x = 0$.
20. $x^3 + 4x = 0$.
21. $9x^2 - 4y^2 = 0$.
22. $x^2 - xy - 6y^2 = 0$.
23. $x^3y + 4xy^3 = 0$.
24. $xy + 2x - y - 2 = 0$.
25. $x^2 - y^2 + 2x - 2y = 0$.
26. $x^3 - x^2y - 2xy^2 = 0$.

27. A function of the form $ax + b$ is called a *linear function* of x, and if some quantity Q varies with x in accordance with the formula

$$Q = ax + b,$$

then Q is said to vary *linearly* with x. Show that a and b have the following interpretations: b is the value of Q when $x = 0$; a is the number of units by which the value of Q changes for each unit of change in x. (Thus if $Q = -\frac{1}{2}x + 6$, then $Q = 6$ when $x = 0$, and Q decreases by $\frac{1}{2}$ unit for each unit of increase in x.)

28. The coefficient of expansion (change in length per unit length per degree change in temperature) for steel is 0.0000065, using the Fahrenheit scale. A steel rod is 30 ft. long at 50°F. Express its length L at $t°$ as a function of t, and make the graph. What are the physical interpretations of its slope and L-intercept (see Prob. 27)?

CHAPTER 4

POLYNOMIALS

4-1. Definition. *A polynomial in **x*** is a function that can be written in the form

$$a_0x^n + a_1x^{n-1} + a_2x^{n-2} + \cdots + a_{n-1}x + a_n,$$

where the a's are constants and n is a positive integer. The polynomial is said to be of degree n if $a_0 \neq 0$. (A constant is usually classed as a polynomial of degree zero.) Thus

$$2x + 5, \qquad (x^2 - 2)^3, \qquad \text{and} \qquad x^5 - \sqrt{2}x^3 + 4$$

are polynomials in x of degree 1, 6, and 5, respectively. The functions

$$\sqrt{x}, \qquad \frac{x^2 - 2}{x^2 + 2}, \qquad \text{and} \qquad x^3 + 4\sqrt{x} + 5$$

are *not* polynomials.

In this chapter we wish to discuss briefly the graph of an equation of the form

$$y = \text{a polynomial in } x.$$

The equation $y = mx + b$ is a special case that we have already studied. We have seen that the graph for this case is a straight line.

4-2. The equation $y = ax^2 + bx + c$. The general shape of the graph of this equation is illustrated by Fig. 4-1. The curve is called a *parabola*. (We shall later define a parabola as the locus of all points that are equidistant from a given fixed point and a given fixed line—and we shall prove that the graph of the equation $y = ax^2 + bx + c$ is such a curve.)

It can be shown that if a is positive the parabola opens upward and has a lowest point which is called its *vertex*. This is the case illustrated.   If a is negative, the parabola opens downward and the vertex is the highest point.

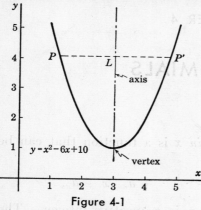

Figure 4-1

The line through the vertex parallel to the y-axis is called the *axis* of the parabola.   The curve is *symmetrical* with respect to this line.   By this we mean that if the paper were folded along this line the two "halves" would coincide.   The proof is not difficult, but it will not be given at this point.

If the parabola crosses the x-axis at two points x_1 and x_2, then the x-coordinate of the vertex is $\frac{1}{2}(x_1 + x_2)$; that is, the abscissa of the vertex is midway between x_1 and x_2.

Example

Make the graph of the equation $y = x - 0.08x^2$.

Solution (Fig. 4-2)

If we put $y = 0$ and solve for x, we find that the parabola crosses the x-axis at 0 and $12\frac{1}{2}$.   The abscissa of the vertex is then $6\frac{1}{4}$.   The value of y corresponding to $x = 6\frac{1}{4}$ is $3\frac{1}{8}$; so the vertex is at $(6\frac{1}{4}, 3\frac{1}{8})$.   By plotting a few additional

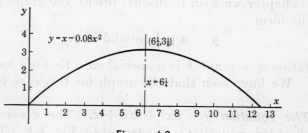

Figure 4-2

points we get the graph shown in the figure.   The axis of the parabola is the line $x = 6\frac{1}{4}$.

If the unit on each axis represents 1 ft., this curve is approximately the path traveled by a ball thrown from the origin with a velocity of 20 ft. per second at an angle of $45°$ with the horizontal x-axis.   This can be proved by using the fundamental laws of physics.

The equation $y = ax^2$ is the special case in which $b = c = 0$. In this case the vertex is at the origin, and the axis of the parabola is the y-axis.

It is evident that the graph of the equation $y = ax^2 + c$ is simply the curve $y = ax^2$ shifted in the y-direction by an amount c. The graph could be obtained by plotting the parabola $y = ax^2$ and the line $y = c$, and adding ordinates as indicated in Fig. 4-3.

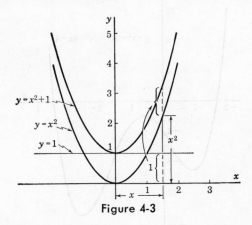

Figure 4-3

Here we have added 1 to each ordinate of the curve $y = x^2$ to obtain the graph of $y = x^2 + 1$.

It can be shown that the graph of the equation $y = ax^2 + bx + c$ is precisely the same curve as the graph of $y = ax^2$. The difference is only in the location of the curve relative to the coordinate axes. This means that the shape of the parabola is completely determined by the absolute value of a. The values of b and c affect only its position.

4-3. Polynomials of higher degree. The graph of a particular polynomial of third degree is shown in Fig. 2-4 (page 50). Figures 4-4 and 4-5 show three examples of the graphs of polynomials of degree four.

If the polynomial is given as a product of linear factors, or if such factors can be found easily, the essential facts about the graph can be obtained by studying these factors. For example, the equation

(1) $y = (x - 1)^2(x - 3)(x - 6)$

becomes

(2) $$y = x^4 - 11x^3 + 37x^2 - 45x + 18$$

when the factors on the right in (1) are multiplied together. It is much easier to sketch the graph from (1) than from (2)—because

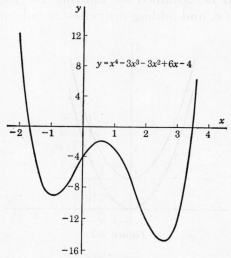

Figure 4-4

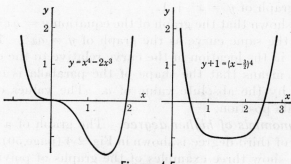

Figure 4-5

from (1) we can readily obtain the intercepts on the x-axis and visualize the general shape of the graph. Thus we see immediately that

$$y = 0 \qquad \text{when } x = 1, 1, 3, \text{ and } 6.$$

These are the x-intercepts. By noting the signs of the factors in the product $(x - 1)^2(x - 3)(x - 6)$ for $x > 6$, for x between 3 and 6, etc., we obtain the following information:

For $x > 6$, all factors are positive; so y is positive.

For $3 < x < 6$, the factor $x - 6$ alone is negative; so y is negative.

For $1 < x < 3$, the factors $x - 3$ and $x - 6$ are negative, while $(x - 1)^2$ is positive; so y is positive.

For $x < 1$, the factors $x - 3$ and $x - 6$ are negative, while $(x - 1)^2$ is positive; so y is positive.

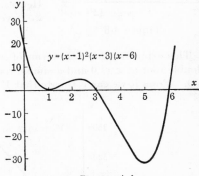

It should be observed that the graph, Fig. 4-6, *crosses* the x-axis at $x = 3$ and $x = 6$, these numbers being *simple* roots of the equation $(x - 1)^2(x - 3)(x - 6) = 0$, but touches it without crossing at $x = 1$, which is a *double* root. The reasoning underlying this behavior is quite simple: the factor $x - 6$, for example, is zero for $x = 6$, negative for $x < 6$, and positive for $x > 6$; the sign of this factor, and consequently the sign of y, changes therefore when x goes through the value 6. On the other hand, the factor $(x - 1)^2$ does not change sign when x goes through the value 1. It is positive for $x > 1$, zero for $x = 1$, and positive again for $x < 1$. Thus the graph must touch the x-axis at $x = 1$—but it does not *cross* the axis.

Figure 4-6

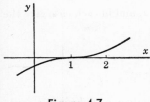

If the factor had been $(x - 1)^3$, the graph would have crossed the x-axis at $x = 1$. It can be shown that in this case the curve would have had roughly the shape shown in Fig. 4-7 in the neighborhood of $x = 1$. It would have been tangent to the x-axis at the crossing point.

Figure 4-7

The graphs of polynomials occur very often in connection with various kinds of physical and geometrical problems.

Example

A right-circular cylinder of radius x (inches) is inscribed in a right circular cone of radius 12 in. and height 9 in. Express the volume V of the cylinder as a function of x. Try to find approximately the value of x for which V is largest.

Solution

The volume of the inscribed cylinder is $\pi x^2 h$, where h must be replaced by its value in terms of x. From similar triangles (Fig. 4-8), we have

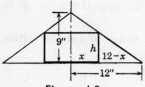

Figure 4-8

$$\frac{h}{12 - x} = \frac{9}{12} \qquad \text{or} \qquad h = \frac{3}{4}(12 - x).$$

Hence, for any value of x between 0 and 12 in., we have

$$V = \tfrac{3}{4}\pi x^2 (12 - x) \qquad \text{cu. in.}$$

This expression for V in terms of x is a polynomial of third degree. It has a double root at $x = 0$ and a simple root at $x = 12$. The graph is shown in Fig. 4-9. From it we can estimate that V would be largest for x in the neighborhood

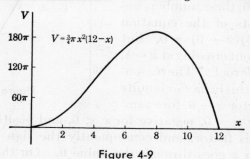

Figure 4-9

of 8. In other words, the largest inscribed cylinder would be one with a radius of about 8 in.

PROBLEMS

1. State which of the following are polynomials in x, and in each case give the degree:

(a) $x^2(x^2 - 1)$.
(b) $\dfrac{x^3}{3x + 1}$.
(c) $x^3 + 5x^2 + 2\sqrt{x}$.
(d) $x^3 + 5x^2 + \sqrt{2}\,x$.

2. What condition must be satisfied by the coefficients a, b, and c in the equation $y = ax^2 + bx + c$, in order that the graph may

(a) Cross the x-axis at two distinct points?
(b) Be tangent to the x-axis?
(c) Fail to touch the x-axis?

3. For what value or values of b is the parabola $y = x^2 + bx + 16$ tangent to the x-axis?

4. For what value or values of a is the parabola $y = ax^2 - 6x + 5$ tangent to the x-axis?

In each of the following cases draw the graph of the given equation:

5. $y = 3x - \frac{1}{4}x^2$.

6. $y = \frac{1}{2}x^2 - 3x - 8$.

7. $y = \frac{1}{2}(x + 3)^2$.

8. $y = 10 - x - 2x^2$.

9. $x^2 + 4y = 16$.

10. $x^2 + 5y = 10x$.

11. $y = x^3 - 3x^2 - 6x + 6$.

12. $y = x^3 - 5x^2 + 3x + 5$.

13. $y = \frac{1}{2}x(x^2 - 7x + 10)$.

14. $y = 3x - x^3 - 3$.

15. $y = x^3 - 6x^2 + 12x + 4$.

16. $4y = x^2(x^2 - 9)$.

17. $y = \frac{1}{4}x(16 - x^2)$.

18. $y = 8x^3 - 3x^4$.

19. $4y = x^2(x + 1)(x - 4)$.

20. $4y = (x + 3)^2(x^2 - 4)$.

21. $y = \frac{1}{2}x(x - 3)^2(x - 5)$.

22. A farmer has 900 ft. of fence and wishes to enclose a rectangular plot and divide it into two equal parts by a cross fence joining the mid-points of two sides. Express the area enclosed as a function of the width x. Make the graph. What dimensions give the largest enclosed area?

23. With 180 ft. of fence it is desired to enclose a rectangular field along the straight bank of a stream. No fence is needed along the stream. Express the area enclosed as a function of the width x of the field. Make the graph, and find the dimensions of the field that make the area largest.

24. A projectile is fired with velocity v_0 ft. per second at an angle α with the horizontal. If air resistance is neglected, the equation of its path can be shown to be

$$y = (\tan \alpha)x - \frac{g}{2v_0{}^2 \cos^2 \alpha}x^2,$$

where g is the gravitational constant ($=32$ ft./sec.^{2} approximately) and the axes are taken as shown in Fig. 4-2. Sketch the path for the case in which $v_0 = 80$ ft. per second and $\alpha = 45°$. Find the maximum height reached by the projectile.

25. If air resistance is neglected, the equation of the path traveled by a baseball that is thrown horizontally can be obtained by putting $\alpha = 0$ in the equation of Prob. 24. What is the minimum initial speed if the ball is to drop not more than $4\frac{1}{2}$ ft. in a horizontal distance of 60 ft.?

26. The base of a right pyramid 15 in. in height is a square with sides 9 in. long. A rectangular box whose base is a square with sides x in. long is inscribed in the pyramid as shown in Fig. 4-10. Express the volume V of the box as a function of x. Make the graph. Estimate the value of x for which V is largest.

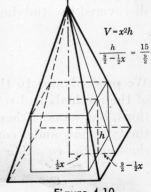

$V = x^2h$

$$\frac{h}{\frac{9}{2} - \frac{1}{2}x} = \frac{15}{\frac{9}{2}}$$

$\frac{1}{2}x$ $\qquad$ $\frac{9}{2} - \frac{1}{2}x$

Figure 4-10

27. A right-circular cylinder of height y is inscribed in a sphere of diameter 12 in. Express the volume V of the cylinder as a function of y. Make the graph. Estimate the value of y for which V is largest.

CHAPTER 5

RATIONAL FRACTIONAL FUNCTIONS

5-1. Introduction. A function of the form

$$\frac{N(x)}{D(x)},$$

where $N(x)$ and $D(x)$ are polynomials in x, is called a *rational fractional function* of x. Examples are

$$\frac{x+1}{x^2-4}, \qquad \frac{6}{x}, \qquad \text{and} \qquad \frac{x^2+2x-7}{x^3+8}.$$

The graphs of rational fractional functions give rise to a wide variety of curves. In many applications one does not need an accurately plotted graph—all that is necessary is a reasonably accurate sketch. This can often be obtained by plotting only a few points and making use of properties of the graph that can be discovered by studying the equation

$$y = \frac{N(x)}{D(x)}.$$

We proceed now to the consideration of such properties. Most of the methods and results are applicable to other kinds of equations, but some of them are particularly useful in connection with the type now under consideration. As an illustrative example we shall use the equation

$$y = \frac{2x+1}{x-1}$$

whose graph is shown in Fig. 5-1.

5-2. Intercepts. By the *intercepts* of the graph on the x-axis, we mean the abscissas of the points where the graph touches or crosses the x-axis. These can be found by setting $y = 0$ and solving for x. By the intercepts on the y-axis, we mean the ordinates of the points where the graph touches or crosses the

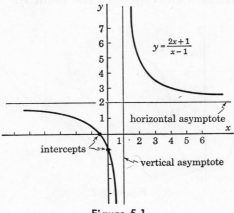

Figure 5-1

y-axis. These can be found by setting $x = 0$ and solving for y. In this manner we find that the graph of the equation

$$y = (2x + 1)/(x - 1)$$

crosses the x-axis at $x = -\frac{1}{2}$, and the y-axis at $y = -1$.

In connection with the problem of finding the intercepts, it is important to remember that *a fraction $N(x)/D(x)$ is equal to zero for those values of x, and only those values, for which its numerator is zero and its denominator is not zero.* Thus to solve the equation

$$\frac{2x + 1}{x - 1} = 0,$$

one first sets the numerator equal to zero and solves for x: $2x + 1 = 0$ if and only if $x = -\frac{1}{2}$. He then makes certain that the denominator is *not* zero for this value of x before concluding that $x = -\frac{1}{2}$ is the solution of the equation.

5-3. Symmetry. A curve is said to be *symmetrical with respect to a line l* if every line drawn from a point P on the curve perpendicular to l cuts the curve at another point P' such that l is the perpendicular bisector of PP'. A curve is said to be *symmetrical with respect to a point O* provided that when the line joining any point P of the curve to O is extended it cuts the curve at another point P' such that $PO = OP'$. The curve on the left in Fig. 5-2 is symmetrical with respect to the line l; that on the right is symmetrical with respect to the point O.

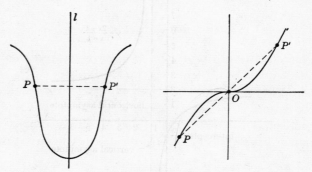

Figure 5-2

In general it would be difficult to determine, by studying a given equation, whether or not there exists some line or point with respect to which the graph is symmetrical. It is easy, however, to determine whether or not the graph is symmetrical with respect to one of the coordinate axes or the origin—and this information is often useful. The tests are as follows:

SYMMETRY TO x-AXIS. The graph of an equation in x and y is symmetrical with respect to the x-axis if and only if the equation that results when y is replaced by $-y$ is identical with the original equation.

Example

The graph of the equation $y^2 = 4x$ is symmetrical with respect to the x-axis. Here, the equation that results when y is replaced by $-y$ is $(-y)^2 = 4x$, or $y^2 = 4x$.

SYMMETRY TO y-AXIS. The graph of an equation is symmetrical with respect to the y-axis if and only if the equation that results when x is replaced by $-x$ is identical with the given equation.

SYMMETRY TO ORIGIN. The graph of an equation is symmetrical with respect to the origin if and only if the equation that results when x is replaced by $-x$ and y is replaced by $-y$ is identical with the original equation.

Example

The graph of the equation $y^3 + 2y = x^3$ is symmetrical with respect to the origin.   For if x is replaced by $-x$ and y is replaced by $-y$, we get

$$(-y)^3 + 2(-y) = (-x)^3.$$

This reduces immediately to $y^3 + 2y = x^3$, which is the original equation.

The student can readily see why the above statements are true. For example, the above condition for symmetry with respect to the y-axis implies that the equation will yield the same value or values for y when $x = -a$ as when $x = a$—so that if $(2,8)$ is a point on the graph, then $(-2,8)$ is also on the graph, etc.

5-4. Vertical asymptotes.   Consider again the equation

$$y = \frac{2x + 1}{x - 1}$$

and let x take the sequence of values

$$2, \ 1\tfrac{1}{2}, \ 1\tfrac{1}{4}, \ 1\tfrac{1}{8}, \ 1\tfrac{1}{16}, \ \cdots$$

getting closer and closer to 1.   The corresponding values of y are

$$5, \ 8, \ 14, \ 26, \ 50, \ \cdots$$

It is obvious that as x approaches nearer and nearer to 1, the corresponding values of y become larger and larger beyond bound. This situation results from the fact that the denominator of the fraction is approaching zero while the numerator is approaching a number different from zero, namely, 3.   It is easy to show that if x approaches 1 from the other side (take $x = \tfrac{1}{2}$, $\tfrac{3}{4}$, $\tfrac{7}{8}$, etc.), the values of y again become indefinitely large in absolute value, but in this case they are negative.

The behavior of the graph in the neighborhood of $x = 1$ is that indicated in Fig. 5-1.   It should be observed that there is no value of y, and consequently no point on the graph, corresponding to x *equals* 1.   Excluding this one point, however, there are values of y for x as *near* 1 as we please.   Furthermore, for x *sufficiently* near 1 the value of y is *arbitrarily* large in absolute value.   The situation is described by saying that the curve approaches the line $x = 1$ "asymptotically."   The line is called an *asymptote* to the curve.   It should be reasonably clear that the graph of the equation

$$y = \frac{N(x)}{D(x)}$$

will have one of these vertical asymptotes at each value of x for which the denominator is zero and the numerator is other than zero.   If the fraction is in lowest terms (numerator and denominator have no common factor), then the numerator cannot be zero for any value of x for which the denominator is zero.   In this case we have the following:

Rule.   *To find the vertical asymptotes to the graph of the equation $y = N(x)/D(x)$, set $D(x) = 0$, and solve for x.*

Example

The graph of the equation $y = \dfrac{2x}{x^2 - 4}$ will have vertical asymptotes at $x = 2$ and $x = -2$.

5-5. *Horizontal asymptotes.*   Returning to the equation

$$y = \frac{2x + 1}{x - 1}$$

let us think of x taking on the values 10, 100, 1,000, $\cdots$, becoming indefinitely large.   The corresponding values of y are $2\frac{1}{3}$, $2\frac{1}{33}$, $2\frac{1}{333}$, $\cdots$.   It is evident that as x gets larger and larger, the value of y gets closer and closer to 2, the difference between the value of y and 2 approaching zero.   The behavior of the curve is therefore that indicated in Fig. 5-1.   Similarly, if x is negative and becomes larger and larger in absolute value, the value of y again approaches 2.   The line $y = 2$ is a *horizontal asymptote* to the curve.

We saw above that the graph of the equation $y = N(x)/D(x)$ may have several vertical asymptotes [if $D(x) = 0$ has several real roots].   Regarding horizontal asymptotes, however, we can say that it either has one or none—and to find the horizontal asymptote, if there is one, one has only to find out what happens to the value of y when x becomes indefinitely large.   There are three cases.

CASE I. *Degree of N lower than that of D.* In this case the value of the fraction approaches zero as x becomes larger and larger in absolute value, and the graph is invariably asymptotic to the x-axis.

Example

The graph of the equation $y = (x + 1)/(x^2 + 4)$ has the x-axis as a horizontal asymptote; i.e., the value of y approaches zero as x becomes larger and larger in absolute value. The student should compute y for $x = 10$, 100, and 1,000. See also Prob. 28 of the next set.

CASE II. *Degree of N same as that of D.* In this case, as x becomes larger and larger in absolute value, the value of the fraction approaches a number which is equal to the quotient of the coefficients of the terms of highest degree in N and D. If $N(x) = a_0x^n + a_1x^{n-1} + \cdots + a_n$ and

$$D(x) = b_0x^n + b_1x^{n-1} + \cdots + b_n,$$

the horizontal asymptote is the line $y = a_0/b_0$.

Example

The graph of the equation $y = (6x^2 + x + 4)/(2x^2 - 1)$ is asymptotic to the horizontal line $y = \frac{6}{2} = 3$. Note that for very large values of x the fraction is nearly the same as $6x^2/2x^2$ because the remaining terms are negligible in comparison with these two. Observe also that by long division

$$\frac{6x^2 + x + 4}{2x^2 - 1} = 3 + \frac{x + 7}{2x^2 - 1}.$$

As x becomes larger and larger in absolute value, the second term on the right approaches zero (by Case I) and the right-hand side must therefore approach 3. This indicates how a proof for Case II can be carried out after Case I has been proved (see also Prob. 29 of the next set).

CASE III. *Degree of N higher than that of D.* In this case, as x becomes larger and larger in absolute value, the absolute value of y also becomes indefinitely large. *There is no horizontal asymptote.*

Example

The graph of the equation $y = (x^2 + 1)/(x - 1)$ has no horizontal asymptote. In this case we have, by division,

$$\frac{x^2 + 1}{x - 1} = x + 1 + \frac{2}{x - 1}.$$

As x becomes larger and larger in absolute value, the fraction $2/(x-1)$ on the right approaches zero. This means that for numerically large values of x the value of the fraction $(x^2+1)/(x-1)$ is nearly the same as that of the linear function $x+1$. The line $y = x+1$ is, in fact, an *inclined asymptote* to the curve (Fig. 5-3). This discussion should make it appear plausible that there is

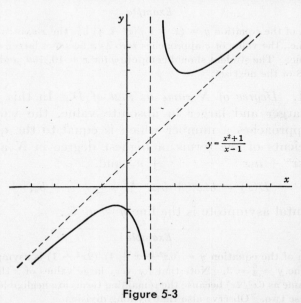

$$y = \frac{x^2+1}{x-1}$$

Figure 5-3

in general an inclined straight line to which the curve is asymptotic if the degree of the numerator exceeds that of the denominator by exactly one.

5-6. *Curve discussion.* By "discussing" the graph of an equation of the form $y = N(x)/D(x)$ we shall mean finding the intercepts, testing for symmetry, and locating all vertical and horizontal asymptotes. Any other information that can be obtained easily from the equation, and that will be useful in sketching the graph, should be included in the discussion. In the problems of the next set, the student should first write out the discussion in the brief form given in the following example. He should then use the discussion and plot only a few necessary points in sketching the graph.

Example

Discuss and sketch: $y = \dfrac{8}{x^2+4}$

Solution

1. *Intercepts:* $\begin{cases} \text{on } x\text{-axis—none.} \\ \text{on } y\text{-axis—at } y = 2. \end{cases}$

2. *Symmetry:* $\begin{cases} \text{to } x\text{-axis—no.} \\ \text{to } y\text{-axis—yes.} \\ \text{to origin—no.} \end{cases}$

3. *Asymptotes:* $\begin{cases} \text{vertical—none.} \\ \text{horizontal—the } x\text{-axis } (y = 0). \end{cases}$

4. *Other information.* It is clear from the equation that y is positive for all values of x. Furthermore, y has its largest value, 2, when $x = 0$, and y decreases from this value as x increases.

The graph is shown in Fig. 5-4. It is necessary to plot a few points near the y-intercept in order to determine the shape of the curve in this region. One might, for example, compute the values of y corresponding to $x = \frac{1}{2}$, 1, $\frac{3}{2}$, and 2.

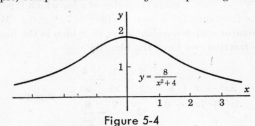

$$y = \frac{8}{x^2 + 4}$$

Figure 5-4

PROBLEMS

Discuss and sketch the graphs of the following equations:

1. $y = \dfrac{2}{3x}$.

2. $y = \dfrac{8}{3x^2}$.

3. $y = \dfrac{9}{x - 3}$.

4. $y = \dfrac{6}{2x + 3}$.

5. $y = \dfrac{3 + x}{2x}$.

6. $y = \dfrac{5 - 2x}{3x}$.

7. $y = \dfrac{2x}{(x + 2)^2}$.

8. $y = \dfrac{5}{x^2 + 2}$.

9. $y = \dfrac{8}{x^2 + 3}$.

10. $y = \dfrac{4x}{x^2 + 4}$.

11. $y = \dfrac{6x}{x^2 + 3}$.

12. $y = \dfrac{6}{x^2 - 4}$.

13. $y = \dfrac{6x}{x^2 - 4}$.

14. $y = \dfrac{8x}{x^2 - 5}$.

15. $y = \dfrac{3x}{2x^2 - 9}$.

16. $y = \dfrac{9 - x^2}{x^2 - 5}$.

17. $y = \dfrac{x^2 + 4}{x^2 - 4}$.

18. $y = \dfrac{x^2 - 4}{x^2 + 4}$.

19. $y = \dfrac{x^2}{x^2 - 12}$.

20. $y = \dfrac{x^3}{x^2 - 3}$.

21. $y = \dfrac{x^3}{3x + 6}$.

22. $y = \dfrac{x(x - 1)}{(x^2 - 4)(x - 6)}$.

23. $y = \dfrac{x^2}{(x - 2)(x - 4)}$.

24. $y = \dfrac{x(x^2 + 4)}{2(x^2 + 2)}.$

25. $y = \dfrac{x^2 + 4x + 1}{x^2 + 1}.$

26. A right circular cone of height y is circumscribed about a sphere whose

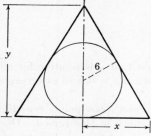

radius is 6 in. (Fig. 5-5). Express its volume V as a function of y, and sketch the graph showing how V varies with y. HINT: $V = \frac{1}{3}\pi x^2 y$, and from similar triangles $x/y = 6/\sqrt{(y-6)^2 - 6^2}$.

27. A rectangular box to contain 108 cu. ft. is to be made with a square base. The cost per square foot of material for bottom, top, and sides is 2, 4, and 6 cents, respectively. Express the cost C of material as a function of the length x of a side of the base. Draw the graph, and estimate the value of x for which C is least.

Figure 5-5

28. Consider the fraction $(3x^2 + x + 4)/(5x^3 + 7x^2 - 6)$. By dividing each term of both numerator and denominator by x^3, which is the highest power of x that occurs in the fraction, we have the identity

$$\frac{3x^2 + x + 4}{5x^3 + 7x^2 - 6} = \frac{\dfrac{3}{x} + \dfrac{1}{x^2} + \dfrac{4}{x^3}}{5 + \dfrac{7}{x} - \dfrac{6}{x^3}} \qquad x \neq 0.$$

Now as x becomes larger and larger in absolute value, each term in the numerator on the right approaches zero. The second and third terms in the denominator also approach zero. The numerator therefore approaches 0 while the denominator approaches 5, and the fraction consequently approaches zero. By using this idea in the general case, write out the proof for Case I, Sec. 5-5.

29. Using the method suggested in Prob. 28, write out a proof for Case II, Sec. 5-5.

In each of the following cases discuss and sketch the graph of the given equation after solving it for y in terms of x:

30. $2xy - 4y + 3x - 8 = 0.$

31. $xy - 2x + y = 4.$

32. $xy + 2y = 4x.$

33. $4y = x^2 y + 4x.$

34. $2xy + 4y = x^2 + 4.$

35. $y(x^2 + 1) = (x + 1)^2.$

36. $xy = x^2 - 4.$

37. $x^2 y + 2x^2 = 8.$

38. $x^2 y + 3y = 2x^2 + 7.$

39. $x^2 y = 4x - y + 3.$

40. $4x^2 y = x^4 - 16x^2 + 4.$

41. $2xy - x^2 = 4y + 2x + 6.$

42. $x^2 y - 9y = x^2 + 4x.$

43. $(x^2 - 1)^2 y = 2x.$

44. $x^2 y + xy = 3x - y + 6.$

45. $(x + 1)^2 y = 8x.$

46. $(x^2 - 9)^2 y = 4x(x^2 - 4).$

CHAPTER 6

TRANSFORMATION OF COORDINATES

6-1. Introduction. The equation of a curve is a statement of the relation that holds between the two coordinates, x and y, of any point on it. The equation is then not something that belongs to the curve itself—it is something that depends also upon the location of the x- and y-axes relative to the curve.

The line shown in Fig. 6-1 has the equation $2x - y = 2$ with respect to the axes shown. [This equation states that, for any point (x,y) on the line, twice the abscissa minus the ordinate is equal to 2.] What is the equation of the line with respect to the axes labeled x' and y' in the figure? It is obvious, in this case, that since the line goes through the origin

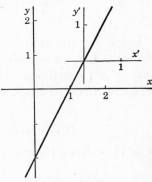

Figure 6-1

of this coordinate system, and has slope 2, its equation is $y' = 2x'$.

It is often necessary to solve the following problem: Given the equation of a curve with respect to an initial set of x- and y-axes, find the equation of this same curve with respect to another specified set of axes. If the new axes are parallel to the original ones, and have the same positive directions, the transformation is called a *translation* of axes. If the new origin is identical with the original one, and the new axes are obtained by revolving the original ones about this fixed point through a specified angle, the transformation is called a *rotation* of axes.

6-2. Translation of axes. Let us assume that we know the equation of a curve with respect to an initial set of x- and y-axes. Let us make a translation of the axes such that the point whose coordinates were (h,k) becomes the new origin. We wish to find the equation of the curve relative to this new coordinate system (Fig. 6-2).

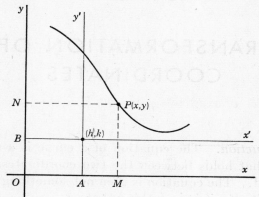

Figure 6-2

Let P be any point on the curve (or, in fact, any point in the plane). Let its coordinates be (x,y) relative to the original axes and (x',y') relative to the new axes. Then, from the basic properties of directed lines, we have the following relations:

$$OM = OA + AM \quad \text{or} \quad x = h + x';$$
$$ON = OB + BN \quad \text{or} \quad y = k + y'.$$

It is thus clear that in order to find the new equation, we simply

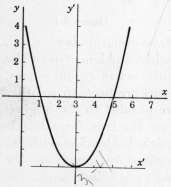

Figure 6-3

take the original equation of the curve and

Replace x by $x' + h$;
Replace y by $y' + k$.

The resulting relation between x' and y' is the desired equation.

Example

The equation of the parabola shown in Fig. 6-3 is $y = x^2 - 6x + 5$. The vertex is at $(3, -4)$. What is the equation relative to axes x' and y' that go through the vertex as shown?

Solution

In this case $h = 3$, and $k = -4$. In the original equation we replace x by $x' + 3$ and y by $y' - 4$. We thus get

$$y' - 4 = (x' + 3)^2 - 6(x' + 3) + 5$$
$$= x'^2 + 6x' + 9 - 6x' - 18 + 5$$
$$= x'^2 - 4.$$

The final result is then

$$y' = x'^2.$$

This was to be expected in view of the discussion on page 85. The parabola whose equation is $y = x^2 - 6x + 5$ is precisely the same curve as the parabola $y = x^2$.

6-3. *Rotation of axes.* We consider now the following problem: The equation of a curve with respect to a set of x- and y-axes is given. A new set of axes, denoted by x' and y', is obtained by rotating the original ones through an angle θ,* Fig. 6-4. It is

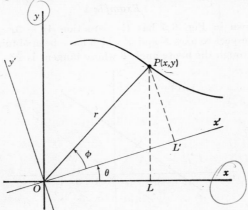

Figure 6-4

required to find the corresponding new equation of the curve.

Let $P(x,y)$ be any point on the curve; then $x = OL$, and $y = LP$. Let the coordinates of P relative to the new axes be x' and y'; then $x' = OL'$, and $y' = L'P$. If we draw OP and let the directed length $OP = r$ (where r is a positive number), and let the angle $L'OP$ be denoted by ϕ, then

$$x = OL = r \cos (\theta + \phi), \qquad y = LP = r \sin (\theta + \phi),$$
$$x' = OL' = r \cos \phi, \qquad y' = L'P = r \sin \phi.$$

Using the formulas for the cosine and sine of the sum of two angles,

* θ is positive when measured counterclockwise and negative when measured clockwise, as in trigonometry.

we have

$$x = r \cos(\theta + \phi) = r(\cos\theta \cos\phi - \sin\theta \sin\phi)$$
$$= (r \cos\phi) \cos\theta - (r \sin\phi) \sin\theta$$
$$= x' \cos\theta - y' \sin\theta.$$

Similarly, $y = r \sin(\theta + \phi) = r(\sin\theta \cos\phi + \cos\theta \sin\phi)$
$$= (r \cos\phi) \sin\theta + (r \sin\phi) \cos\theta$$
$$= x' \sin\theta + y' \cos\theta.$$

It follows that in order to find the new equation of the curve (in x' and y') we must take the original equation in x and y and

Replace x by $x' \cos\theta - y' \sin\theta$;
Replace y by $x' \sin\theta + y' \cos\theta$.

Example 1

The line shown in Fig. 6-5 has the equation $4y - 3x = 10$. What is its equation with respect to axes x' and y' which have been obtained by rotating the original axes through the acute angle θ whose tangent is $\frac{3}{4}$?

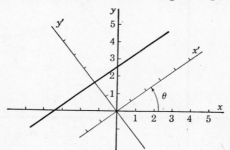

Figure 6-5

Solution

The sine and cosine of the acute angle whose tangent is $\frac{3}{4}$ are $\sin\theta = \frac{3}{5}$ and $\cos\theta = \frac{4}{5}$. We therefore take the original equation $4y - 3x = 10$ and

Replace x by $\frac{4}{5}x' - \frac{3}{5}y'$;
Replace y by $\frac{3}{5}x' + \frac{4}{5}y'$.

The result is
$$4\left(\tfrac{3}{5}x' + \tfrac{4}{5}y'\right) - 3\left(\tfrac{4}{5}x' - \tfrac{3}{5}y'\right) = 10;$$
$$\tfrac{12}{5}x' + \tfrac{16}{5}y' - \tfrac{12}{5}x' + \tfrac{9}{5}y' = 10;$$
$$5y' = 10;$$
$$y' = 2.$$

This final result was to be expected, for the slope of the given line is $\frac{3}{4}$, and its distance from the origin is 2. Thus the line is parallel to the new x'-axis and 2 units above it.

Example 2

The circle shown in Fig. 6-6 has the equation $x^2 + y^2 = 25$. Show that, for any value of the angle θ of rotation, the new equation of the circle is $x'^2 + y'^2 = 25$.

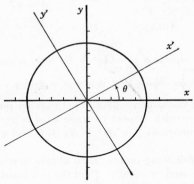

Figure 6-6

Solution

We take the given equation and replace x by $x' \cos \theta - y' \sin \theta$ and replace y by $x' \sin \theta + y' \cos \theta$, without specifying the value of θ. We get

$$(x' \cos \theta - y' \sin \theta)^2 + (x' \sin \theta + y' \cos \theta)^2 = 25.$$

This can be simplified as follows:

$$x'^2 \cos^2 \theta - 2x'y' \sin \theta \cos \theta + y'^2 \sin^2 \theta + x'^2 \sin^2 \theta$$
$$+ 2x'y' \sin \theta \cos \theta + y'^2 \cos^2 \theta = 25;$$
$$x'^2(\cos^2 \theta + \sin^2 \theta) + y'^2(\sin^2 \theta + \cos^2 \theta) = 25.$$

Now, for any value of θ, $\sin^2 \theta + \cos^2 \theta = 1$. The above result therefore becomes

$$x'^2 + y'^2 = 25.$$

PROBLEMS

In each of the following cases sketch the graph of the given equation, and plot the given point A. Then draw new axes x' and y' through A parallel to the original axes and having the same positive directions. Find the equation of the given line or curve with respect to these new axes:

1. $2y = x + 4$; $A(2,3)$.   **2.** $x - y = 5$; $A(1,-1)$.

3. $\dfrac{x}{6} + \dfrac{y}{4} = 1$; $A(0,4)$.   **4.** $y - 3 = \frac{2}{3}(x - 5)$; $A(5,3)$.

5. $y = 6x - x^2$; $A(3,9)$.   **6.** $y = 2x^2 - 7x - 15$; $A(5,0)$.

7. $y = 8 + 2x - x^2$; $A(1,9)$.   **8.** $y = \frac{1}{2}(x^2 + 8x)$; $A(-4,0)$.

9. $y - 8 = x(x^2 + 6x + 12)$; $A(-2,0)$.

10. $x + y = x^3 - 3x^2 + 3$; $A(1,0)$.

11. $y = x(x^3 - 4x^2 + 2x + 4)$; $A(1,3)$.

12. $y = \dfrac{2x + 1}{x - 1}$; $A(1,2)$.

13. $y = \dfrac{-2x^2}{x^2 + 4}$; $A(0,-2)$.

14. $y = \dfrac{3x^2 + x + 3}{x^2 + 1}$; $A(0,3)$.

15. $y = \dfrac{x(2x - 3)}{x^2 - 4x + 5}$; $A(2,2)$.

16. The graph of the equation $y = Ax^2 + Bx + C$ is a parabola with vertex at $\left(-\dfrac{B}{2A}, -\dfrac{B^2 - 4AC}{4A}\right)$. Show that if new $x'-$ and $y'-$ axes, parallel to the original ones and having the same positive directions, are put through this point, the equation of the curve with respect to these axes is $y = Ax'^2$. Hence infer that the graphs of the equations $y = Ax^2 + Bx + C$ and $y = Ax^2$ are precisely the same curve.

17. Plot each of the following points; then obtain new axes by rotating the original ones through an angle $\theta = 30°$. Find the new coordinates of each point. $A(8,-6)$; $B(-4,-4)$; $C(0,10)$.

18. Same as Prob. 17 but with $\theta = -45°$.

19. Same as Prob. 17 but with $\theta = 90°$.

20. Draw the line whose equation is $2y + x = 4$. Rotate the axes through the acute angle θ whose tangent is 2, and find the new equation of the line.

21. Draw the line whose equation is $5x - 12y = 52$. Rotate the axes through the acute angle whose tangent is $\frac{5}{12}$, and find the new equation of the line.

22. Sketch the parabola whose equation is $y = \sqrt{2}\, x^2$. Rotate the axes through an angle $\theta = 45°$, and find the new equation of the curve.

23. Sketch the curve whose equation is $y = 1/x$. Rotate the axes through an angle $\theta = 45°$, and find the new equation of the curve.

24. Solve the system of equations $x = x' \cos \theta - y' \sin \theta$, $y = x' \sin \theta + y' \cos \theta$, for x' and y' in terms of x and y.

25. Show that the equation $5x^2 + 4xy + 8y^2 = 9$ is transformed into $9x'^2 + 4y'^2 = 9$ when the axes are rotated through the acute angle whose tangent is 2.

CHAPTER 7

THE CIRCLE

7-1. The standard form. A circle may be defined as *the locus of all points that lie in a given plane and are at a given distance from a fixed point of the plane.* The fixed point is called the *center*, and the given distance is called the *ra-dius* of the circle.

We derive the equation directly from this definition as follows: Let the center be the point (h,k), and let the radius be r, Fig. 7-1. Then if $P(x,y)$ is any point of the plane, its undirected distance from the point (h,k) is

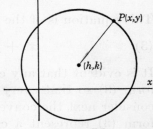

Figure 7-1

$$d = \sqrt{(x - h)^2 + (y - k)^2}.$$

Every point P which lies on the circle must have $d = r$; hence its coordinates must satisfy the equation

$$(1) \qquad \sqrt{(x - h)^2 + (y - k)^2} = r,$$

or

$$(2) \qquad (x - h)^2 + (y - k)^2 = r^2.$$

Conversely, every point in the plane whose coordinates (x,y) satisfy (2) lies on the circle—for if (2) is true for a point (x,y), then (1) is also true and the point is therefore at a distance r from the point (h,k). Equation (2) is thus the equation of the circle with center at the point (h,k) and radius r. It is called the *standard form* of the equation of the circle. If $h = k = 0$, the equation reduces to

$$x^2 + y^2 = r^2$$

which is the equation of a circle with center at the *origin* and radius r.

Example

The equation of the circle with center at $(2, -1)$ and radius 3 is

$$(x - 2)^2 + (y + 1)^2 = 9.$$

By performing the indicated operations and simplifying, we may reduce the equation to the form

$$x^2 + y^2 - 4x + 2y - 4 = 0.$$

This is the *general form* to be discussed in the next section.

7-2. *The general form.* If the indicated operations in equation (2) above are carried out, the result can be written in the form

$$x^2 + y^2 - 2hx - 2ky + h^2 + k^2 - r^2 = 0.$$

This equation is of the general type

(3) $$x^2 + y^2 + Dx + Ey + F = 0.$$

It is evident that any equation of the form (2) can be reduced to form (3) so that every circle has an equation of this type. We consider next the converse question, "Does every equation of the form (3) represent a circle?" We first give an example which indicates that, with suitable restrictions on the values of D, E, and F, this is true.

Example

Transform the equation $x^2 + y^2 - 6x + 2y + 4 = 0$ into the standard form.

Solution

We first write the equation in the following way:

$$x^2 - 6x + \quad + y^2 + 2y + \quad = -4.$$

Now, in order to complete the square in x we must add 9, and in order to complete the square in y we must add 1. We thus have

$$x^2 - 6x + 9 + y^2 + 2y + 1 = -4 + 9 + 1,$$
or $$(x - 3)^2 + (y + 1)^2 = 6.$$

It is now clear that the given equation is that of a circle with center at $(3, -1)$ and radius $\sqrt{6}$. Observe, however, that if the constant term in the given equation had been 10 instead of 4, our result would have been

$$(x - 3)^2 + (y + 1)^2 = 0.$$

The graph in this case is a circle of radius *zero* with center at $(3, -1)$, or a *point circle*. Finally, if the constant term had been greater than 10, say 12, the result would have been

$$(x - 3)^2 + (y + 1)^2 = -2.$$

In this case there is no graph; i.e., the equation is not satisfied by any pair of real numbers.

By similarly completing the square in the general case, one can prove that the equation $x^2 + y^2 + Dx + Ey + F = 0$ invariably represents a circle or has no graph at all. The word circle is to be understood to include a point circle, or circle of radius zero. The equation $x^2 + y^2 + Dx + Ey + F = 0$ is called the *general form* of the equation of a circle. It is obvious, in view of the result of completing the square, that the center of the circle is at $(-\frac{1}{2}D, -\frac{1}{2}E)$ (see Prob. 4 of the next set).

7-3. Circle satisfying three conditions. Both the standard form and the general form of the equation of a circle contain three arbitrary constants. These are h, k, and r in the standard form and D, E, and F in the general form.

If one is given three conditions which determine a circle, he can usually find its equation by setting up three equations in h, k, and r, or D, E, and F, and solving for these constants. In most cases either form may be used, but, depending upon the nature of the given conditions, one form may be more convenient than the other.

Example 1

Find the equation of the circle that passes through the points $(1,1)$, $(4,0)$, and $(2, -1)$.

Solution (Fig. 7-2)

The circle certainly has an equation of the form

$$x^2 + y^2 + Dx + Ey + F = 0.$$

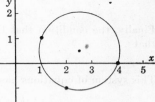

Figure 7-2

We must determine the values of D, E, and F, so that the equation is satisfied by the coordinates of each of the given points—since each is to be on the circle. We thus must have

$$1 + 1 + D + E + F = 0,$$
$$16 + 0 + 4D + 0 + F = 0,$$
$$4 + 1 + 2D - E + F = 0.$$

By the usual methods of algebra we find that this system of equations has the solution $D = -5$, $E = -1$, $F = 4$, and no other solution. The required equation is then

$$x^2 + y^2 - 5x - y + 4 = 0.$$

If we wish to find the center and radius of the circle, we may complete the squares in x and y. The result is

$$(x - \tfrac{5}{2})^2 + (y - \tfrac{1}{2})^2 = \tfrac{10}{4}.$$

The center is at the point $(\tfrac{5}{2}, \tfrac{1}{2})$, and the radius is $\tfrac{1}{2}\sqrt{10}$.

The student will perhaps see other ways of solving the problem.

Example 2

Find the equation of a circle that is tangent to the x-axis, has its center on the line $y = 2x + 1$, and passes through the point $(-2, 8)$.

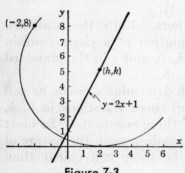

Figure 7-3

Solution (Fig. 7-3)

In this case we shall assume an equation of the form

$$(x - h)^2 + (y - k)^2 = r^2$$

and try to determine h, k, and r so as to satisfy the specified conditions.

The fact that the center is on the line $y = 2x + 1$ means that its coordinates (h, k) must satisfy this equation; that is,

$$k = 2h + 1.$$

The condition that the circle is tangent to the x-axis means that the y-coordinate of the center is equal to r or $-r$.

$$k = \pm r.$$

Finally, the condition that the circle passes through the point $(-2, 8)$ requires that

$$(-2 - h)^2 + (8 - k)^2 = r^2.$$

This system of equations has two (and only two) solutions as follows:

$$h = 2, \qquad k = 5, \qquad r = 5;$$
$$h = 26, \qquad k = 53, \qquad r = 53.$$

There are then two circles satisfying the given conditions. Their equations are

$$(x - 2)^2 + (y - 5)^2 = 25;$$
$$(x - 26)^2 + (y - 53)^2 = 2,809.$$

The first of these is shown in the figure.

PROBLEMS

1. In each of the following cases write the equation of the circle with center at C and radius r in both the standard and the general form:

(a) $C(4,-2)$; $r = 3$.　　　　　　(b) $C(-2,-6)$; $r = 2$.
(c) $C(0,-5)$; $r = 5$.　　　　　　(d) $C(2,0)$; $r = 4$.
(e) $C(4,1)$; $r = 4$.　　　　　　(f) $C(-3,4)$; $r = 5$.

2. In each of the following cases complete the squares in x and y, and thus determine the center and radius of the circle represented by the equation—or determine that the equation has no graph. Draw the graph if there is one.

(a) $x^2 + y^2 - 4x + 6y = 12$.　　　(b) $x^2 + y^2 + 2x + 10y + 1 = 0$.
(c) $x^2 + y^2 - 3x + 5y + 7 = 0$.　　(d) $x^2 + y^2 = x + y$.
(e) $2x^2 + 2y^2 = 5y - 4x - 2$.　　(f) $x^2 + y^2 + 4x + 4y + 10 = 0$.

3. Show that the equation of the circle with center at $(r,0)$ and radius r (Fig. 7-4) is $x^2 + y^2 = 2rx$. What is the corresponding equation of a circle with center at $(0,r)$ and radius r?

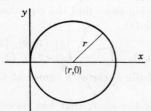

Figure 7-4

4. Show that the equation $x^2 + y^2 + Dx + Ey + F = 0$ represents a circle with center at $(-\frac{1}{2}D, -\frac{1}{2}E)$ and radius $\sqrt{\dfrac{D^2}{4} + \dfrac{E^2}{4} - F}$ if $\dfrac{D^2}{4} + \dfrac{E^2}{4} - F$ is a positive number, and that it represents a point circle if this latter quantity is zero.

5. Show that the equation $x^2 + y^2 = ax + by$ always represents a circle and that this is a point circle if and only if $a = b = 0$.

6. In each of the following cases find the equations of all circles that satisfy the given conditions:

(a) Has the segment $A(-2,-4)$　$B(6,4)$ as a diameter.
(b) Passes through $(3,0)$ and $(12,0)$ and is tangent to the y-axis.
(c) Has its center on the line $y = \frac{1}{2}x + 3$ and is tangent to both axes.
(d) Passes through $(3,6)$ and $(-4,-1)$ and has its center on the y-axis.
(e) Has its center at $(8,4)$ and is tangent to the line whose intercepts are $a = 6$ and $b = 3$.

7. A point moves so as to be always twice as far from the origin as from the point $(12,0)$. Find the equation of its path, and sketch it.

8. Find the equation of the locus of all points that are twice as far from the point $(-3,0)$ as from the point $(6,6)$.

9. Find the equation of the locus of all points which are three times as far from the point $(-4,2)$ as from the point $(8,6)$.   Sketch the locus.

10. What equation represents the family of all circles with center on the x-axis and passing through the origin?

11. What equation represents the family of all circles with center on the line $y = x$ and passing through the origin?

12. What equation represents the family of all circles with center on the line $x + y = 0$ and tangent to both axes?

13. Write an equation which represents the family of all circles with center on the line $y = 2x$ and passing through the origin.   Find the particular member of the family that passes through the point $(6,2)$.

14. Draw a square with center at the origin and with each side 6 units long, the sides being parallel to the coordinate axes.   A point moves in the plane so that the sum of the squares of its distances from the lines of which the sides of the square are segments is 100.   Find the equation of its path.

15. Does the circle whose equation is $4x^2 + 4y^2 - 32x - 48y + 127 = 0$ intersect the line $x - 2y = 2$ at two points, at one point, or not at all?   HINT: Compare the radius of the circle with the distance from its center to the line.

16. In each of the following cases find the equation of the circle that passes through the three given points:

   (a) $(6,10)$, $(0,2)$, $(2,8)$.   (b) $(10,2)$, $(3,9)$, $(-2,10)$.

   (c) $(-2,-2)$, $(-1,6)$, $(0,1)$.   (d) $(0,6)$, $(2,2)$, $(3,5)$.

17. Find the equation of the circle with center at $(5,-3)$ and tangent to the line $3x - 4y = 12$.

18. Find the equation of the circle that has its center on the y-axis and is tangent to the line $x + 4y = 10$ at the point $(2,2)$.

19. Find the equation of the circle that is tangent to the line $4x - 3y = 2$ at the point $(-1,-2)$ and passes through the point $(6,-1)$.

20. Find the equation of the circle that is tangent to the line $x + 2y = 4$ at the point $(6,-1)$ and passes through the point $(5,2)$.

21. Find the equations of all circles that pass through the origin and the point $(-1,-3)$ and are tangent to the line $2x + y + 10 = 0$.

22. Find the equation of the line that is tangent to the circle

$$x^2 + y^2 - 10x - 6y + 29 = 0$$

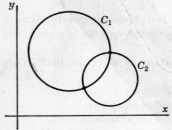

Figure 7-5

at the point $(3,4)$.   HINT: The tangent line is perpendicular to the radius.

23. Show that the line drawn tangent to the circle $x^2 + y^2 = r^2$ at any point (x_1,y_1) on the circle has the equation $x_1x + y_1y = r^2$.

24. Let the equations of two intersecting circles C_1 and C_2 (Fig. 7-5) be

$$x^2 + y^2 + D_1x + E_1y + F_1 = 0$$

and $$x^2 + y^2 + D_2x + E_2y + F_2 = 0.$$

Show that, for every value of k except -1, the equation

$$(x^2 + y^2 + D_1 x + E_1 y + F_1) + k(x^2 + y^2 + D_2 x + E_2 y + F_2) = 0$$

represents a circle that goes through the points of intersection of C_1 and C_2. What does it represent for $k = -1$? HINT: If $k \neq -1$, the equation represents a circle. Furthermore, it is satisfied by the coordinates of the points of intersection of C_1 and C_2. Why?

25. Let $A(x_1, y_1)$, $B(x_2, y_2)$, and $C(x_3, y_3)$ be three distinct points, not all on the same straight line, and having rational numbers as coordinates. Is it possible that the coordinates of the center of the circle passing through A, B, and C may be irrational numbers? Is it possible that the radius may be an irrational number?

CHAPTER 8

THE PARABOLA, ELLIPSE, AND HYPERBOLA

8-1. *Introduction.* In the chapter on Polynomials we stated that the graph of the equation $y = ax^2 + bx + c$ is a curve called a *parabola*. We shall now give general definitions for this and two closely related curves called, respectively, the *ellipse* and *hyperbola*. Using these definitions, we shall derive standard equations for these curves and discuss briefly their most important properties. These standard equations will all be special cases of the general equation of second degree in x and y; that is, they will be special cases of the equation

$$Ax^2 + Bxy + Cy^2 + Dx + Ey + F = 0,$$

in which some of the coefficients will be zero. (We have already seen that if $B = 0$ and $A = C$, the above equation represents a circle or has no locus.)

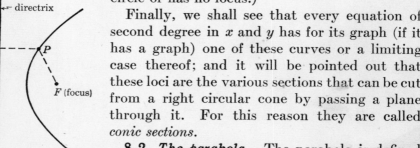

Figure 8-1

Finally, we shall see that every equation of second degree in x and y has for its graph (if it has a graph) one of these curves or a limiting case thereof; and it will be pointed out that these loci are the various sections that can be cut from a right circular cone by passing a plane through it. For this reason they are called *conic sections*.

8-2. *The parabola.* The parabola is defined as *the locus of all points that are equidistant from a fixed point and a fixed line.* (The distances referred to here are undirected distances.) Thus if a point P (Fig. 8-1) moves so that the undirected distances FP and LP remain equal, it will trace out a parabola. The fixed point

112

F is called the *focus*, and the fixed line l is called the *directrix* of the parabola.

Naturally, the equation that one obtains for the curve depends on his choice of coordinate axes relative to the focus and directrix. It turns out that we get the simplest equation if we choose the axes as indicated in Fig. 8-2. Here, we have taken the origin at the mid-point of the segment drawn from the focus perpendicular to the directrix and have let the x-axis coincide with this perpendicular. If we let p denote the directed distance from the directrix to the focus, then, with our choice of axes, the focus has the coordinates $(\frac{1}{2}p,0)$ and the directrix has the equation $x = -\frac{1}{2}p$. We find the equation

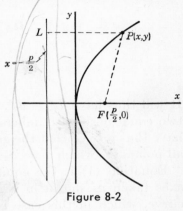

Figure 8-2

of the curve with respect to these axes as follows: Let $P(x,y)$ be a point of the plane, and let d_1 and d_2 be the undirected lengths of FP and LP, respectively; then

$$d_1 = \sqrt{\left(x - \frac{p}{2}\right)^2 + y^2}; \qquad d_2 = \sqrt{\left(x + \frac{p}{2}\right)^2}.$$

Every point such that $d_1 = d_2$ must have $d_1{}^2 = d_2{}^2$; so it must satisfy the equation

$$\left(x - \frac{p}{2}\right)^2 + y^2 = \left(x + \frac{p}{2}\right)^2.$$

By performing the indicated operations and simplifying we get

$$x^2 - px + \frac{p^2}{4} + y^2 = x^2 + px + \frac{p^2}{4},$$

or

(1) $$y^2 = 2px.$$

We thus know that every point in the plane having $d_1 = d_2$ must satisfy (1). We do not know yet that there are not also other points that satisfy (1)—points for which $d_1 \neq d_2$. We may now prove that any point (x,y) which satisfies (1) has $d_1 = d_2$, as follows: Any point (x,y) for which $y^2 = 2px$ will be such that

$$y^2 + \left(x - \frac{p}{2}\right)^2 = 2px + \left(x - \frac{p}{2}\right)^2$$

$$= 2px + x^2 - px + \frac{p^2}{4}$$

$$= x^2 + px + \frac{p^2}{4}$$

$$= \left(x + \frac{p}{2}\right)^2.$$

It will thus have $d_1{}^2 = d_2{}^2$, and since the positive square roots of two equal positive numbers are equal, it will have $d_1 = d_2$. We have thus proved that the graph of the equation $y^2 = 2px$ includes all points for which $d_1 = d_2$ *and no points for which* $d_1 \neq d_2$.

Equation (1) is the equation of the parabola with respect to axes taken as shown in Fig. 8-2. The line of symmetry of the curve, which in this case is the x-axis, is called the *axis* of the parabola. The point where the axis intersects the curve is called the *vertex* of the parabola. The vertex in this case is at the origin.

The case illustrated is that in which p is positive. If p is negative, the focus is to the left of the directrix.

Example

In the equation $y^2 = -8x$, $p = -4$; the focus is at $(-2,0)$, and the directrix is the line $x = 2$ (see Fig. 8-3).

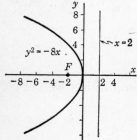

$y^2 = -8x$

Figure 8-3

If the axes are chosen so that the focus is on the y-axis at the point $(0,\frac{1}{2}p)$, and the directrix is the line $y = -\frac{1}{2}p$, the corresponding equation is of course

$$(2) \qquad x^2 = 2py.$$

In this case the focus is above the directrix and the parabola opens upward if p is positive; the focus is below the directrix and the parabola opens downward if p is negative.

Example

In the equation $x^2 = 6y$, or $y = \frac{1}{6}x^2$, we have $p = 3$; the focus is at $F(0,1\frac{1}{2})$, and the directrix is the line $y = -1\frac{1}{2}$ (see Fig. 8-4).

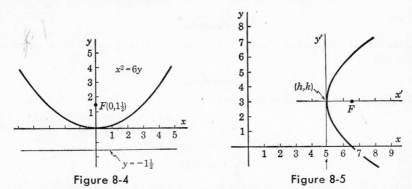

Figure 8-4   Figure 8-5

8-3. Parabola with vertex at (h,k). Let a parabola have its vertex at (h,k) and its axis parallel to the x-axis as indicated in Fig. 8-5. We may insert new axes x' and y' through the vertex as shown, and the equation of the curve relative to these axes is

$$y'^2 = 2px'.$$

In order to find the equation relative to the x- and y-axes, we may use the transformation for translation of axes, in the inverse sense:

$$x = x' + h, \qquad \therefore\ x' = x - h;$$
$$y = y' + k, \qquad \therefore\ y' = y - k.$$

Making these substitutions, we have

(3) $$(y - k)^2 = 2p(x - h).$$

This is the standard form of the equation of a parabola with vertex at (h,k) and axis parallel to the x-axis. The parabola opens to the right if p is positive and to the left if p is negative. Equation (1) is of course the special case of (3) in which $h = k = 0$.

If (3) is simplified, the result is an equation of the form

(4) $$y^2 + Dx + Ey + F = 0.$$

Conversely, any equation of the form (4) can be transformed into form (3) by completing the square in y if $D \neq 0$. It is therefore evident that *any equation of the form* (4) *represents a parabola with its axis parallel to the x-axis unless* $D = 0$.*

* In this exceptional case the equation contains only one variable and represents a pair of parallel or coincident lines, or has no locus. Thus the graph of $y^2 - 7y + 10 = 0$ is two parallel lines, $y = 2$ and $y = 5$; the equation

$$y^2 + 2y + 3 = 0$$

has no graph.

Example

Transform the equation $y^2 - 6y - 6x + 39 = 0$ into standard form, and draw the graph.

Solution

First write the equation in the form

$$y^2 - 6y = 6x - 39.$$

Now to complete the square in y, add 9 to both sides:

$$y^2 - 6y + 9 = 6x - 30.$$

This equation may be written in the standard form (3) as follows:

$$(y - 3)^2 = 6(x - 5).$$

The graph is a parabola with vertex at $(5,3)$. The value of p is 3; so the focus is $1\frac{1}{2}$ units to the right of the vertex. We have then

Coordinates of focus: $(6\frac{1}{2}, 3)$;
Equation of directrix: $x = 3\frac{1}{2}$.

The graph is shown in Fig. 8-5.

By similarly completing the square in x, any equation of the form $x^2 + Dx + Ey + F = 0$ can be put into the form

(5) $$(x - h)^2 = 2p(y - k)$$

if $E \neq 0$. This is the standard form of the equation of a parabola with vertex at (h,k) and axis parallel to the y-axis. It opens upward if p is positive and downward if p is negative. *It should be observed that the equation*

$$y = ax^2 + bx + c$$

which we met in the discussion of polynomial curves is of this form.

Example

The equation $y = x^2 + 4x + 1$ may be put into standard form (5) by completing the square in x.

$$y + 3 = x^2 + 4x + 4,$$
$$(x + 2)^2 = y + 3.$$

The graph is a parabola with vertex at $(-2, -3)$ and axis parallel to the y-axis. In this case $2p = 1$; so the parabola opens upward, and the focus is $\frac{1}{4}$ unit above the vertex.

8-4. Applications. The parabola has a multitude of scientific applications, only a few of which can be mentioned here.

It has already been stated (page 84) that when a projectile such as a ball or stone is thrown into the air its path is a parabola except for a slight deviation due to air resistance. This deviation is appreciable in the case of a projectile fired at high velocity from a gun.

Certain types of bridge construction employ parabolic arches; the curve in which a suspension-bridge cable hangs is approximately a parabola if the load is distributed uniformly along the horizontal roadbed.

If a parabola be rotated about its axis, a surface called a *paraboloid* is generated. This surface is used as a reflector in automobile headlights and other searchlights because of the following property of the parabola: From any point P on the curve, draw a line PF to the focus and a line PL parallel to the axis (Fig. 8-6). It can be proved that *these lines make equal angles with the tangent to the curve at P*. This means that if a source of light is placed at F the light rays upon striking the reflecting surface will be reflected in rays parallel to the axis, thus throwing a cylindrical beam of light in this direction. This same principle is used in the reverse sense in the reflecting telescope; if the axis of a parabolic mirror is pointed toward a star, the rays from the star, upon striking the mirror, will all be reflected to the focus.

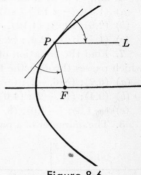

Figure 8-6

PROBLEMS

1. In each of the following cases, find the coordinates of the focus and the equation of the directrix of the parabola whose equation is given; sketch the graph:

(a) $y^2 = 6x.$ (b) $y^2 = -4x.$ (c) $x^2 = -8y.$

(d) $y = 4x^2.$ (e) $x = 0.6y^2.$ (f) $x^2 = -0.4y.$

(g) $4y^2 = x.$ (h) $3x = -8y^2.$ (i) $9y = 4x^2.$

2. In each of the following cases, find the equation of the parabola satisfying the given conditions:

(a) Vertex at the origin, axis along the x-axis, and passing through $A(3,6)$. HINT: The equation can be written as $y^2 = 2px$ or as $y^2 = kx$; then p or k can be found from the condition that $y = 6$ when $x = 3$.

(b) Vertex at the origin, axis along the y-axis, and passing through $B(-2,-1)$.

(c) Vertex at the origin, axis along the x-axis, and passing through $C(-3,4)$.

3. In each of the following cases, find the equation of the parabola satisfying the given conditions:

(a) Vertex at $(4,2)$, axis parallel to the x-axis, and passing through $A(8,7)$.

(b) Vertex at $(5,-3)$, axis parallel to the y-axis, and passing through $B(1,2)$

(c) Vertex at $(0,-6)$, axis along the y-axis, and passing through $(8,0)$.

4. A parabola has its focus at $(3,4)$ and its vertex at $(3,-2)$. What is its equation?

5. The chord drawn through the focus of a parabola perpendicular to its axis is called the *latus rectum* of the parabola. Show that its length is $2p$. [This means that the "width" of a parabola at its focus is $|2p|$; for example, the parabola $y^2 = 8x$ is 8 units wide at its focus, which is the point $(2,0)$.]

6. Find the equation of the parabola whose axis is parallel to the y-axis, and which passes through the three given points. (HINT: The equation can be written in the form $x^2 + Dx + Ey + F = 0$ or $y = ax^2 + bx + c$. Solve for D, E, and F, or a, b, and c.)

(a) $(1,3)$; $(-2,15)$; $(3,5)$.

(b) $(2,3)$; $(0,2)$; $(4,12)$.

(c) $(1,-5)$; $(-2,6)$; $(2,-2)$.

7. Find the equation of the parabola whose axis is parallel to the x-axis, and which passes through the three given points.

(a) $(6,2)$; $(-6,-2)$; $(-2,0)$.

(b) $(0,4)$; $(12,-2)$; $(4,0)$.

(c) $(-1,3)$; $(-4,0)$; $(8,-6)$.

8. The diameter of a parabolic reflector is 12 in., and its depth is 4 in. Locate the focus.

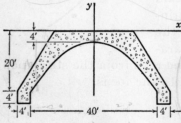

9. A parabola is 16 in. wide at a distance of 6 in. from the vertex. How wide is it at the focus?

10. A parabolic arch has the dimensions shown in Fig. 8-7. Find the equation of the parabola with respect to the axes shown. Compute the values of y at the points where $x = 5$, 10, and 15 ft.

Figure 8-7

11. Draw a graph that shows the way in which cos 2θ varies with cos θ; that is, take cos θ as the abscissa and cos 2θ as the ordinate. Show that the curve is a parabola.

12. If a ball is thrown vertically upward from the ground with initial velocity v_0 ft. per second, its distance above the ground at the end of t sec. is given approximately by the formula

$$y = v_0 t - 16t^2.$$

Draw this "distance-time graph," taking $v_0 = 40$ ft. per second.

13. Prove that if a point is equidistant from the y-axis and the point $F(6,0)$, then its coordinates (x,y) must satisfy the equation $y^2 = 12(x - 3)$. Prove,

conversely, that every point (x,y) having $y^2 = 12(x - 3)$ is equidistant from the point $F(6,0)$ and the y-axis.   It is to be understood that the distances involved are undirected distances.

14. Prove that if a point (x,y) is equidistant from $A(8,0)$ and the line $x = 4$, then its coordinates must satisfy the equation $y^2 = 8(x - 6)$.   Prove, conversely, that every point (x,y) having $y^2 = 8(x - 6)$ is equidistant from the point $A(8,0)$ and the line $x = 4$.

15. Let d_1 and d_2 be the undirected distances of a point $P(x,y)$ from the point $A(10,0)$ and from the line $x = 4$, respectively.   Show that if $d_1 = d_2$ then $y^2 = 12(x - 7)$.   Which, if any, of the following assertions is thereby proved?

(a) Every point whose coordinates satisfy the equation $y^2 = 12(x - 7)$ is equidistant from the given line and the given point.

(b) There are no points on the graph of the equation $y^2 = 12(x - 7)$ which are not equidistant from the given line and the given point.

(c) Every point (of the plane) that is equidistant from the given line and the given point lies on the graph of the equation $y^2 = 12(x - 7)$.

16. By completing the square, transform the equation

$$y = ax^2 + bx + c$$

into the standard form (5); find the coordinates of the vertex and the value of p in terms of a, b, and c, and show that the directed distance from the vertex to the focus is $1/4a$.

17. In each of the following cases, transform the given equation into the standard form (3) or (5), and sketch the curve.   In making the sketch it may be convenient to use the fact that the width of the parabola at its focus is $2p$ (see Prob. 5).

(a) $y^2 - 8y - 3x + 22 = 0$.   (b) $y^2 - 4y - 6x - 10 = 0$.
(c) $x^2 + 2x - 4y = 11$.   (d) $x^2 - 8x - 4y + 8 = 0$.
(e) $y = 12x - x^2$.   (f) $y^2 = 4(x + y)$.
(g) $4y^2 - 12y - 12x + 33 = 0$.   (h) $2x^2 - 10x - 3y + 8 = 0$.

18. The length of fencing available to enclose a rectangular plot of ground is 100 ft.   Let x (feet) be the width of the plot, and express the enclosed area as a function of x.   Make the graph.   For what value of x is the area greatest?

19. A rectangular field is to be enclosed and divided into four lots by fences parallel to one of the sides.   A total of 1,200 yd. of fencing is available.   Find the dimensions of the largest field that can be enclosed.

20. When a ball is thrown with initial velocity v_0 ft. per second at an angle $45°$ with the horizontal, it travels a path whose equation is approximately

$$y = x - \frac{32x^2}{v_0^2}.$$

If $v_0 = 96$ ft. per second, find the horizontal distance traveled and the height reached by the ball.

8-5. *The ellipse.* The ellipse is defined as *the locus of all points each of which has the sum of its undirected distances from two fixed points equal to a constant.* In Fig. 8-8 the points F and F' are 8 units apart. If P moves so that the sum of its undirected distances from F and F' is equal to 10 units, it will trace out the ellipse shown. F and F' are called the *foci* of the ellipse, and the point midway between them is called its *center.*

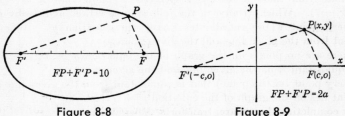

Figure 8-8   Figure 8-9

In order to obtain a simple equation for this curve, we choose axes as shown in Fig. 8-9 with the x-axis through the foci and the origin at the mid-point of the segment $F'F$. If the distance between the foci is denoted by $2c$, the coordinates of F' and F are $(-c,0)$ and $(c,0)$, respectively.

Now let $P(x,y)$ be a point of the plane, and let its undirected distances from F' and F be d_1 and d_2, respectively; then

$$d_1 = \sqrt{(x+c)^2 + y^2}; \qquad d_2 = \sqrt{(x-c)^2 + y^2}.$$

We want the equation in x and y that must be satisfied by the coordinates of all points for which $d_1 + d_2$ is equal to some specified constant—which must of course be greater than $2c$. We denote this constant by $2a$, it being understood that $a > c$. Then the coordinates of every point for which $d_1 + d_2 = 2a$ must satisfy the relation

$$\sqrt{(x+c)^2 + y^2} + \sqrt{(x-c)^2 + y^2} = 2a.$$

f we transpose the second radical to the right side, square both
des, and simplify, we get

$$a\sqrt{(x-c)^2 + y^2} = a^2 - cx.$$

ng again, we have

$$a^2(x^2 - 2cx + c^2 + y^2) = a^4 - 2a^2cx + c^2x^2$$
$$(a^2 - c^2)x^2 + a^2y^2 = a^2(a^2 - c^2).$$

If we now divide both sides by $a^2(a^2 - c^2)$, we get

$$\frac{x^2}{a^2} + \frac{y^2}{a^2 - c^2} = 1.$$

Now the quantity $a^2 - c^2$ is positive because $a > c$; if we wish, we may denote it by the new symbol b^2. Our equation then takes the form

(1) $$\frac{x^2}{a^2} + \frac{y^2}{b^2} = 1,$$

where a, b, and c are connected by the relation

(2) $$a^2 = b^2 + c^2.$$

We have proved that the coordinates of every point in the plane that has $d_1 + d_2 = 2a$ must satisfy equation (1). It can be proved, conversely, that the locus of (1) does not contain any points other than those for which $d_1 + d_2 = 2a$. We shall not give this part of the proof. Equation (1) is called the *standard equation* of the ellipse with center at the origin and foci on the x-axis.

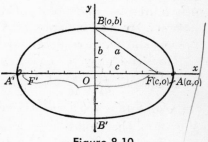

Figure 8-10

The intercepts of the ellipse on the axes are readily found to be $(\pm a, 0)$ and $(0, \pm b)$. The points A' and A (Fig. 8-10) are called the *vertices* of the ellipse; the line segment $A'A$, whose length is $2a$, is called its *major axis*, and the segment $B'B$, whose length is $2b$, is called its *minor axis*. We thus have a graphical interpretation of the constants a and b.

c = *distance from center to focus* = **OF**;
a = *distance from center to end of major axis* = **OA**;
b = *distance from center to end of minor axis* = **OB**.

The relation between a, b, and c appears in the triangle in Fig. 8-10; note that $BF = OA = a$.

Example

In the equation $\dfrac{x^2}{25} + \dfrac{y^2}{9} = 1$, $a = 5$ and $b = 3$; $c = \sqrt{a^2 - b^2} = 4$, and the foci are at $(\pm 4, 0)$. This is the case shown in Fig. 8-10.

If we choose the y-axis through the foci, making their coordinates $(0, \pm c)$, the equation of the ellipse is

(3)
$$\frac{x^2}{b^2} + \frac{y^2}{a^2} = 1.$$

Example

In the equation $\frac{x^2}{9} + \frac{y^2}{16} = 1$, $a = 4$ and $b = 3$; $c = \sqrt{a^2 - b^2} = \sqrt{7}$, and the foci are at $(0, \pm \sqrt{7})$.

Observe that since $a^2 = b^2 + c^2$, *the larger of the two denominators is always a^2.* The foci are on the x-axis if this larger number is under x^2 and on the y-axis if it is under y^2.

8-6. Eccentricity. The shape of the ellipse is determined by the ratio of c to a. This ratio, which is a number between 0 and 1 since $a > c > 0$, is called the *eccentricity* of the ellipse and is denoted by the letter e.

$$e = \frac{c}{a}.$$

Example

The equation $\frac{x^2}{64} + \frac{y^2}{16} = 1$ represents an ellipse in which $a = 8$ and $b = 4$; $c = \sqrt{64 - 16} = 4\sqrt{3}$, and its eccentricity is

$$\frac{4\sqrt{3}}{8} = \frac{\sqrt{3}}{2} = 0.866.$$

The student may show that if c/a, which is the same as $\sqrt{a^2 - b^2}/a$, is near 1, then b is small compared with a and the ellipse is long and narrow. On the other hand, if c/a is near zero, then b is nearly equal to a and the ellipse is nearly a circle. In fact as c approaches zero, and the foci consequently approach the center of the ellipse, the value of b approaches that of a. If $b = a$, the equation $x^2/a^2 + y^2/b^2 = 1$ becomes $x^2 + y^2 = a^2$. *The circle may therefore be regarded as an ellipse with eccentricity 0.*

8-7. Ellipse with center at (h,k). Let an ellipse have its center at (h,k) and its major and minor axes parallel to the coordinate axes as shown in Fig. 8-11. We may insert new axes x' and y' through the center as shown, and the equation of the curve relative to these axes is

$$\frac{x'^2}{a^2} + \frac{y'^2}{b^2} = 1.$$

In order to find the equation relative to the x- and y-axes, we let $x' = x - h$ and $y' = y - k$ as we did in the case of the parabola. The result is

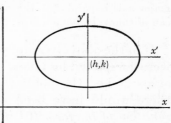

(4) $\dfrac{(x - h)^2}{a^2} + \dfrac{(y - k)^2}{b^2} = 1.$

This is the standard equation of the ellipse with center at (h,k) and major axis parallel to the x-axis.

Figure 8-11

If the major axis is parallel to the y-axis, the equation is

(5) $\dfrac{(x - h)^2}{b^2} + \dfrac{(y - k)^2}{a^2} = 1.$

If either of these equations is multiplied out, the result is an equation of the form

(6) $Ax^2 + Cy^2 + Dx + Ey + F = 0,$

in which A and C have the same sign.   Conversely, any equation of the form (6) can be put into form (4) or (5) by completing the squares in x and y provided that A and C have the same sign and provided also that the constant appearing on the right side when the left side is expressed as a sum of squares is positive.

Example

Transform the equation $x^2 + 4y^2 - 16x + 16y + 76 = 0$ into standard form.

Solution

First write the equation in the form

$$(x^2 - 16x) + 4(y^2 + 4y) = -76.$$

Now add the numbers necessary to complete the squares.

$$(x^2 - 16x + 64) + 4(y^2 + 4y + 4) = -76 + 64 + 16.$$

Note that the value of the right-hand member is now positive.   The equation may be written as

$$(x - 8)^2 + 4(y + 2)^2 = 4$$

or, in standard form, as

$$\frac{(x-8)^2}{4} + \frac{(y+2)^2}{1} = 1.$$

The graph is an ellipse with center at $(8,-2)$ and with $a = 2$ and $b = 1$; the major axis is parallel to the x-axis, and $c = \sqrt{3}$. The coordinates of the foci can of course be found easily.

If in the above example the number on the right after the squares were completed had been zero, the graph would have been a "point ellipse," i.e., the point (h,k). If the number had been negative, there would have been no locus. It is evident then that *every equation of the form* (6) *in which A and C have the same sign represents an ellipse, a single point, or no locus.*

Example

Upon completing the squares, the equation

$$x^2 + 2y^2 - 2x + 16y + 45 = 0$$

becomes $(x-1)^2 + 2(y+4)^2 = -12$. There is no locus. If the constant 45 is replaced by 33, the locus is the point $(1,-4)$.

8-8. Applications. The ellipse, like the parabola, has many scientific applications. Elliptic gears are used in certain kinds of machinery; arches in the form of semi-ellipses are often employed in the construction of stone and concrete bridges. The orbits in which the planets revolve about the sun are ellipses, the sun being at one focus. In the case of the earth the eccentricity of the ellipse is about $\frac{1}{60}$. In engineering drawing one must frequently draw ellipses because the orthographic projection of a circle on a plane not parallel to the plane of the circle is an ellipse.

PROBLEMS

1. In each of the following cases, draw the ellipse whose equation is given. Find the coordinates of its foci, and compute its eccentricity.

(a) $\dfrac{x^2}{9} + \dfrac{y^2}{25} = 1.$

(b) $\dfrac{x^2}{27} + \dfrac{y^2}{4} = 1.$

(c) $4x^2 + 3y^2 = 36.$

(d) $x^2 + \frac{3}{4}y^2 = 24.$

(e) $\dfrac{2x^2}{3} + \dfrac{3y^2}{2} = 24.$

(f) $\frac{3}{4}x^2 + 4y^2 = 108.$

2. In each of the following cases, find the equation of the ellipse with center at the origin that satisfies the given conditions:

(a) One focus at $(0,6)$; $e = \frac{1}{2}$.
(b) One vertex at $(9,0)$; $e = \frac{2}{3}$.
(c) One end of minor axis $(0,4)$; $e = 0.6$.

3. In each of the following cases, find the equation of the ellipse that satisfies the given conditions:

(a) Center at $(6,-4)$; one vertex at $(10,-4)$; $e = \frac{1}{2}$.
(b) Vertices at $(-5,-2)$, $(7,-2)$; one focus at $(5,-2)$.
(c) Center at $(4,-4)$; one end of minor axis at $(0,-4)$; one focus at $(4,0)$.
(d) Foci at $(-2,3)$, $(6,3)$; one vertex at $(8,3)$.

4. What is the eccentricity of an ellipse whose major axis is twice as long as its minor axis? Ten times as long?

5. Show that an ellipse is symmetrical with respect to its major and minor axes, and with respect to its center.

6. The chord drawn through either focus of an ellipse perpendicular to its major axis is called the *latus rectum* of the ellipse. Show that its length is $2b^2/a$.

7. Let the undirected distances of a point $P(x,y)$ from $A(1,0)$ and $B(9,0)$ be d_1 and d_2, respectively. Show that if $d_1 + d_2 = 10$, then the coordinates of P must satisfy the equation $9x^2 + 25y^2 = 90x$. Have you proved that every point whose coordinates satisfy this equation has $d_1 + d_2 = 10$?

8. A point moves so that the sum of its undirected distances from $A(0,-3)$ and $B(0,-9)$ is equal to 10. Find the equation of its path, and sketch it.

9. A point moves so that its undirected distance from the origin is equal to one-half its undirected distance from the line $x + 9 = 0$. Find the equation of its path, and sketch it.

10. A point moves so that its undirected distance from the point $A(0,-2)$ is equal to one-half its undirected distance from the line $y = 4$. Find the equation of its path, and sketch it.

11. Find the equation of the locus of points that are two-thirds as far from the point $A(6,0)$ as from the y-axis, it being understood that the distances are undirected.

12. A semielliptic arch in a stone bridge has a span of 20 ft. and a height of 6 ft. as shown in Fig. 8-12. In constructing the arch it is necessary to know its height at distances of 2, 4, 6, 8, and 9 ft. from its center, as indicated by the dotted lines. Compute these heights to the nearest tenth of a foot.

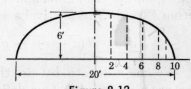

Figure 8-12

13. A rod PQ of length 24 units moves so that P is always on the y-axis and Q is on the x-axis. A point M is on PQ two-thirds of the way from P to Q. Find the equation of the path traveled by M.

14. The orbit in which the earth travels about the sun is an ellipse with the sun at one focus. The semimajor axis of the ellipse is 92.9 million miles, and its eccentricity is 0.0168. Compute the greatest and least distances of the earth from the sun.

In each of the following cases, transform the given equation into standard form. Draw the corresponding graph if there is one.

15. $9x^2 + 4y^2 - 54x + 8y + 49 = 0$.   **16.** $4x^2 + 9y^2 + 24x - 36y + 36 = 0$.

17. $x^2 + 4y^2 - 32y + 48 = 0$.   **18.** $4x^2 + y^2 - 16x = 0$.

19. $x^2 + y^2 + 3x - 4y = 0$.   **20.** $x^2 + 2y^2 + 4x + 6y = 0$.

21. $2x^2 + 3y^2 = 8x + 18y - 29$.   **22.** $9x^2 + 4y^2 + 36x + 24y + 72 = 0$.

23. Find the points of intersection of the line $3x - 5y + 3 = 0$ and the ellipse $9x^2 + 25y^2 = 225$. Draw the graph.

24. Find the points of intersection of the line $9x - 5y = 60$ and the ellipse $9x^2 + 25y^2 = 90x$. Draw the graph.

25. A point moves so that its undirected distance from the point $A(-2,0)$ remains equal to one-half its undirected distance from the line $x + 5 = 0$. Find the coordinates of the point or points on its path that are farthest from the x-axis.

8-9. The hyperbola. The hyperbola is defined as *the locus of all points each of which has the difference of its undirected distances from two fixed points equal to a constant.* The fixed points are called the *foci* of the hyperbola, and the point midway between them is called its *center*. The derivation of the standard equation for this curve parallels that for the ellipse. We choose the axes as shown in Fig. 8-13 and denote the distance between the foci by $2c$, just as in the case of the ellipse. The foci

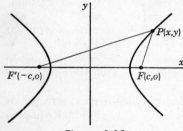

Figure 8-13

are then the points $F'(-c,0)$ and $F(c,0)$, as shown. Let $P(x,y)$ be a point of the plane, and let d_1 and d_2 be its undirected distances from F' and F, respectively; then

$$d_1 = \sqrt{(x + c)^2 + y^2}; \qquad d_2 = \sqrt{(x - c)^2 + y^2}.$$

We may denote by $2a$ the absolute value of the difference between d_1 and d_2. Our definition then implies that if P is to be a point of the locus, its coordinates must be such that either $d_1 - d_2 = 2a$ or $d_2 - d_1 = 2a$, according as $d_1 > d_2$ or $d_2 > d_1$. Thus we must have

$$\sqrt{(x + c)^2 + y^2} - \sqrt{(x - c)^2 + y^2} = \pm 2a.$$

By going through the same operations of transposing, squaring, etc., that we used in the case of the ellipse we get from this the equation

$$\frac{x^2}{a^2} - \frac{y^2}{c^2 - a^2} = 1.$$

Observe now that $a < c$ because the difference of two sides of a triangle is less than the third side. The quantity $c^2 - a^2$ is therefore positive, and if we wish, we may denote it by the symbol b^2. Our equation then becomes

(1) $$\frac{x^2}{a^2} - \frac{y^2}{b^2} = 1$$

where a, b, and c are connected by the relation

(2) $$c^2 = b^2 + a^2.$$

The graph has the general shape shown in Fig. 8-13. It is easy to see from equation (1) that it is symmetrical with respect to both axes and the origin, that its intercepts on the x-axis are the points $(\pm a, 0)$, and that it does not intersect the y-axis. In fact, if we solve the equation for y in terms of x, we get

$$y = \pm \frac{b}{a} \sqrt{x^2 - a^2},$$

from which it is clear that there is no value of y corresponding to any value of x between $-a$ and $+a$. It is also evident that y increases indefinitely in absolute value as x increases. If we write the above equation in the form

$$y = \pm \frac{bx}{a} \sqrt{1 - \frac{a^2}{x^2}}$$

and note that the expression $\sqrt{1 - \frac{a^2}{x^2}}$ approaches 1 as x becomes larger and larger in absolute value, we suspect that for numerically large values of x the graph of the hyperbola nearly coincides with that of the lines

$$y = \pm \frac{b}{a} x.$$

It can be proved that these lines are asymptotes to the curve (see **Prob.** 10 of the next set).

The segment $A'A$, Fig. 8-14, is called the *transverse axis* of the hyperbola, and segment $B'B$ is called its *conjugate axis*. The diagonals of the rectangle drawn as shown in the figure obviously have the equations $y = \pm \dfrac{b}{a} x$; they are therefore the asymptotes.

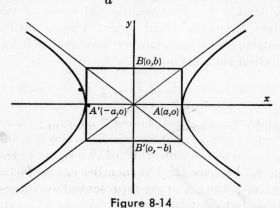

Figure 8-14

The ratio of c to a is called the *eccentricity* of the hyperbola and is denoted by the letter e.

$$e = \frac{c}{a}.$$

Since $a < c$, the eccentricity is greater than 1.

If we had chosen the y-axis through the foci, making their coordinates $(0, \pm c)$, the equation would have been

$$(3) \qquad \frac{y^2}{a^2} - \frac{x^2}{b^2} = 1.$$

In the equation of the hyperbola a may be less than, equal to, or greater than b. One determines whether the foci are on the x- or y-axis by putting the equation in the standard form (1) or (3) with $+1$ on the right-hand side; if the coefficient of x^2 is then positive, the foci are on the x-axis, while if that of y^2 is positive, they are on the y-axis.

The standard form of the equation of a hyperbola with center at (h,k) and transverse axis parallel to the x-axis is

$$(4) \qquad \frac{(x - h)^2}{a^2} - \frac{(y - k)^2}{b^2} = 1;$$

if the transverse axis is parallel to the y-axis, the corresponding equation is

(5)
$$\frac{(y - k)^2}{a^2} - \frac{(x - h)^2}{b^2} = 1.$$

If either (4) or (5) is multiplied out, the result is an equation of the form

(6)
$$Ax^2 + Cy^2 + Dx + Ey + F = 0$$

in which A and C have *opposite signs*.   Conversely, an equation of the form (6) can be transformed into form (4) or (5) by completing the squares, provided A and C have opposite signs.   The only exceptional case is that in which, when the left-hand side has been expressed as the difference of two squares, the right-hand side is zero.   In this case the left member can be factored into real linear factors, and the equation represents two intersecting lines. Otherwise it of course represents a hyperbola.

8-10. Equilateral hyperbola.   If $b = a$, the equation

$$\frac{x^2}{a^2} - \frac{y^2}{b^2} = 1$$

takes the form

$$x^2 - y^2 = a^2.$$

The asymptotes in this special case are the lines $y = \pm x$ which are *mutually perpendicular*.   This hyperbola is called an *equilateral* or *rectangular hyperbola*.   It will be left to the student to show that if the axes are rotated through $-45°$ the equation becomes

$$2xy = a^2.$$

In applications the equation of the equilateral hyperbola is often encountered in the form $xy = k$.   Thus, the law connecting the pressure and volume of a perfect gas under constant temperature is $pv = k$.   The graph (Fig. 8-15)

Figure 8-15

shows pictorially the way in which the pressure of a given quantity of gas decreases as its volume increases.

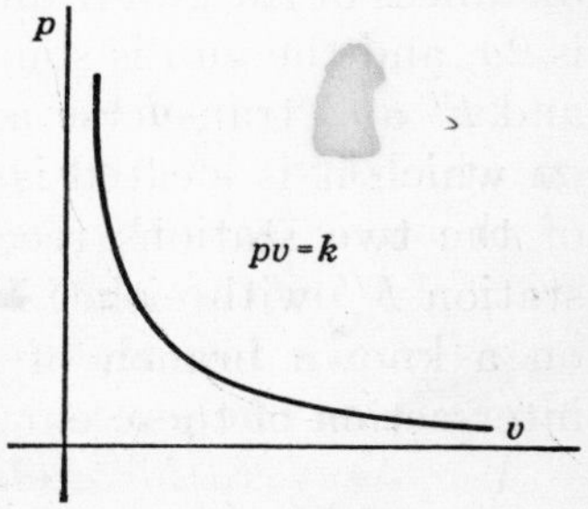

A more general form of the equation of the equilateral hyperbola is

$$axy + by + cx + d = 0.$$

Upon solving for y, the equation becomes

$$y = -\frac{cx + d}{ax + b}.$$

This equation was studied in Chap. 5 on Rational Fractional Functions. The student can easily show, using the methods of that chapter, that the line $x = -b/a$ is the vertical asymptote and the line $y = -c/a$ is the horizontal asymptote. Figure 5-1, page 91, is an example.

It should be fairly obvious that the equation

$$axy + by + cx + d = 0$$

can be changed into the form $x'y' = k$ by making a translation of axes so as to move the origin to the center of the hyperbola. The required substitution is of course

$$x = x' - \frac{b}{a}; \qquad y = y' - \frac{c}{a}.$$

8-11. Application. One of the applications of the hyperbola is in range finding. If the precise time at which the sound of a gun reaches two listening posts F and F' is recorded, this difference multiplied by the velocity of sound gives the difference of the distances of the gun from F and F'. In our notation this difference is $2a$, and the gun is somewhere on the hyperbola having foci at F and F' and transverse axis $2a$. The "branch" of the hyperbola on which it is located is known since this depends only on which of the two stations received the sound first. By using a third station F'' with either F or F', the gun can similarly be located on a known branch of another hyperbola. Finally, a point of intersection of these curves gives the position of the gun.

PROBLEMS

1. In each of the following cases, sketch the hyperbola whose equation is given. Draw its asymptotes (as indicated in Fig. 8-14), and give the coordinates of its vertices and foci.

(a) $x^2 - 4y^2 = 100.$ (b) $3x^2 - 4y^2 = -144.$

(c) $16x^2 - 9y^2 = 144.$ (d) $9y^2 - 4x^2 + 36 = 0.$

(e) $x^2 - 4y^2 = 36.$ (f) $0.4x^2 - 0.6y^2 = 14.4.$

2. What is the eccentricity of an equilateral hyperbola?

3. The two hyperbolas $\dfrac{x^2}{a^2} - \dfrac{y^2}{b^2} = 1$ and $\dfrac{y^2}{b^2} - \dfrac{x^2}{a^2} = 1$ are called *conjugate* hyperbolas. Show that the conjugate axis of either is the transverse axis of the other, and vice versa, and that they have the same asymptotes. Draw both on the same axes, taking $a = 5$ and $b = 3$.

4. Sketch the graph of the equation $x^2 - y^2 = 4$. Rotate the axes through $45°$, and find the new equation for the curve.

5. Show that when the axes are rotated through an angle of $-45°$, the new equation for the hyperbola $x^2 - y^2 = a^2$ is $2x'y' = a^2$.

6. The chord drawn through either focus of a hyperbola perpendicular to its transverse axis is called its *latus rectum*. Show that its length is $2b^2/a$.

7. Find the equation of the hyperbola satisfying the following conditions:

(a) Vertices at $(\pm 6,0)$; $e = \frac{4}{3}$.   (b) Vertices at $(0, \pm 4)$; foci at $(0, \pm 5)$.

(c) Foci at $(0, \pm 6)$; $e = \frac{3}{2}$.   (d) Vertices at $(\pm 8,0)$; $e = \sqrt{2}$.

8. Find the equation of the hyperbola satisfying the following conditions:

(a) Center at $(4,2)$; one focus at $(4,7)$; $e = \frac{5}{3}$.

(b) Vertices at $(-2,3)$, $(6,3)$; one focus at $(-4,3)$.

(c) Center at $(-1,-2)$; one vertex at $(-1,1)$; $e = 2$.

9. A point moves so that the difference of its undirected distances from the origin and the point $(10,0)$ is 6 units. Find the equation of its path, and sketch it.

10. Show that the difference between the ordinate to the line $y = \dfrac{bx}{a}$ and the positive ordinate to the hyperbola $\dfrac{x^2}{a^2} - \dfrac{y^2}{b^2} = 1$ approaches zero as x increases indefinitely. HINT: The difference is

$$\frac{b}{a}(x - \sqrt{x^2 - a^2});$$

multiply and divide by $x + \sqrt{x^2 - a^2}$.

11. Let d_1 and d_2 be the undirected distances of a point $P(x,y)$ from $A(-10,0)$ and $B(10,0)$, respectively. Show that if $d_1 - d_2 = 12$, then the coordinates of P must satisfy the relation $\dfrac{x^2}{36} - \dfrac{y^2}{64} = 1$. Is it true that *every* point whose coordinates satisfy this equation has $d_1 - d_2 = 12$? What is the locus of all points for which $d_1 - d_2 = 12$?

12. Let d_1 and d_2 be the undirected distances of a point $P(x,y)$ from the origin and from $B(8,0)$, respectively. Show that if $d_1 - d_2 = 4$, then the coordinates of P must satisfy the equation $3x^2 - y^2 = 12(2x - 3)$. Is it true that *every*

point whose coordinates satisfy this equation has $d_1 - d_2 = 4$? What is the locus of all points for which $d_1 - d_2 = 4$?

13. Let d_1 and d_2 be the undirected distances of a point $P(x,y)$ from the points $A(0,-2)$ and $B(0,8)$, respectively. Show that if $d_1 - d_2 = 6$, then the coordinates of P must satisfy the equation $16y^2 - 96y - 9x^2 = 0$. Is it true that *every* point whose coordinates satisfy this equation has $d_1 - d_2 = 6$? What is the locus of all points for which $d_1 - d_2 = 6$?

14. In each of the following cases, transform the given equation into the standard form and sketch the graph:

(a) $4x^2 - y^2 - 4y - 8x = 4$.   (b) $x^2 - y^2 - 2x - 4y - 7 = 0$.

(c) $3x^2 - y^2 + 18x - 2y + 14 = 0$.   (d) $5x^2 - 4y^2 = 40x$.

(e) $4x^2 - 3y^2 = 8x - 12y + 8$.   (f) $3x^2 - y^2 + 18x + 6y = 9$.

(g) $4x^2 - 9y^2 - 32x + 54y = 17$.

In each of the following cases, draw the graph of the given equation by solving for y in terms of x and using the methods of Chap. 5:

15. $xy + 2y - 3x + 1 = 0$.   **16.** $xy + y - 2x = 5$.

17. $2xy + 3y + x = 5$.   **18.** $2y - xy - 3x = 6$.

19. $3xy + 4y = 6x + 6$.   **20.** $xy = x + y$.

In each of the following cases, translate the axes, choosing the new origin so that the resulting equation will not contain any terms of first degree. Sketch the graph, and show both sets of axes:

21. $xy + 2y - x + 1 = 0$.   **22.** $xy + 4y - 2x - 3 = 0$.

23. $2xy + 3y = 3x - 5$.   **24.** $2y - 5x = 3xy + 2$.

25. $y + 3x = 2 - 2xy$.   **26.** $5xy + 3x = 6 - 2y$.

27. If we solve the equation $axy + by + cx + d = 0$ for y in terms of x, we get

$$y = -\frac{cx + d}{ax + b}.$$

We thus see that the lines $x = -b/a$ and $y = -c/a$ are vertical and horizontal asymptotes, respectively, to the hyperbola. The center is then the point

$$\left(-\frac{b}{a}, -\frac{c}{a}\right).$$

Show that if the axes are translated so that this point becomes the new origin, then the new equation has the form $x'y' = k$, where $k = (cb - ad)/a^2$.

8-12. *Sections of a cone.* It can be proved that when a right circular cone (including both its upper and lower nappes) is cut by a plane, the section is a parabola, ellipse, or hyperbola if the plane does not pass through the vertex of the cone. If the plane does pass through the vertex, the section may be a single point, or two intersecting or coincident lines. All these loci are called *conic sections*, or simply *conics*. We may use the term *regular conic* to designate sections cut by planes that do not pass through the vertex and *degenerate conic* to denote those cut by planes through the vertex.*

8-13. *The general equation of second degree.* The most general equation of second degree in x and y is

(1) $$Ax^2 + Bxy + Cy^2 + Dx + Ey + F = 0$$

where A, B, and C are not all zero. The special case in which $B = 0$ is

(2) $$Ax^2 + Cy^2 + Dx + Ey + F = 0.$$

We have found that when (2) has a locus it is always a conic section. If the conic is not degenerate, it is

> *A parabola if **A** or **C** = 0;*
> *An ellipse (or circle) if **A** and **C** have the same sign;*
> *A hyperbola if **A** and **C** have opposite signs.*

Furthermore, in each case the axis or axes of the conic are parallel to the coordinate axes.

We shall now show that if the xy term is present, it can be removed by rotating the axes through a proper angle. This means that the most general equation of second degree (1) also represents a conic section (or no locus). When the xy term is present, the axis or axes of the conic are inclined to the coordinate axes.

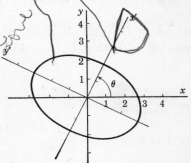

Example

The equation $5x^2 + 4xy + 8y^2 - 36 = 0$ represents an ellipse whose minor axis makes an angle θ whose tangent is 2 with the x-axis

Figure 8-16

(Fig. 8-16). If the axes are rotated through this angle, the xy term disappears and the equation, with respect to the new axes, becomes $(x'^2/4) + (y'^2/9) = 1$.

---

* We shall include also in this last designation a pair of parallel lines. They could not be cut from a cone but could be cut from a cylinder, which is a limiting case.

In order to show that the xy term can be removed by rotating the axes through a proper angle, and to determine this angle, we take the equation

$$Ax^2 + Bxy + Cy^2 + Dx + Ey + F = 0$$

and let $x = x' \cos \theta - y' \sin \theta$, $y = x' \sin \theta + y' \cos \theta$; the result is a new equation of the form

$$(3) \qquad A'x'^2 + B'x'y' + C'y'^2 + D'x' + E'y' + F' = 0,$$

where

$$(4) \qquad \begin{cases} A' = A \cos^2 \theta + B \sin \theta \cos \theta + C \sin^2 \theta \\ B' = B \cos 2\theta - (A - C) \sin 2\theta \\ C' = A \sin^2 \theta - B \sin \theta \cos \theta + C \cos^2 \theta \\ D' = D \cos \theta + E \sin \theta \\ E' = E \cos \theta - D \sin \theta \\ F' = F. \end{cases}$$

To eliminate the $x'y'$ term, we must make $B' = 0$; that is, we must choose θ so that

$$B \cos 2\theta - (A - C) \sin 2\theta = 0.$$

The solution of this equation is

$$\tan 2\theta = \frac{B}{A - C} \qquad \text{if } A \neq C.$$

If $A = C$ (and $B \neq 0$), the required value of θ is given by $\cos 2\theta = 0$; that is, $\theta \pm 45°$.

Example

The angle through which the axes must be rotated to remove the xy term from the equation

$$5x^2 + 4xy + 8y^2 - 36 = 0$$

is given by

$$\tan 2\theta = \frac{4}{5 - 8} = -\frac{4}{3}.$$

Since $\tan 2\theta = \dfrac{2 \tan \theta}{1 - \tan^2 \theta}$, this means that

$$\frac{2 \tan \theta}{1 - \tan^2 \theta} = -\frac{4}{3}$$

or

$$2 \tan^2 \theta - 3 \tan \theta - 2 = 0.$$

Solving this equation, we find that

$$\tan \theta = 2 \text{ or } -\tfrac{1}{2}.$$

The xy term will disappear if the axes are rotated through either of these angles (see Fig. 8-16).

8-14. Identification of a conic. After the xy term has been removed from a general equation of second degree by rotating the axes, the conic can be easily identified: If there is a graph, then

(**a**) If A' or $C' = 0$, it is a parabola;
       (Degenerate case a pair of parallel or coincident lines)
(**b**) If A' and C' have the same sign, it is an ellipse;
       (Degenerate case a single point)
(**c**) If A' and C' have opposite signs, it is a hyperbola.
       (Degenerate case a pair of intersecting lines)

It is possible to give rules by which the conic can be identified without first removing the xy term.   For this purpose we state the following:
Theorem.   The graph (if it has a graph) of the equation

$$Ax^2 + Bxy + Cy^2 + Dx + Ey + F = 0$$

is

(1) A parabola (or its degenerate case) if $B^2 - 4AC = 0$;
(2) An ellipse (or its degenerate case) if $B^2 - 4AC < 0$;
(3) A hyperbola (or its degenerate case) if $B^2 - 4AC > 0$.

The proof of this theorem depends upon the fact (proof of which is left to the student) that the value of the quantity $B^2 - 4AC$ is unchanged when the axes are rotated through any angle; i.e., no matter what the angle θ of rotation may be,

$$B^2 - 4AC = B'^2 - 4A'C'.$$

Now if θ is chosen so that $B' = 0$, we have

$$B^2 - 4AC = -4A'C'.$$

It is immediately evident that

(1) $B^2 - 4AC = 0$ if and only if A' or $C' = 0$;
(2) $B^2 - 4AC < 0$ if and only if A' and C' have the same sign;
(3) $B^2 - 4AC > 0$ if and only if A' and C' have opposite signs.

The theorem follows immediately in view of statements (*a*), (*b*), and (*c*).

Finally we state as a matter of interest, but without giving the proof, that the graph will be the regular conic if $\Delta \neq 0$ and the degenerate conic if $\Delta = 0$, where

$$\Delta = \begin{vmatrix} 2A & B & D \\ B & 2C & E \\ D & E & 2F \end{vmatrix}$$

8-15. *Second definition of a conic.* An alternate definition of a regular conic is as follows:

*A regular conic is the locus of a point which moves so that the ratio of its undirected distance from a fixed point **F** to that from a fixed line **l** is a constant **e**.* This positive constant is the eccentricity of the conic, and if

$e < 1$, the conic is an ellipse;
$e = 1$, the conic is a parabola;
$e > 1$, the conic is a hyperbola.

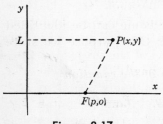

Figure 8-17

In order to derive an equation for the conic from this definition, we proceed as follows: Choose the coordinate axes so that the fixed line *l* coincides with the *y*-axis, and the fixed point *F* has coordinates $(p,0)$ as indicated in Fig. 8-17. Let $P(x,y)$ be a point of the plane, and let d_1 and d_2 be its undirected distances from the point *F* and from the line *l*, respectively. Then

$$d_1 = |FP| = \sqrt{(x-p)^2 + y^2}; \qquad d_2 = |LP| = |x| = \sqrt{x^2}.$$

The coordinates of every point for which $d_1/d_2 = e$ (or $d_1 = ed_2$) must satisfy the equation

(1) $$\sqrt{(x-p)^2 + y^2} = e\sqrt{x^2}.$$

If we square both sides and simplify, we get the following results:

(2) $$x^2 - 2px + p^2 + y^2 = e^2x^2,$$
(3) $$(1 - e^2)x^2 + y^2 - 2px + p^2 = 0.$$

Thus the coordinates of every point for which $d_1 = ed_2$ must satisfy (3). It is easy to show, by reversing the above steps, that every point whose coordinates satisfy (3) has $d_1 = ed_2$. Thus if (3) is true for a point (x,y), then (2) must be true. If (2) is true, then (1) must be true because the positive square roots of two equal positive numbers are equal.

We have proved that (3) is the equation of the locus of a point which moves so that the ratio of its undirected distance from the point $(p,0)$ to its undirected distance from the y-axis is always equal to a constant e. By examining this equation we can readily see the following facts:

If $e < 1$, the coefficients of x^2 and y^2 have the same sign, and the locus is an ellipse.

If $e = 1$, the coefficient of x^2 is zero, and the locus is a parabola.

If $e > 1$, the coefficients of x^2 and y^2 have opposite signs, and the locus is a hyperbola.

The fixed point F is called a *focus* of the conic, and the fixed line l is called a *directrix*. In the case of the parabola ($e = 1$) these are precisely the focus and directrix of our previous definition. In the case of the ellipse and hyperbola the "focus" as used in this definition coincides with one of the two foci of the previous definition. Thus the ellipse of Example 3, page 60, has the line $x = -3$ as a directrix and the origin as a focus. In this case $e = \frac{1}{2}$. The student may show that the origin and the point $(2,0)$ are the foci in the sense that this term was used in our previous definition.

PROBLEMS

1. In each of the following cases, identify the graph, assuming that there is one and that it is not a degenerate conic:

(a) $x^2 + y^2 = x + y.$ (b) $x^2 - 3x + 2y^2 = 4.$

(c) $3x^2 = y^2 + y + 1.$ (d) $4x - y = 4 + 2x^2.$

(e) $x^2 + 2 = 3x - 2y^2.$ (f) $x^2 + 6x = y^2 + 2y - 3.$

2. In each of the following cases, show that the given equation has no graph or that it represents a degenerate conic:

(a) $x^2 + y^2 - 4x + 8y + 26 = 0.$ (b) $(x + y)^2 = 0.$

(c) $x^2 - 6x = y^2 - 6y.$ (d) $(x + 2y)^2 + 4 = 0.$

3. In each of the following cases, identify the conic represented by the given equation, and find the sine and cosine of the positive acute angle through which the axes should be rotated in order that the new equation shall not contain an $x'y'$ term:

(a) $4x^2 + 4xy + 7y^2 = 10.$ (b) $5x^2 + 6xy - 3y^2 = 6.$

(c) $5x^2 + 24xy - 2y^2 = 30.$ (d) $3x^2 + 4xy + 3y^2 = 8.$

(e) $8x^2 + 8xy - 7y^2 = 25.$ (f) $34x^2 - 24xy + 41y^2 = 50.$

242/1 ALE

4. In each of the following cases, rotate the axes through a positive acute angle, choosing the angle so that the resulting equation will not have an $x'y'$ term. Draw the curve, and show both sets of axes.

(a) $3x^2 + 4xy - 4 = 0.$

(b) $5x^2 + 4xy + 8y^2 - 36 = 0.$

(c) $16x^2 - 24xy + 9y^2 - 90x - 120y = 0.$

(d) $16x^2 + 24xy + 9y^2 + 20x - 110y + 125 = 0.$

(e) $3x^2 - 10xy + 3y^2 + 32 = 0.$

(f) $2x^2 + xy + 2y^2 = 90.$

(g) $5x^2 + 8xy + 5y^2 = 25.$

5. Show that, for any angle θ through which the axes may be rotated, $B'^2 - 4A'C' = B^2 - 4AC.$

6. Show that, for any angle θ through which the axes may be rotated, $A' + C' = A + C.$

7. In each of the following cases, evaluate both Δ and $B^2 - 4AC$; identify the locus, if there is one, with the aid of this information:

(a) $x^2 - xy - 6y^2 + x - 3y = 0.$

(b) $x^2 - 2xy + y^2 + x + 2y + 1 = 0.$

(c) $x^2 - xy - 2y^2 - x + 2y = 0.$

(d) $x^2 + xy + y^2 + 4y = 0.$

(e) $x^2 + 2xy + y^2 - 1 = 0.$

8. A point moves so that its undirected distance from $A(5,0)$ is always equal to one-half its undirected distance from the line $x + 4 = 0.$ Find the equation of its path, and sketch it.

9. A point moves so that its undirected distance from $A(3,0)$ is always equal to one-half its undirected distance from the y-axis. Find the equation of its path, and sketch it.

10. A point moves so that the ratio of its undirected distances from the point $A(0,5)$ and from the x-axis remains equal to $\frac{3}{2}.$ Find the equation of its path, and sketch it.

11. Find the equation of the locus of all points each of which is twice as far from the point $(0,6)$ as from the x-axis. Sketch the graph.

12. A point moves so that its undirected distance from $A(3,0)$ remains equal to one-half its undirected distance from the y-axis. Show that the sum of its undirected distances from $A(3,0)$ and $B(5,0)$ remains equal to 4.

13. A point moves so that its undirected distance from $A(7,0)$ is always equal to two-thirds its undirected distance from the line $x - 2 = 0.$ Show that the sum of its undirected distances from $A(7,0)$ and $B(15,0)$ remains equal to 12.

14. A point moves so that its undirected distance from the origin remains always equal to one-third its undirected distance from the line $x + 2 = 0.$ Find the coordinates of the point or points on its path that are farthest from the x-axis.

15. A point moves so that its undirected distance from the point $A(4,0)$ is always equal to four-thirds its undirected distance from the y-axis. Find the equation of its path, and sketch it.

CHAPTER 9

ALGEBRAIC CURVES OF HIGHER DEGREE

9-1. Definitions. A plane curve is said to be an *algebraic curve* if it is the locus of an equation $f(x,y) = 0$, where $f(x,y)$ is a *polynomial* in x and y. The general equation of this type of first degree is

$$Ax + By + C = 0.$$

Its graph is a straight line. The corresponding equation of second degree is

$$Ax^2 + Bxy + Cy^2 + Dx + Ey + F = 0.$$

We have seen that such an equation may have no locus at all, but if it has one, it is a conic section.

It would be natural, as a next step, to consider polynomials of higher degree. We have already studied some special cases in Chaps. 4 and 5. For example, the equation

$$y = \frac{x + 2}{x(x^2 + 1)},$$

which is of the type studied in Chap. 5, is equivalent to

$$x^3y + xy - x - 2 = 0.$$

The left-hand member of this last equation is a polynomial in x and y degree four.* It is, however, of only the first degree in y, and this is characteristic of the equations studied in Chaps. 4 and 5. In this chapter we shall take up a few cases of a more general nature.

* The student will recall that the degree of any particular term of a polynomial in x and y is the sum of the exponents of x and y in that term—and that the degree of the polynomial is that of the term of highest degree.

9-2. *Discussion of algebraic curves.* The sketching of an algebraic curve is often facilitated by first writing out a "discussion" similar to that employed in Chap. 5. More general methods of finding horizontal and vertical asymptotes are needed, and certain items included below should be added to the discussion.

1. INTERCEPTS. These are of course found as before by substituting zero for y and solving the resulting equation for x, and then similarly substituting zero for x and solving for y.

2. SYMMETRY. The tests previously given for symmetry with respect to the coordinate axes and to the origin apply to any equation in x and y. In addition, it may be worthwhile to note that if the equation that results when x is replaced by y and y is replaced by x is identical with the original equation, then the graph is symmetrical with respect to the line $y = x$. The equations $3xy = 5$ and $x^2 - 7xy + y^2 = 10$ are examples.

3. ASYMPTOTES. If the equation can be solved for y in terms of x and thus put into the form $y = F(x)$, then any vertical asymptotes that exist can be found by the method of Chap. 5; that is, by finding any values of x for which the denominator of $F(x)$ is zero and the numerator is not zero.

Similarly, if the equation can be solved for x in terms of y and thus put into the form $x = \phi(y)$, then any horizontal asymptotes that exist can be found by determining the values of y for which the denominator of $\phi(y)$ is zero and the numerator is not zero.

Example

If we solve the equation $x^2y^2 - 4y^2 - x^2 = 0$ for y in terms of x and for x in terms of y, we get the two equations

$$y = \pm \sqrt{\frac{x^2}{x^2 - 4}}; \qquad x = \pm \sqrt{\frac{4y^2}{y^2 - 1}}.$$

From the first of these we see that the lines $x = 2$ and $x = -2$ are vertical asymptotes, and from the second we see that the lines $y = 1$ and $y = -1$ are horizontal asymptotes. (For as y approaches either 1 or -1, the denominator under the radical on the right approaches zero while the numerator approaches 4. Thus x becomes arbitrarily large in absolute value.)

Since it is sometimes difficult, or even impossible, to solve the given equation for y and for x as we did in the above example, we need a method of finding the horizontal and vertical asymptotes that does not require this step. The following reasoning yields such a method:

The root of the equation $ax + b = 0$ becomes indefinitely large if and only if we let a approach zero. Similarly, one root of the quadratic equation $ax^2 + bx + c = 0$ becomes indefinitely large if and only if we let a approach zero; one root of the cubic equation $ax^3 + bx^2 + cx + d = 0$ becomes indefinitely large if and only if we let a (the coefficient of the term of highest degree in x) approach zero, and so on. Consider now the equation

$$(y - 2)x^3 + 3yx^2 + y^3x + 6 = 0.$$

The left member is a polynomial in x and y, and we have arranged it in descending powers of x—putting the term involving x^3 first, that involving x^2 next, and so on. Let us think of assigning values to y and finding the corresponding values of x from this equation. From the above discussion we know that it is only when we assign values approaching 2 to y that one of the corresponding values of x will become indefinitely large. Thus the line $y = 2$ is a horizontal asymptote, and there is no other one.

Similarly, if we arrange the polynomial in descending powers of y, we have

$$xy^3 + (3x^2 + x^3)y - 2x^3 + 6 = 0.$$

We may think of assigning values to x and determining the corresponding values of y from this equation. The coefficient of the highest power of y is x—and it is when and only when this approaches zero that one of the corresponding values of y becomes indefinitely large. This means that the line $x = 0$ is a vertical asymptote and that there is no other vertical asymptote.

We have the following general rule: To find the horizontal asymptotes to an algebraic curve, *equate to zero the coefficient of the highest power of x that occurs in the equation, and solve this resulting equation for y.* To find the vertical asymptotes, *equate to zero the coefficient of the highest power of y that occurs in the equation, and solve this resulting equation for x.* In each case the real roots of the equation being solved yield the corresponding asymptotes. If the equation has no real roots, then the algebraic curve has no horizontal or no vertical asymptotes, as the case may be. In particular, of course, there is no horizontal asymptote if the coefficient of the highest power of x is a constant, and there is no vertical asymptote if the coefficient of the highest power of y is a constant.

Examples

The highest power of x in the equation $x^2y^2 - 2y^2 + 3x^2 + 4x = 0$ is x^2. Its coefficient is $y^2 + 3$. The equation $y^2 + 3 = 0$ has no real roots; so the curve has no horizontal asymptote.

The highest power of y is y^2. Its coefficient is $x^2 - 2$. The equation $x^2 - 2 = 0$ has $x = \pm \sqrt{2}$ as real roots; so the curve has two vertical asymptotes, namely, the lines $x = \sqrt{2}$ and $x = -\sqrt{2}$.

In the equation $x^3y + 2y^3 + 3xy + y^2 = 6$, the coefficient of the highest power of x is y. The curve therefore has one horizontal asymptote, namely, the line $y = 0$. The coefficient of the highest power of y is 2. This means that the curve has no vertical asymptote.

4. TANGENT LINES AT THE ORIGIN. An algebraic curve passes through the origin if and only if the constant term in its equation is zero. For example, the curve whose equation is

$$x^3y + x^2 - 4y^2 = 0$$

goes through the origin, but the curve whose equation is

$$x^3y + x^2 - 4y^2 + 5 = 0$$

does not—for obviously the coordinates $(0,0)$ satisfy the first equation but do not satisfy the second.

If the curve goes through the origin, its behavior near that point may be studied by striking out from the equation all terms except the one or ones of *lowest* degree, and studying this simpler equation. Thus if the equation has one or more terms of first degree, strike out all terms except those of first degree. If the equation has no terms of first degree, but has one or more terms of second degree, strike out all terms except those of second degree, etc. It can be shown, in particular, that if this resulting equation represents one or more straight lines, then these lines are the tangent lines to the curve at the origin.

Examples

Consider the curve whose equation is

$$x^2y + y^2 + 3x - y = 0.$$

The curve goes through the origin and has the line $3x - y = 0$ as its tangent line at that point.

Similarly, the curve whose equation is

$$x^3y + x^2 - 4y^2 = 0$$

goes through the origin.   If we strike out the term that is of degree higher than the second, we have the equation $x^2 - 4y^2 = 0$.   This can be written as

$$(x - 2y)(x + 2y) = 0,$$

and it represents the two lines $y = \frac{1}{2}x$ and $y = -\frac{1}{2}x$.   These are the tangent lines to the curve at the origin.   Incidentally, the curve has the line $y = 0$ as its only horizontal asymptote, and it has no vertical asymptote (since the coefficient of the highest power of y is a constant).   The graph is shown in Fig. 9-1.

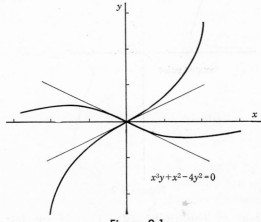

$$x^3y + x^2 - 4y^2 = 0$$

Figure 9-1

The reason why we can strike out all terms except those of lowest degree in studying the behavior of the graph near the origin is that for values of x and y that are near zero the terms of higher degree are small in numerical value compared with those of lowest degree.   Thus, for example, the equation $x^2 - 4y^2 = 0$ is satisfied by the coordinates $(0.02, 0.01)$.   These coordinates *almost* satisfy the equation $x^3y + x^2 - 4y^2 = 0$, because the value of the term x^3y is $(0.02)^3(0.01)$, or 0.00000008.

If the equation has one or more terms of first degree, then the graph has one and only one tangent line at the origin.   Thus the graph of the equation $x^2 + y^2 + x + y = 0$ has the one tangent line $x + y = 0$ at the origin.   If there are no terms of first degree but are some of second degree, there may be two distinct or coincident tangent lines at the origin (see Fig. 9-1), or the origin may be an isolated point as in Fig. 9-2.

If one wishes to investigate the behavior of the curve at some particular point, he can of course make a translation of axes so that this point becomes the origin. Suppose, for example, that we wish to investigate the behavior of the curve of Fig. 9-2 in

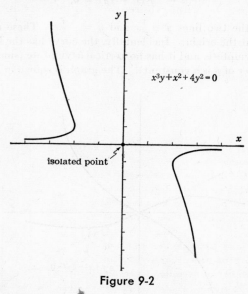

Figure 9-2

the neighborhood of the point $(2, -1)$. If we let $x = x' + 2$, $y = y' - 1$, we get the equation

$$x'^3 y' - x'^3 + 6x'^2 y' - 5x'^2 + 12x'y' + 4y'^2 - 8x' = 0.$$

From this we see that the curve has the new y'-axis as its tangent line at the new origin.

5. EXCLUDED INTERVALS. It may be possible to determine from the given equation that there will be no real value of y corresponding to values of x in a certain interval. For example, it is clear that in the case of the equation $y^2 = 4 - x$ there are no real values of y corresponding to any value of x that is greater than 4. In the case of the equation $x^2 + y^2 = 25$ there are no real values of y corresponding to any value of x that is greater than 5 or less than -5. In other words, we get real values of y only if $-5 \leqq x \leqq 5$, and the entire graph lies in this interval.

If the equation can be solved for y in terms of x, the resulting expression may be such that terms involving x appear under square-root signs. If the expression under such a radical sign is negative for a certain range of values of x, then there will be no real value of y corresponding to values of x in this interval. Such a range of values of x is called an *excluded interval* on the x-axis. Similarly, it may be that there are certain excluded intervals along the y-axis.

Example

If we solve the equation $x^3 + xy^2 + 2x^2 - 2y^2 = 0$ for y in terms of x, we get

$$y = \pm x \sqrt{\frac{x+2}{2-x}}.$$

If $x > 2$, the fraction under the radical is negative because the denominator is negative and the numerator is positive. Also, if $x < -2$, the fraction is again negative because the numerator is negative and the denominator is positive. There is then no real value of y corresponding to values of x that are greater than 2 or less than -2.

It would be difficult to solve the equation for x in terms of y in order to investigate similarly the possibility of excluded intervals along the y-axis. However, we can conclude that there is no such interval from the following consideration: If we substitute any value, y_1, for y in the given equation, the resulting equation is a cubic in x with real numbers as coefficients. Such a cubic must have at least one real root; so there must be at least one real value of x corresponding to every real value of y (see Fig. 9-3).

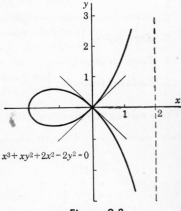

$$x^3 + xy^2 + 2x^2 - 2y^2 = 0$$

Figure 9-3

In working out the problems of the next set, the student should arrange the results of his discussion in an orderly fashion as indicated in the following examples.

Example 1

Discuss and sketch the graph of the equation

$$x^3 + xy^2 + 2x^2 - 2y^2 = 0.$$

Solution

1. *Intercepts:* $\begin{cases} \text{on } x\text{-axis—}(0,0) \text{ and } (-2,0). \\ \text{on } y\text{-axis—}(0,0). \end{cases}$

2. *Symmetry:* symmetrical to x-axis.

3. *Asymptotes:* $\begin{cases} \text{vertical—}x = 2. \\ \text{horizontal—none.} \end{cases}$

4. *Tangents at origin:* $y = x$ and $y = -x$.

5. *Excluded intervals:* $\begin{cases} \text{on } x\text{-axis—}x \text{ cannot be } >2 \text{ or } <-2. \\ \text{on } y\text{-axis—no excluded interval.} \end{cases}$

The graph, which is shown in Fig. 9-3, is called a *strophoid*. The general equation of a strophoid is $x^3 + xy^2 + kx^2 - ky^2 = 0$, where k is a constant.

Example 2

Discuss and sketch the graph of the equation

$$x^2y + y - 4x = 0.$$

Solution

1. *Intercepts:* $\begin{cases} \text{on } x\text{-axis—}(0,0). \\ \text{on } y\text{-axis—}(0,0). \end{cases}$

2. *Symmetry:* symmetrical to origin.

3. *Asymptotes:* $\begin{cases} \text{vertical—none.} \\ \text{horizontal—}y = 0 \ (x\text{-axis}). \end{cases}$

4. *Tangents at origin:* $y - 4x = 0$ or $y = 4x$.

5. *Excluded intervals:* $\begin{cases} \text{on } x\text{-axis—no excluded interval.} \\ \text{on } y\text{-axis—}y \text{ cannot be } >2 \text{ or } <-2. \end{cases}$

(Upon solving the given equation for x in terms of y we get $x = \dfrac{2 \pm \sqrt{4 - y^2}}{y}$, from which the last result above follows.) The graph is shown in Fig. 9-4.

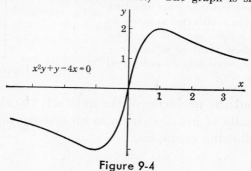

$x^2y + y - 4x = 0$

Figure 9-4

Since the equation can be written in the form $y = \dfrac{4x}{x^2 + 1}$, it is of the type discussed in Chap. 5. The curve is called a *serpentine*, and its general equation is $x^2y + b^2y - a^2x = 0$, where a and b are constants.

Example 3

Discuss and sketch the graph of the equation

$$x^3 + y^3 = 3xy.$$

Solution

1. *Intercepts:* $\begin{cases} \text{on } x\text{-axis—}(0,0). \\ \text{on } y\text{-axis—}(0,0). \end{cases}$

2. *Symmetry:* symmetrical with respect to the line $y = x$ (since interchanging x and y leaves the equation unaltered).

3. *Asymptotes:* $\begin{cases} \text{vertical—none.} \\ \text{horizontal—none.} \end{cases}$

4. *Tangents at origin:* $xy = 0$, or $x = 0$ and $y = 0$ (both axes).

5. *Excluded intervals:* none (since substituting a value for x or y results in a cubic equation in the other variable).

The curve is shown in Fig. 9-5. It is called the *folium of Descartes*, and it has the general equation $x^3 + y^3 = 3axy$, where a is a constant.

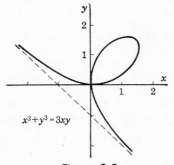

Figure 9-5

This last example illustrates the fact that in some cases the discussion does not yield enough information to enable one to sketch the curve without plotting a fairly large number of points. Observe also that when one substitutes a value for x he must solve a cubic equation in order to get the corresponding values of y. This is of course a laborious process, and it is partly for this reason that algebraic curves of higher degree are often studied by means of parametric equations, which are discussed in Chap. 12. It will be shown there that the above folium can be defined by means of the two equations

$$x = \frac{3t}{1 + t^3}, \qquad y = \frac{3t^2}{1 + t^3},$$

where t is a third variable called a *parameter* (see Prob. 13, page 187). The equation $x^3 + y^3 = 3xy$ results from the operation of eliminating t between these two equations. The graph shown in Fig. 9-5 was actually plotted from these equations. When one substitutes a number for t, the equations yield a pair of values of x and y that correspond to a point on the curve. Thus if we put $t = 2$, we get $x = \frac{2}{3}$ from the first equation and $y = \frac{4}{3}$ from the second. The point $(\frac{2}{3}, \frac{4}{3})$ is then a point on the graph.

PROBLEMS

In each of the following cases the equation of a parabola, circle, ellipse, or hyperbola is given. Identify the curve, and sketch it after discussing it for intercepts, symmetry, asymptotes, and tangent lines at the origin.

1. $x^2 + y^2 + 3x + 3y = 0$.
2. $x^2 + 4y^2 + 2x - 8y = 0$.
3. $9x^2 + 16y^2 = 72x$.
4. $2x^2 + xy + 2y^2 + 6x + 6y = 0$.
5. $xy + 2x + 2y = 0$.
6. $x^2 + 4xy + 4y^2 + 4x + 8y = 0$.
7. $3xy + 6x - 8y = 0$.
8. $(x + y)^2 = 2(y - x)$.

9. Describe and sketch the locus of all points (x,y) for which the sum of the two coordinates is equal to the sum of their cubes: $x + y = x^3 + y^3$.

10. Describe and sketch the locus of all points (x,y) for which the sum of the squares of the two coordinates is equal to the sum of their cubes:

$$x^2 + y^2 = x^3 + y^3.$$

11. Describe and sketch the locus of all points (x,y) for which the product of the squares and the sum of the squares of the two coordinates are equal:

$$x^2y^2 = x^2 + y^2.$$

12. Draw a line through the origin with inclination θ, and draw a line through the point $(2a,0)$ with inclination 3θ. Show that the locus of the point of intersection of these lines consists of the x-axis and a curve having the equation

$$x^3 + xy^2 = a(3x^2 - y^2).$$

Discuss and sketch this curve. It is called a *trisectrix*. In what way could it be used to trisect a given angle?

In each of the following cases discuss and sketch the graph of the given equation:

13. $x^2y + 4y = 8$.
14. $x^2y + 6y = 12x$.
15. $x^2y - 4y - 4x = 0$.
16. $x^2y = x^2 + 4y$.
17. $y^2 = x^2(x - 4)$.
18. $y^2 = x(x - 2)(x - 4)$.
19. $x(x^2 + y^2) = 4y^2$.
20. $x^4 + y^4 = 16$.
21. $x^3 + xy^2 = 2(3x^2 - y^2)$.
22. $x^2y^2 - 9y^2 = 4x^2$.
23. $x^3 + y^3 - 4xy = 0$.
24. $x^2 = 2y^2(y + 4)$.

25. Discuss and sketch the curve whose equation is $x^2y + 4y - 4x = 0$. By translating the axes so that the point $(2,1)$ on the curve becomes the new origin, investigate the direction of the tangent line to the curve at this point.

26. A curve consists of all points (x,y) for which

$$x(x^2 + y^2) = 5(y^2 - x^2).$$

Show that no point of the curve lies outside the interval $-5 \leq x < 5$.

27. Discuss and sketch the curve whose equation is $xy^2 - 4y = 9x$.

28. Discuss and sketch the curve whose equation is $y^4 - 4y^3 + 4x^2 = 0$.

29. Discuss and sketch the curve whose equation is $x^4 - 3xy^2 + 2y^3 = 0$ (see Fig. 12-2, page 185).

30. Discuss and sketch the curve whose equation is $(x^2 + y^2)^2 = 16x^2y$.

31. A point moves so that the product of its undirected distances from the points $(-a,0)$ and $(a,0)$ is equal to a constant b^2. Show that its path has the equation

$$(x^2 + y^2 + a^2)^2 - 4a^2x^2 = b^4.$$

Sketch the curve for the case in which $a = 2$, $b = 2$.

CHAPTER 10

THE TRIGONOMETRIC CURVES

10-1. Introduction. The definitions of the trigonometric functions and the basic facts and formulas of trigonometry are reviewed on pages 8 to 13. Any student who is not thoroughly familiar with these matters should study that material before proceeding with this chapter. It is particularly important that he have in mind the definition of a radian and that he understand the relation between the radian measure and the degree measure of an angle. When we write sin x in this chapter, it is to be understood that x is a *number*, and that the value of sin x is another number— namely, the number that results when one lays out an angle of x radians, chooses a point P on the terminal side, and divides the ordinate of P by the undirected distance from the origin to P, as required by the definition on page 9. Thus the relation $y = \sin x$ associates a definite number y with every real number x.

Consider, as an example, the relation

$$W = 5 \sin \frac{2\pi t}{3}.$$

If t is any given real number then $2\pi t/3$ is a real number which can be taken as the number x in the above discussion of sin x. The relation thus yields a definite value of W for every real number t. If we assign to t the value 1.8, we have

$$\frac{2\pi t}{3} = \frac{2(3.1416)(1.8)}{3} = 3.7699;$$
$$W = 5 \sin 3.7699 = -5 \sin 0.6283$$
$$= -5(0.5878)$$
$$= -2.939.$$

We used the formula sin $(\theta + \pi) = -\sin \theta$ to replace sin 3.7699 by

— sin 0.6283.   We obtained the value of sin 0.6283 from a table after first finding that 0.6283 radian corresponds to 36°0′.

It is unfortunate that students sometimes get the impression that the radian measure of an angle always involves the number π explicitly—that we may have 10° or 4.8°, but never 10 radians or 4.8 radians.   The idea that radians come in "packages" that are

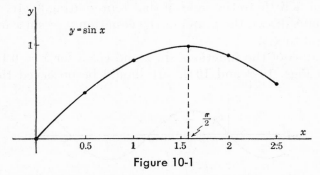

Figure 10-1

multiples of $\pi/180$ comes from the fact that 1° is equivalent to $\pi/180$ (or 0.017453) radians.   This means that an angle of $n°$ contains $n \cdot \pi/180$ or $n(0.017453)$ radians:

$$30° = 30 \cdot \frac{\pi}{180} = \frac{\pi}{6} \text{ radians};$$

$$270° = 270 \cdot \frac{\pi}{180} = \frac{3}{2}\pi \text{ radians.}$$

In the above example it is easy to find the value of W corresponding to certain special values of t.   Thus if $t = 2$, we have

$$W = 5 \sin \frac{2\pi}{3}(2) = 5 \sin \frac{4}{3}\pi$$

$$= 5\left(-\frac{\sqrt{3}}{2}\right) = -4.33.$$

10-2. *The graphs of the functions* sin *x and* cos *x.*   These graphs can be sketched by substituting numbers for x, finding the corresponding values of y from tables, and plotting the points.   Thus in the case of sin x we have sin 0 = 0, sin 0.5 = 0.479, sin 1 = 0.841, sin 1.5 = 0.997, etc.   If one does not have a table giving the values for the trigonometric functions for angles in radian measure, it is convenient to use numbers such as $\pi/6$, $\pi/3$, and $\pi/2$ for x.

$_{.5}$ sin $(\pi/6) = 0.500$, sin $(\pi/4) = 0.707$, sin $(\pi/3) = 0.866$, sin $(\pi/2) = 1.00$, etc. In laying out our number scale along the x-axis we may find it convenient to mark not only the points 1, 2, 3, 4, etc., but also points such as $\frac{1}{6}\pi$, $\frac{1}{2}\pi$, and π. Since $\frac{1}{6}\pi = \frac{1}{6}(3.1416) = 0.5236$, the point corresponding to this number lies just a little to the right of that representing $\frac{1}{2}$; the point representing π is a little to the right of that representing 3, etc. In Fig. 10-1 we have drawn the graph of the equation $y = \sin x$ for values of x from 0 to 2.5.

The graphs of the functions sin x and cos x for $x = 0$ to 2π are shown in Figs. 10-2 and 10-3. It should be observed that since

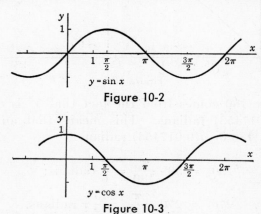

$$y = \sin x$$

Figure 10-2

$$y = \cos x$$

Figure 10-3

sin $(x + \frac{1}{2}\pi) = \cos x$, the graph of cos x is identical with that of sin $(x + \frac{1}{2}\pi)$. This graph, in turn, is simply the graph of sin x with the axes translated so that the point $(\frac{1}{2}\pi,0)$ becomes the new origin.

10-3. *Periodic functions.* A function $f(x)$ is said to be *periodic* with period k if the relation

$$f(x + k) = f(x)$$

holds for all values of x for which $f(x)$ is defined.

Since sin $(x + 2\pi) = \sin x$ for all values of x, the function sin x is periodic with period 2π. If the graph were constructed over the interval $x = 0$ to 2π, that for $x = 2\pi$ to 4π could be obtained by repeating this part, and so on. Any piece covering a length of 2π along the x-axis is called a *complete cycle* of the curve.

It follows from the above definition of period that sin x also has 4π, 6π, etc., as periods. Ordinarily when we speak of the period of a periodic function $f(x)$, we shall mean the *smallest* number k for which $f(x + k) \equiv f(x)$.

It follows from the definitions of the trigonometric functions that they are all periodic with period 2π; tan x and cot x also have the period π.

10-4. *The graphs of the functions a* sin *nx and a* cos *nx.* The largest and smallest values of sin θ or cos θ are $+1$ and -1, respectively; the corresponding largest and smallest values of a sin nx or a cos nx are $\pm a$. The constant a is called the *amplitude* of the function.

Example

The largest value of 5 sin $(2x/3)$ is 5, and its smallest value is -5. In the x-interval from 0 to 3π the largest value of the function occurs when x is such that $2x/3 = \pi/2$; that is, when $x = 3\pi/4$. The smallest value occurs when $2x/3 = 3\pi/2$, or $x = 9\pi/4$.

It is easy to prove that the functions sin nx and cos nx are periodic with period $2\pi/n$. Thus, for all values of x,

$$\sin n\left(x + \frac{2\pi}{n}\right) = \sin(nx + 2\pi) = \sin nx.$$

Examples

The function sin $3x$ is periodic with period $\frac{2}{3}\pi$, so that in a length of 2π units along the x-axis one would get three complete cycles of the curve. The function

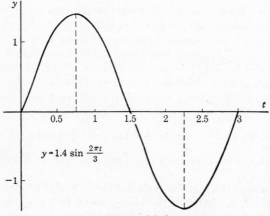

$$y = 1.4 \sin \frac{2\pi t}{3}$$

Figure 10-4

$\cos \frac{1}{2}x$ has the period $2\pi/\frac{1}{2} = 4\pi$; hence one gets only one-half of a complete cycle in a distance of 2π. The function $1.4 \sin (2\pi t/3)$ has period $2\pi/(2\pi/3) = 3$. In any interval of length 3 units along the t-axis one gets a complete cycle of the curve. The graph for $t = 0$ to 3 is shown in Fig. 10-4.

Our final conclusions about the graphs of $a \sin nx$ and $a \cos nx$ are as follows:

The graphs of the equations $y = a \sin nx$ *and* $y = a \cos nx$ *are sine and cosine curves, respectively, with amplitude* a *and period* $2\pi/n$.

Example

The graph of the equation $y = 2 \cos \frac{2}{3}x$ is like that of $y = \cos x$—but the amplitude is 2 instead of 1, and the period is $2\pi/\frac{2}{3} = 3\pi$ instead of 2π (see Fig. 10-5).

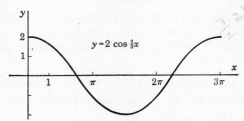

$$y = 2 \cos \tfrac{2}{3}x$$

Figure 10-5

PROBLEMS

1. Prove that if x is any number, then

$$\sin^2 x + \cos^2 x = 1; \qquad 1 + \tan^2 x = \sec^2 x; \qquad 1 + \cot^2 x = \csc^2 x.$$

2. Prove that if x is a positive number less than $\frac{1}{4}\pi$ then $\sin 2x = 2 \sin x \times \cos x$. Does this relation hold for all values of x; that is, if x is *any* real number?

3. Prove that if x is any number between $\pi/2$ and π then $\sin (-x) = -\sin x$ and $\cos (-x) = \cos x$. Are these relations true for all real values of x?

4. A function $f(x)$ is said to be an *even* function if the relation $f(-x) = f(x)$ holds for all values of x for which $f(x)$ is defined. Similarly, $f(x)$ is said to be an *odd* function if $f(-x) = -f(x)$. Which of the following functions are even and which are odd:

$$\sin x, \ \cos 3x, \ 2^x, \ x^3, \ x^2 - 3x, \ 3x + 2 \tan x, \ x^2 + 4 \sec x, \ x^2 - 3 \tan x?$$

5. Find the value of the function $10 \cos \frac{3}{2}\pi t$ for each of the following values of t: $-0.25, 0, 0.25, 0.5, 1$.

6. Find the value of the function $5 \sin \frac{1}{3}\pi t$ for each of the following values of t: $-0.5, 0, 0.5, 0.75, 1, 2$. What is the largest value that the function can have, and what is the smallest positive value of t for which it takes on this largest value?

7. Find the value of the function $4 \sin \frac{2}{3}t$ for each of the following values of t: 0, 0.5, 1, $\frac{1}{2}\pi$, 2, 3, π. What is the largest value that the function can have, and what is the smallest positive value of t for which it takes on this largest value?

8. Between what largest and smallest values does the function $4 + 5 \cos (\pi t/3)$ oscillate? Find a value of t for which the function takes on its largest value, and a value of t for which it takes on its smallest value.

9. Between what largest and smallest values does the function $7 - 5 \sin x \cos x$ oscillate? Find a value of x for which the function takes on its largest value, and a value of x for which it takes on its smallest value. HINT: Use the fact that $2 \sin x \cos x = \sin 2x$.

10. If $W = 4 \sin \frac{1}{3}t + 4 \cos \frac{2}{3}\pi t$, find the value of W when $t = 2$ and when $t = \frac{1}{3}\pi$.

In each of the following cases find the period and amplitude of the given function, and sketch its graph. Mark the units on both axes.

11. $3 \cos \frac{2}{3}x$.   **12.** $5 \sin \frac{1}{2}\pi x$.

13. $\frac{1}{2} \sin \frac{1}{2}\pi t$.   **14.** $2 \cos \frac{3}{2}t$.

15. $5 \cos 2t$.   **16.** $2.6 \sin 0.25\pi x$.

17. $2.5 \sin \frac{1}{2}x$.   **18.** $3.4 \cos \pi t$.

19. $6 \cos \frac{3}{4}x$.   **20.** $10 \sin \dfrac{5\pi x}{4}$.

21. The value of a certain quantity E varies with the time in accordance with the formula

$$E = 2 + 2 \sin \tfrac{1}{5}\pi t,$$

where t is the number of seconds. Show that, for all values of t, $0 \leqq E \leqq 4$, and that E goes through a complete cycle of values every 10 sec. Sketch the graph showing how E varies with t.

22. A certain quantity E varies with the time in accordance with the formula $E = 40 \cos \omega t$, where t is the number of seconds. For what value of ω will E go through a complete cycle of values in $\frac{1}{60}$ sec.?

23. Sketch the graph of the function $\sin x$, and on the same axes sketch the graph of $\sin^2 x$. Show that $\sin^2 x$ is periodic with period π.

24. Sketch the graph of the function $\sin x$, and on the same axes sketch the graph of $\sin^3 x$.

25. A certain quantity Q varies with the time in accordance with the formula

$$Q = 2 \sin \tfrac{1}{2}\pi t + 3 \cos \tfrac{2}{3}\pi t$$

where t is the number of seconds. Is Q a periodic function of t, and if so, what is the period?

26. A certain quantity E varies with the time in accordance with the formula

$$E = 1.8 \sin 0.4\pi t + 3.6 \cos \tfrac{2}{3}\pi t$$

where t is the number of seconds. Show that E will go through a complete cycle of its values every 15 sec. What would be the period if the number π were deleted from the above formula?

27. Two quantities E_1 and E_2 vary with the time t in accordance with the formulas

$$E_1 = 3 \sin \tfrac{1}{4}\pi t, \qquad E_2 = -6 \cos \tfrac{1}{8}\pi t,$$

where t is the number of seconds. For what value or values of t between 0 and 16 is $E_1 = E_2$?

10-5. The functions $a \sin (nx + \alpha)$ and $a \cos (nx + \alpha)$. The graphs of the equations $y = \sin x$ and $y = \sin (x + \tfrac{1}{4}\pi)$ are shown in Fig. 10-6. They are of course identical except that the wave

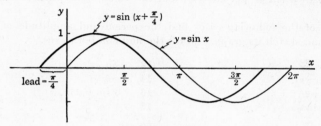

Figure 10-6

whose equation is $y = \sin (x + \tfrac{1}{4}\pi)$ "leads" the one whose equation is $y = \sin x$ by an amount $\tfrac{1}{4}\pi$. If x represents time in seconds, for example, the function $\sin (x + \tfrac{1}{4}\pi)$ reaches its maximum value $\tfrac{1}{4}\pi$ sec. earlier, etc. Similarly, the graph of the equation

$$y = \sin (x - \tfrac{1}{4}\pi)$$

would be identical with that of $y = \sin x$ but displaced in the opposite direction by an amount $\tfrac{1}{4}\pi$. This displacement to the right is usually called a "lag."

We may now show that the graph of the function $\sin (nx + \alpha)$ is identical with that of $\sin nx$ but has a *phase displacement* (lag or lead) whose amount is α/n. The proof is as follows: Take the equation

$$y = \sin (nx + \alpha),$$

and let $x = x' - \dfrac{\alpha}{n}$. This translates the origin to the left or right by an amount α/n, according as α is positive or negative, and the new equation is

$$y = \sin \left[n \left(x' - \frac{\alpha}{n} \right) + \alpha \right] = \sin nx'.$$

Similar considerations of course apply to the function $\cos (nx + \alpha)$. Our final conclusion is as follows:

The graphs of the functions $a \sin (nx + \alpha)$ and $a \cos (nx + \alpha)$ are sine and cosine curves, respectively, having amplitude a, period $2\pi/n$, and a lead (if $\alpha > 0$) or lag (if $\alpha < 0$) whose amount is α/n.

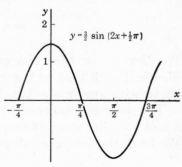

Figure 10-7

Example

The graph of the equation

$$y = \tfrac{3}{2} \sin (2x + \tfrac{1}{2}\pi)$$

is a sine curve with amplitude $\tfrac{3}{2}$, period $2\pi/2$ or π, and a lead of $\tfrac{1}{2}\pi/2$ or $\tfrac{1}{4}\pi$. One complete cycle is shown in Fig. 10-7.

10-6. *The function $a \sin nx + b \cos nx$*. The graphs of the functions $\sin x$ and $\cos x$ are drawn lightly in Fig. 10-8. By graphically adding the two ordinates for each value of x we have constructed the graph of the equation

$$y = \sin x + \cos x.$$

(The method used is discussed on page 85 and illustrated in Fig. 4-3.) This result of adding a sine wave and a cosine wave with

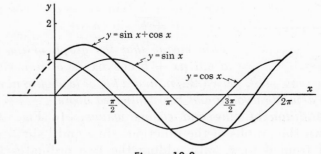

Figure 10-8

equal periods appears to be another sine or cosine wave with a larger amplitude and with a lag or lead. In order to show that this is actually the case, we observe that for all values of x

$$\sin x + \cos x = \sqrt{2} \left(\frac{1}{\sqrt{2}} \sin x + \frac{1}{\sqrt{2}} \cos x \right).$$

Now $\sin(\pi/4) = \cos(\pi/4) = 1/\sqrt{2}$; so we have

$$\sin x + \cos x = \sqrt{2}\left(\sin x \cos\frac{\pi}{4} + \cos x \sin\frac{\pi}{4}\right)$$
$$= \sqrt{2}\sin\left(x + \frac{\pi}{4}\right).$$

We thus know that the graph of the function $\sin x + \cos x$ is identical with that of the function $\sqrt{2}\sin(x + \frac{1}{4}\pi)$. It is a sine curve with amplitude $\sqrt{2}$, period 2π, and lead $\frac{1}{4}\pi$.

The more general case is that of adding a sine wave of amplitude a and a cosine wave of amplitude b, both having the same period. We have the following situation: The equation

$$y = a\sin nx + b\cos nx$$

is equivalent to the equation

$$y = \sqrt{a^2 + b^2}\left[\frac{a}{\sqrt{a^2 + b^2}}\sin nx + \frac{b}{\sqrt{a^2 + b^2}}\cos nx\right].$$

If we let α denote a number such that the sine and cosine of α radians are $b/\sqrt{a^2 + b^2}$ and $a/\sqrt{a^2 + b^2}$, respectively, as indicated in Fig. 10-9, then the above equation becomes

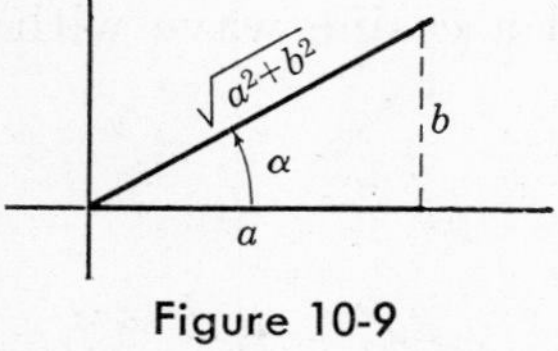

$$y = \sqrt{a^2 + b^2}(\sin nx \cos\alpha + \cos nx \sin\alpha)$$
$$= \sqrt{a^2 + b^2}\sin(nx + \alpha).$$

Figure 10-9

This means that the graph of the function $a\sin nx + b\cos nx$ *is a sine curve with amplitude* $\sqrt{a^2 + b^2}$, *period* $2\pi/n$, *and a lag or lead of* α/n, *where the value of* α *depends upon* a *and* b *as indicated above.*

10-7. Addition of sine and cosine waves. In Fig. 10-10 we have drawn the graphs of the functions $\sin x$ and $\frac{1}{3}\sin 3x$ over the x-interval from 0 to π. By adding the two ordinates for each value of x we have obtained the graph of the equation

$$y = \sin x + \frac{1}{3}\sin 3x.$$

We have also drawn the line $y = \frac{1}{4}\pi$, and we may observe that the last curve lies rather close to this line throughout most of the interval from $x = 0$ to π.

In Fig. 10-11 we have drawn the graphs of the functions $\sin x$, $\frac{1}{3} \sin 3x$, and $\frac{1}{5} \sin 5x$. By adding the three ordinates for each value of x we have obtained the graph of the equation

$$y = \sin x + \tfrac{1}{3} \sin 3x + \tfrac{1}{5} \sin 5x.$$

It may again be observed that the curve lies near the line $y = \frac{1}{4}\pi$ throughout most of the interval. It can be proved, by methods

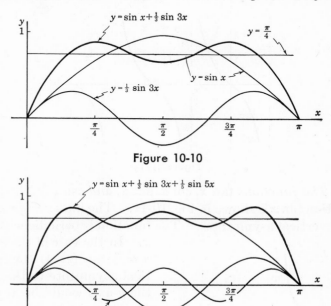

Figure 10-10

Figure 10-11

that are studied in more advanced courses in mathematics, that if one should construct successively the graphs of the equations

$$y = \sin x + \tfrac{1}{3} \sin 3x + \tfrac{1}{5} \sin 5x + \tfrac{1}{7} \sin 7x,$$
$$y = \sin x + \tfrac{1}{3} \sin 3x + \tfrac{1}{5} \sin 5x + \tfrac{1}{7} \sin 7x + \tfrac{1}{9} \sin 9x,$$

and so on, these graphs would come progressively nearer and nearer to coinciding with the line $y = \frac{1}{4}\pi$ throughout any interval that lies inside the interval $x = 0$ to π. In the interval $x = \pi$ to 2π the curve would similarly approximate the line $y = -\frac{1}{4}\pi$; and since all terms have 2π as a period, the behavior outside the interval $x = 0$ to 2π is obvious.

In the study of alternating current and voltage, in the analysis of vibrations, and in fact in the problems of many branches of applied mathematics, use is made of the fact that a function $f(x)$ which is defined over an interval from $x = a$ to b, and satisfies certain conditions, can be thus approximated by a *series* of sine and cosine terms.

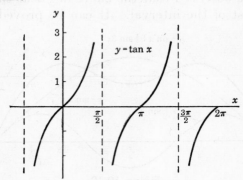

Figure 10-12

10-8. *The functions* tan x, cot x, sec x, *and* csc x.   The graph of the function tan x is shown in Fig. 10-12.   The lines $x = \frac{1}{2}\pi$, $x = \frac{3}{2}\pi$, etc., are vertical asymptotes.   The function is periodic with period

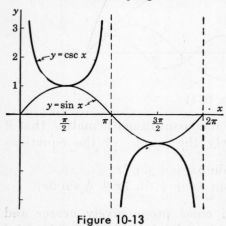

Figure 10-13

π.   In the case of the equation $y = \frac{1}{2} \tan (\pi t/4)$ the first vertical asymptote to the right of the y-axis would be at $t = 2$—for if we set

$$\frac{\pi t}{4} = \frac{\pi}{2}$$

and solve for t, we get $t = 2$. The period in this case would be 4, and we would therefore get a complete cycle of the graph in a distance of 4 units along the t-axis.

Similar considerations apply in the case of the function cot x, and the details will be left to the student.

In Fig. 10-13 we have drawn the graph of the function sin x, and on the same axes that of the function csc x.   The latter graph is readily sketched and easily remembered because of the relation

$$\csc x = \frac{1}{\sin x}.$$

Thus where $\sin x = \frac{1}{2}$, $\csc x = 2$; where $\sin x = 1$, $\csc x = 1$; where $\sin x$ approaches zero, $\csc x$ becomes indefinitely large. This last statement means that the lines $x = 0$, $x = \pi$, etc., are vertical asymptotes to the graph of the function $\csc x$.

The same reciprocal relation exists between the functions $\sec x$ and $\cos x$. Hence the graph of $\sec x$ bears the same relation to that of $\cos x$ as that of $\csc x$ bears to that of $\sin x$. The details are left to the student.

PROBLEMS

In each of the following cases, make the graph of the given equation. Mark the units on both axes.

1. $y = \sin (x - \frac{1}{6}\pi)$.
2. $y = 2 \cos (x + \frac{1}{4}\pi)$.
3. $y = 0.8 \cos (x + \frac{1}{4}\pi)$.
4. $y = 1.2 \sin (x + \frac{2}{3}\pi)$.
5. $y = 1.6 \sin (2t - \frac{1}{2}\pi)$.
6. $y = 2.8 \cos (\frac{1}{2}t + \frac{1}{2}\pi)$.
7. $y = 2 \cos (0.25t + \frac{1}{2}\pi)$.
8. $y = 3 \sin (0.6t + 3.6\pi)$.
9. $y = \frac{3}{2} \sin \pi(x + 1)$.
10. $y = 2.4 \cos \frac{1}{2}\pi(4x - 1)$.

Each of the following equations is of the form $y = a \cos mx + b \sin nx$. In each case, sketch the graphs of the separate functions $a \cos mx$ and $b \sin nx$ on the same axes, and then obtain the graph of the given equation by adding ordinates.

11. $y = 3 \sin x + \cos x$.
12. $y = 3 \cos x + 4 \sin x$.
13. $y = 2 \cos x + \sin 2x$.
14. $y = 3 \sin x + \cos 2x$.
15. $y = 3 \cos x - 2 \sin \frac{1}{2}x$.
16. $y = 2 \cos \frac{1}{2}x + 3 \sin x$.
17. $y = 2 \sin \frac{1}{2}\pi x + \cos \pi x$.
18. $y = 3 \cos \frac{1}{3}\pi x - 2 \sin \frac{2}{3}\pi x$.
19. $y = 3 \cos \frac{1}{2}\pi x - 4 \sin \frac{1}{2}\pi x$.
20. $y = \sin \frac{1}{2}\pi x - 2 \cos \frac{1}{3}\pi x$.

21. Using the method of Sec. 10-6, show that the function $\sin 2x + \cos 2x$ is equivalent to $\sqrt{2} \sin \left(2x + \frac{\pi}{4}\right)$. Hence infer that its graph is a sine curve with amplitude $\sqrt{2}$, period π, and lead $\frac{1}{8}\pi$. Sketch the graph.

22. Using the method of Sec. 10-6, show that the function $4 \sin x + 3 \cos x$ is equivalent to $5 \sin (x + \alpha)$, where α is a number such that $\sin \alpha = \frac{3}{5}$ and $\cos \alpha = \frac{4}{5}$. Sketch the graph.

23. A certain quantity E varies with the time in accordance with the formula

$$E = 3 \cos 0.25\pi t + 2 \sin 0.25\pi t,$$

where t is the number of seconds. Between what largest and smallest values does E vary? In how many seconds does E go through a complete cycle of values?

24. A quantity Q varies with the time in accordance with the formula

$$Q = 4 + 3 \cos \frac{\pi t}{10} + 4 \sin \frac{\pi t}{10}$$

where t is the number of seconds. What are the largest and smallest values of Q? In how many seconds does Q go through a complete cycle of values? Sketch the graph.

25. A quantity E varies with the time in accordance with the formula

$$E = 3.5 + 1.2 \cos \frac{\pi t}{6} - 1.6 \sin \frac{\pi t}{6}$$

where t is the number of seconds. Show that E is never greater than 5.5, nor less than 1.5, and that E goes through a complete cycle of values every 12 sec. Sketch the graph.

26. Sketch the graph of the equation

$$y = 2 \sin x - \sin 2x + \tfrac{2}{3} \sin 3x$$

by sketching the graphs of the three terms on the right separately and then adding ordinates as illustrated in Fig. 10-11.

In each of the following cases, sketch the graph of the given equation:

27. $y = \tfrac{1}{2} \tan \tfrac{1}{2}x$.   **28.** $y = \cot x$.
29. $y = \tfrac{1}{2} \cot 2x$.   **30.** $y = \sec x$.
31. $y = \sec \tfrac{1}{2}\pi t$.   **32.** $y = 2 \csc \tfrac{1}{4}\pi t$.
33. $y = \tan\left(x + \dfrac{\pi}{4}\right)$.   **34.** $y = \cot \tfrac{1}{2}\left(x - \dfrac{\pi}{2}\right)$.

In each of the following cases, solve the given pair of equations to find the coordinates of the points of intersection of their graphs in the given interval. Illustrate by drawing the graphs.

35. $y = \sin x$; $y = \tfrac{1}{2}\tan x$; $0 \leqq x < 2\pi$.
36. $y = \sin 2x$; $y = \cos x$; $0 \leqq x < 2\pi$.
37. $y = 3 \tan \tfrac{1}{4}x$; $y = 2 \sin \tfrac{1}{2}x$; $0 \leqq x \leqq 4\pi$.
38. $y = \cot 2x$; $y = 2 \sin 4x$; $0 \leqq x \leqq \tfrac{1}{2}\pi$.
39. $y = \sin \tfrac{1}{2}\pi t$; $y = \cos \tfrac{1}{4}\pi t$; $0 \leqq t < 8$.

10-9. *The inverse trigonometric functions.* We define the abbreviation

(1) $y = \arcsin x$ or $y = \sin^{-1} x$

to mean *y is the number of radians in an angle whose sine is **x***. We may assign to x any value from -1 to $+1$, and to each such value of x there corresponds an indefinite number of values of y. Thus if $x = \frac{1}{2}$, we have $y = \arcsin \frac{1}{2} =$ the number of radians in an angle whose sine is $\frac{1}{2} = \pi/6$, or $5\pi/6$, or $-7\pi/6$, etc.

The function arcsin x is thus a *multiple-valued function* defined over the interval $-1 \leqq x \leqq 1$. If we solve (1) for x in terms of y, we obtain the equation

$$x = \sin y.$$

The graph of the equation $y = \arcsin x$ is then identical with that of the equation $x = \sin y$, which in turn is simply the graph of the equation $y = \sin x$ with the axes interchanged. It is shown in Fig. 10-14.

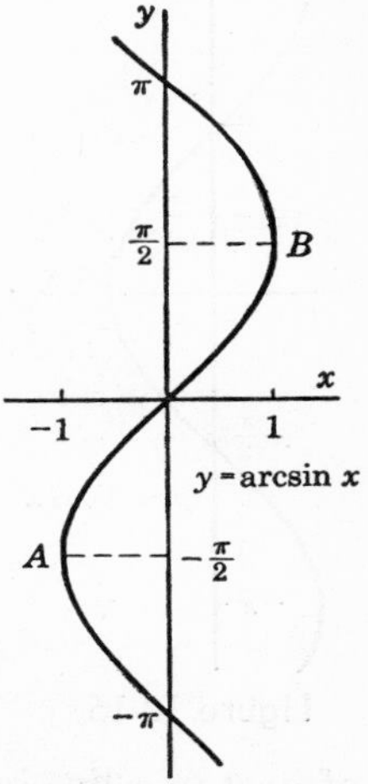

Corresponding to every number x in the interval $-1 \leqq x \leqq 1$ there is one and only one value of arcsin x which lies in the interval from $-\frac{1}{2}\pi$ to $+\frac{1}{2}\pi$. We call this value of arcsin x its *principal value*. If we agree to use only the principal values, then the graph of the equation $y = \arcsin x$ is just the arc AB in Fig. 10-14. In this case arcsin $\frac{1}{2} = \frac{1}{6}\pi$, arcsin $1 = \frac{1}{2}\pi$, arcsin $(-1) = -\frac{1}{2}\pi$ (not $\frac{3}{2}\pi$), etc. The arc AB is called the *principal branch* of the graph.

Figure 10-14

For most purposes it is desirable to restrict the symbol arcsin x to denote the principal value for essentially the same reason that we restrict the symbol $\sqrt{x}$ $(x > 0)$ to denote a particular square root of x. It will be recalled that there are two numbers whose square is 16, namely, $+4$ and -4. We called $+4$ the *principal square root* and denoted it by the symbol $\sqrt{16}$. Then the symbol $-\sqrt{16}$ of course stands for -4. The present situation is analogous. If one asks for an angle whose sine is $-\frac{1}{2}$, there are many correct answers—one is $-\frac{1}{6}\pi$, another is $\frac{7}{6}\pi$, etc. We call the one that is between $-\frac{1}{2}\pi$ and $+\frac{1}{2}\pi$ the *principal* one, and agree to mean this particular one when we write arcsin x. In trigonometry one frequently uses a capital A and writes Arcsin x when he means the principal value. We shall not do this, but we shall agree that in the rest of this chapter the symbol arcsin x will always mean the principal value unless the contrary is specifically stated.

The situation regarding the equation $y = \arccos x$ is entirely analogous. The equation is equivalent to the equation $x = \cos y$; so the graph is that of $y = \cos x$ with the axes interchanged. It is shown in Fig. 10-15. We call arc AB the *principal branch,* and

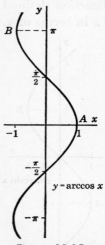

we call the function values that correspond to points on this arc the *principal values.* They are the values of arccos x that lie in the interval from 0 to π. Thus, if we restrict ourselves to this branch, $\arccos \frac{1}{2} = \frac{1}{3}\pi$, $\arccos -\frac{1}{2} = \frac{2}{3}\pi$, $\arccos 0 = \frac{1}{2}\pi$, etc. For the remainder of this chapter we shall assume that this restriction is made unless the contrary is specifically stated. Then arccos x is a single-valued function defined over the interval $-1 \leqq x \leqq 1$ and having values that lie in the interval from 0 to π.

The corresponding situation regarding the equations $y = \arctan x$ and $y = \text{arccot } x$ are indicated in Figs. 10-16 and 10-17. In each case the principal branch is the arc AB. The functions are defined for all values of x. The principal value

Figure 10-15

of arctan x lies in the interval from $-\frac{1}{2}\pi$ to $\frac{1}{2}\pi$, and that of arccot x lies in the interval from 0 to π.

We shall not discuss the functions arcsec x and arccsc x. They are of course defined for $|x| \geqq 1$, and their graphs are identical

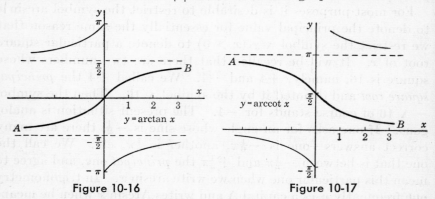

Figure 10-16   **Figure 10-17**

with those of sec x and csc x, respectively, with the axes interchanged. One can usually avoid the use of these functions by substituting arccos $(1/x)$ for arcsec x and arcsin $(1/x)$ for arccsc x.

The following examples, and the problems of the next set, illustrate various ways in which the inverse trigonometric functions are used.

Example 1

Find the value of $\sin \left(2 \text{ arc tan } \tfrac{2}{3}\right)$.

Solution

We are asked to find the sine of 2θ, where θ is the principal value of arctan $\tfrac{2}{3}$,

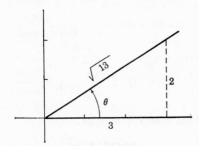

Figure 10-18

that is, to find the sine of twice the principal angle whose tangent is $\tfrac{2}{3}$.   Now we know from trigonometry that

$$\sin 2\theta = 2 \sin \theta \cos \theta,$$

and in our case, since $\tan \theta = \tfrac{2}{3}$ and θ is in the first quadrant (Fig. 10-18),

$$\sin \theta = \frac{2}{\sqrt{13}} \quad \text{and} \quad \cos \theta = \frac{3}{\sqrt{13}}.$$

We have then $\sin \left(2 \arctan \dfrac{2}{3}\right) = 2 \cdot \dfrac{2}{\sqrt{13}} \cdot \dfrac{3}{\sqrt{13}} = \dfrac{12}{13}.$

Example 2

Prove that $\arctan \tfrac{1}{4} + \arctan \tfrac{3}{5} = \tfrac{1}{4}\pi$.

Solution

We are asked to prove that the number of radians in the angle whose tangent is $\tfrac{1}{4}$ plus the number of radians in the angle whose tangent is $\tfrac{3}{5}$ (principal values, of course) is equal to $\tfrac{1}{4}\pi$.   If we let these numbers be α and β, respectively, as indicated in Fig. 10-19, our first thought might be to find them from tables and add them.   This would be unsatisfactory because we would probably have to interpolate, and we could expect only to get an approximation that is *near* $\tfrac{1}{4}\pi$. We therefore use the following plan of attack: It is obvious that $\alpha + \beta$ is a number between 0 and $\tfrac{1}{2}\pi$.   If and only if this number is $\tfrac{1}{4}\pi$ is $\tan (\alpha + \beta)$ equal

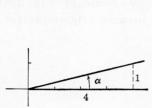

Figure 10-19

to 1. Now

$$\tan (\alpha + \beta) = \frac{\tan \alpha + \tan \beta}{1 - \tan \alpha \tan \beta}$$

$$= \frac{\frac{1}{4} + \frac{3}{5}}{1 - \frac{1}{4} \cdot \frac{3}{5}}$$

$$= \frac{\frac{17}{20}}{\frac{17}{20}} = 1.$$

We can therefore conclude that $\alpha + \beta = \frac{1}{4}\pi$.

PROBLEMS

Find the value of each of the following, it being understood that only the principal values of the inverse trigonometric functions are to be considered:

1. $\sin (\arccos \frac{4}{5})$. **2.** $\tan (\arcsin 0.3)$.
3. $\sin [\arccos (-\frac{1}{2})]$. **4.** $\cos [\arctan (-1)]$.
5. $\sec [\arctan (-\frac{3}{4})]$. **6.** $\csc (\arcsin \frac{2}{3})$.
7. $\sin [\text{arccot} (-\frac{5}{12})]$. **8.** $\tan (\text{arccot } 0.2)$.
9. $\cos (\arcsin 1)$. **10.** $\sin (\text{arccot } 0)$.
11. $5 \cos [\arctan (-\frac{3}{4})] + 2 \tan^2 (\arcsin \frac{1}{2})$.
12. $8 \tan (\arctan \frac{1}{2}) - 6 \cos^2 [\arcsin (-\frac{2}{3})]$.
13. $2 \sin (\arctan 2) - 6 \cos [\text{arccot} (-\frac{1}{2})]$.
14. $5 \cos^2 (\arcsin 1) + 3 \sin^2 (\arccos \frac{1}{2})$.
15. $3 \sin^2 (\arctan \frac{1}{3}) - 5 \tan^2 (\arcsin \frac{1}{3})$.

In each of the following cases, evaluate the given expression. The needed formulas for the functions of $(\alpha + \beta)$, $(\alpha - \beta)$, 2α, and $\frac{1}{2}\alpha$, are given in the Introduction, pages 12 to 13.

16. $\tan (2 \arcsin \frac{3}{5})$. **17.** $\sin (2 \arctan \frac{1}{2})$.
18. $\cos [2 \arcsin (-\frac{2}{3})]$. **19.** $\tan [2 \arctan (-\frac{5}{2})]$.
20. $\tan (\frac{1}{2} \arccos \frac{4}{5})$. **21.** $\sin (\frac{1}{2} \arcsin \frac{1}{2})$.
22. $2 \tan (\frac{1}{2} \arctan 1)$. **23.** $4 \sin [\frac{1}{2} \arccos (-\frac{1}{2})]$.
24. $\sin (\arcsin 1 + \arctan \frac{3}{4})$. **25.** $\tan (\arcsin \frac{3}{5} - \arctan \frac{1}{3})$.
26. $\cos [\arctan \frac{12}{5} + \arccos (-\frac{4}{5})]$. **27.** $\sin [2 \arcsin (-1) + \arccos (-\frac{4}{5})]$.
28. $\cos [2 \arccos 0 - \arctan (-\frac{3}{4})]$. **29.** $\sin [\arctan \frac{2}{3} - \arctan \frac{1}{3}]$.

30. Prove that arctan $\frac{1}{3}$ + arctan $\frac{1}{5}$ = arctan $\frac{4}{7}$.

31. Prove that arctan $\frac{1}{2}$ + arctan $\frac{1}{3}$ = $\frac{1}{4}\pi$.

Solve each of the following equations for x, considering only the principal values of the inverse trigonometric functions:

32. arcsin $2x$ − arcsin x = $\frac{1}{3}\pi$.

33. arctan $2x$ + arctan $3x$ = $\frac{1}{4}\pi$.

34. tan $(\frac{1}{4}\pi + $ arctan $x)$ = 7.

35. arcsin $2x$ + arctan $\frac{3}{4}$ = $\frac{1}{2}\pi$.

36. The radius of the base of a right circular cone is 4 ft. The height is 3 ft. when the time $t = 0$, and increases at 0.2 ft. per minute. Express the vertex angle θ as a function of t.

37. A picture 2 ft. high hangs on a wall with its lower edge 3 ft. above the observer's eye (Fig. 10-20). Express the number of radians θ in the angle sub-

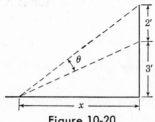

Figure 10-20

tended by the picture at the eye as a function of the distance x (feet) of the observer from the wall. Sketch a graph showing approximately how θ varies with x.

In each of the following cases, draw the graph of the given equation. Mark the units on both axes.

38. $y = 3$ arcsin $2x$.

39. $y = 2$ arccos $2x$.

40. $y = $ arctan $(x - 1)$.

41. $y = 2$ arccot $\frac{1}{2}x$.

42. $y = $ arcsin $(x - 2)$.

43. $y = 2$ arccos $(x + 1)$.

44. $y = 3$ arcsin $\frac{1}{6}x$.

45. $y = 2$ arccos $\frac{1}{3}x$.

CHAPTER 11

THE EXPONENTIAL AND LOGARITHMIC CURVES

11-1. *The laws of exponents.* The student will recall that in algebra we first define the symbol a^n for n a positive integer only. The definition is

$$a^n = a \cdot a \cdot a \cdots \quad \text{to } n \text{ factors.}$$

We call this the *nth power of a*, and we call a the *base* and n the *exponent* of the power.

From this definition one easily proves that the following laws apply to positive integral exponents:

(I) $$a^m \cdot a^n = a^{m+n}.$$

(II) $$\frac{a^m}{a^n} = a^{m-n} \quad \text{if } m > n \text{ and } a \neq 0$$

$$= \frac{1}{a^{n-m}} \quad \text{if } m < n \text{ and } a \neq 0.$$

(III) $$(a^m)^n = a^{mn}.$$

(IV) $$(a \cdot b)^n = a^n \cdot b^n.$$

(V) $$\left(\frac{a}{b}\right)^n = \frac{a^n}{b^n} \quad \text{if } b \neq 0.$$

When we extend our definition of a^n so as to give meanings to symbols such as 2^0, $5^{\frac{2}{3}}$, and 4^{-3}, we let the requirement that the above laws should hold for all exponents be our guide in deciding upon the needed definitions. For example, we desire that

$$\frac{2^5}{2^5} = 2^{5-5} = 2^0, \qquad \text{and} \qquad 2^0 \cdot 2^6 = 2^{0+6} = 2^6.$$

These things are true if and only if $2^0 = 1$. If we replace 2 by any real number a and examine the situation carefully, we see that *the above laws will hold if and only if* $a^0 = 1$ *for all values of* a *except zero.* We do not need here to define the symbol 0^0 at all.

If we wish that

$$2^3 \cdot 2^{-3} = 2^{3-3} = 2^0 = 1, \qquad \text{and} \qquad \frac{2^5}{2^{-3}} = 2^{5-(-3)} = 2^8,$$

we must define 2^{-3} to mean $1/2^3$. More generally, *we define* a^{-n} *to mean* $1/a^n$ if a is any number other than zero.

If we wish that

$$a^{\frac{1}{2}} \cdot a^{\frac{1}{2}} = a^{\frac{1}{2}+\frac{1}{2}} = a^1 = a,$$

we must define $a^{\frac{1}{2}}$ to denote a number whose square is a, that is, a *square root* of a. To avoid ambiguity, we define it to stand for the *positive square root* if a is any positive number. More generally, we define the symbol $a^{1/n}$, where n is a positive integer, to denote the *principal nth root of* a. This is the positive nth root if a is positive and the negative one if a is negative and n is odd. Thus $16^{\frac{1}{2}} = 4$, and $(-8)^{\frac{1}{3}} = -2$.

Finally, we consider the symbol $a^{m/n}$, where a is a positive number. If law (III) is to hold, then we must have

$$(a^{1/n})^m = (a^m)^{1/n} = a^{m/n}.$$

Consequently we define $a^{m/n}$ to denote the mth power of the principal nth root of a, or the principal nth root of a^m, these two numbers being equal if a is positive. We need not consider other cases at this time.

The above definitions give a meaning to the symbol a^x $(a > 0)$ if x is any *rational* number. We shall not discuss in detail the case in which x is irrational. The student is probably willing to assume that there is a unique number that is properly denoted by the symbol $5^{\sqrt{2}}$—and that this number is between $5^{1.41}$ and $5^{1.42}$, between $5^{1.414}$ and $5^{1.415}$, etc.

11-2. The exponential function. Let us assume now that, for any given positive number a, the symbol a^x denotes a definite number for every real value of x, in accordance with the discussion of the preceding section. We can then draw an approximation to the graph of the function by the usual procedure of making up a table of values, plotting the points, and drawing a smooth curve through them. Thus for the equation

$$y = (1.5)^x$$

we can construct the following table:

x	0	1	2	3	4	5	−1	−2	−3	−4
y	1	1.50	2.25	3.38	5.06	7.59	0.67	0.44	0.30	0.20

The corresponding graph is shown in Fig. 11-1. We could of course obtain points between those actually plotted by using

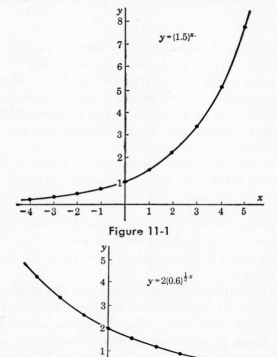

Figure 11-1

Figure 11-2

nonintegral values of x. Thus, corresponding to $x = 2.5$, we would find that

$$y = (1.5)^{2.5} = (1.5)^2 \sqrt{1.5} = 2.76.$$

The function a^x, where a is positive, is called the *exponential function*. The value of the function is positive for all real values of x, and it increases as x increases if $a > 1$, the graph having the general shape shown in Fig. 11-1.   If a is between 0 and 1, the value of a^x decreases as x increases, and the graph has the general form shown in Fig. 11-2.

11-3. *The logarithmic function.* The student will recall that it is possible to express any given positive number N in the form 10^x by properly choosing the exponent x.   Thus $437 = 10^x$ for one and only one value of x.   It is obvious that this value of x must be between 2 and 3, and it turns out that to three significant figures $x = 2.64$.   This number is called the *logarithm of 437 to the base* 10.

$$\log_{10} 437 = 2.64 \qquad \text{since} \qquad 10^{2.64} = 437.$$

More generally, it can be proved that if a is any positive number different from 1, and N is any given positive number, there exists one and only one number x such that $a^x = N$.   This number x is called the *logarithm of N to the base a*.   For a given base $a > 1$, the value of x increases as N increases.

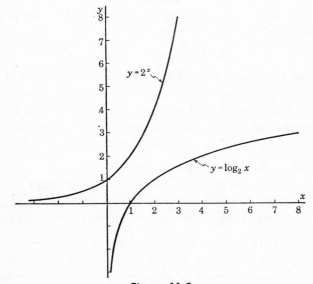

Figure 11-3

The relation $y = \log_a x$ implies that $x = a^y$.   These equations therefore have the same graph, and this graph is simply the graph of the equation $y = a^x$ with the axes interchanged.   The graphs of the equations $y = 2^x$ and $y = \log_2 x$ are shown in Fig. 11-3.

The student will recall that the logarithmic function has the following properties:

$$\log_a (M \cdot N) = \log_a M + \log_a N$$
$$\log_a \left(\frac{M}{N}\right) = \log_a M - \log_a N$$
$$\log_a N^q = q \cdot \log_a N.$$

It follows from the first of these properties that

$$\log_a 10N = \log_a N + \log_a 10.$$

If we use 10 as the base, we have

$$\log_{10} 10N = \log_{10} N + \log_{10} 10$$
$$= \log_{10} N + 1.$$

Thus, *multiplying a number by 10 increases its logarithm to the base 10 by one.*

Example

If $\log_{10} 4.87 = 0.6875$, then $\log_{10} 48.7 = 1.6875$ and $\log_{10} 487 = 2.6875$, etc. Similarly, $\log_{10} 0.487 = 0.6875 - 1$ or $9.6875 - 10$, and

$$\log_{10} 0.0487 = 8.6875 - 10.$$

11-4. *The functions e^x and $\log_e x$.* Let us take the expression $(1 + v)^{1/v}$, and let v approach closer and closer to zero—for example, let $v = 1.0$, then 0.1, then 0.01, etc. It can be proved that the corresponding values of the expression approach a certain irrational number which to five significant figures is 2.7183. Thus

If $v = 1$, then $(1 + v)^{1/v} = 2^1 = 2$;
If $v = 0.1$, then $(1 + v)^{1/v} = (1.1)^{10} = 2.5937$;
If $v = 0.01$, then $(1 + v)^{1/v} = (1.01)^{100} = 2.7048$;
If $v = 0.001$, then $(1 + v)^{1/v} = (1.001)^{1,000} = 2.7169$.

The proof of the fact that the sequence of numbers on the right approaches arbitrarily near to a definite number as v approaches zero is not elementary and of course cannot be given here. We denote the number by the letter e: $e = 2.7183$.

It is shown in calculus that the function e^x is simpler than 2^x or 3^x or 7^x in the following respect: *The line drawn tangent to the graph of the equation $y = e^x$ at any point P on the curve has a slope which is equal to the value of y at that point.* Thus, at the point where $y = 3$ the slope of the tangent line is 3, at the point where $y = 5$ the slope is 5, etc. (Fig. 11-4).   In the more general case of $y = a^x$ this slope is *proportional* to the value of y, that is, equal to ky—but it is only when e is the base that $k = 1$.

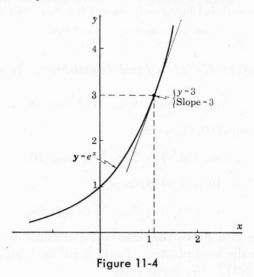

Figure 11-4

The corresponding logarithmic function $\log_e x$ or $\ln x$ is called the *natural logarithm* of x.   Figure 11-5 shows how the graph of $\log_e x$ compares with that of $\log_2 x$.   It is shown in calculus that the graph of $\log_e x$ is simpler in the following respect: *The line drawn tangent to the graph of the equation* $y = \log_e x$ *at any point* P *on the curve has a slope which is equal to the reciprocal of the value of* x *at that point.*   Thus, where $x = 4$, the slope is $\frac{1}{4}$, etc.   In the general case of the function $\log_a x$ this slope is *proportional* to $1/x$, that is, equal to $k(1/x)$—but it is only if e is the base that $k = 1$.

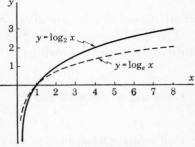

Figure 11-5

Since any positive number b can be expressed in the form e^k, the function b^{rx} is equivalent $(e^k)^{rx}$ or e^{krx}.   This means that we can always use e as the base for the exponential function if we wish. This is usually done because it turns out to be simpler.

Example

Express the function $5^{2.64x}$ in the form e^{kx}.

Solution

From tables we find that $\log_e 5 = 1.609$, and it follows that $5 = e^{1.609}$. Then

$$5^{2.64x} = (e^{1.609})^{2.64x} = e^{(1.609)(2.64)x}$$
$$= e^{4.25x}.$$

11-5. Use of tables of natural logarithms. If we apply the formula

$$\log_a (MN) = \log_a M + \log_a N$$

to the case of $\log_e (10N)$, we have

$$\log_e (10N) = \log_e N + \log_e 10.$$

The value of $\log_e 10$ is 2.3026; hence

$$\log_e (10N) = \log_e N + 2.3026.$$

Table IV, page 294, gives the natural logarithms of numbers from 1 to 10, to four decimal places. From it we find, for example, that $\log_e 4.87 = 1.5831$. We have then

$$\log_e 48.7 = 1.5831 + 2.3026 = 3.8857;$$
$$\log_e 487 = 1.5831 + 2(2.3026) = 6.1883.$$

Similarly, $\log_e 0.487 = 1.5831 - 2.3026$
$$= 1.5831 + (7.6974 - 10) = 9.2805 - 10.$$

Multiples of $\log_e 10$ are given at the bottom of the page.

The problem of finding N when $\log_e N$ is given is solved as indicated in the following:

Example

Given $\log_e N = 8.3465$, find N.

Solution

First subtract $3 \log_e 10$ from the given logarithm.

$$8.3465 - 6.9078 = 1.4387$$

Next, find the number in the table whose natural logarithm is 1.4387. This number is 4.215. Now multiply this number by 10^3 to obtain the final result, $N = 4{,}215$.

When a table of natural logarithms of the desired accuracy is not available, one can compute $\log_e N$ from the formula

$$\log_e N = \log_{10} N \cdot \log_e 10 = 2.3026 \log_{10} N.*$$

This is of course a special case of the general formula for change of base,

$$\log_b N = \frac{\log_a N}{\log_a b} \doteq \log_a N \cdot \log_b a.$$

PROBLEMS

1. Prove that if m and n are positive integers then

$$a^m \cdot a^n = a^{m+n}, \quad \text{and} \quad \frac{a^m}{a^n} = a^{m-n} \quad \text{if } m > n.$$

2. Prove that $(a^m)^n = a^{mn}$ if m and n are positive integers.

3. Evaluate: $3(16)^{-\frac{1}{2}} + 4(7)^0 - 8^{\frac{2}{3}}$.

4. Evaluate: $\dfrac{5}{(4)^{\frac{3}{2}}} - \dfrac{4}{(8)^{\frac{2}{3}}} + 3(32)^{-0.4}$.

5. Solve for x: $(2x)^{\frac{2}{3}} = 27$.

6. Solve for x: $16x^{-\frac{3}{4}} = 9$.

7. Prove: $\log_a (MN) = \log_a M + \log_a N$.

8. Prove: $\log_a N^q = q \log_a N$.

9. Prove: $\log_b N = \log_a N \cdot \log_b a$.

In each of the following cases, sketch the graph of the given equation. Mark the units on both axes.

10. $y = \frac{1}{2}(\frac{3}{2})^x$.

11. $y = 2^{-\frac{1}{2}x}$.

12. $y = (1.4)^x$.

13. $y = 4(1.2)^{2x}$.

14. $y = 8(0.25)^{-x}$.

15. $y = 3(\frac{3}{2})^{-2x}$.

16. $y = 2^{3x-2}$.

17. $y = (1.5)^{1-x}$.

18. $8y = 2^{x+2}$.

19. $\frac{1}{4}y = 2^{1-2x}$.

In each of the following cases, sketch the graph of the given equation. Use Table V, page 296, to find values of e^k.

20. $y = e^{0.5x}$.

21. $y = \frac{1}{2}e^{-0.5x}$.

22. $y = 0.5e^{\frac{3}{2}x}$.

23. $y = 0.6e^{-0.2x}$.

24. $y = e^x + e^{-x}$.

25. $y = 3e^{-\frac{1}{4}x}$.

26. $y = \log_e (1 + x)$.

27. $y = \log_2 (1 - x)$.

28. $y = 1 - x + (1.5)^x$.

29. $y = 2^x - x^2$.

30. $x^3 + y = 3^x$.

31. $y = \frac{1}{2}x + 2^{-x}$.

* To eight places the value of $\log_e 10$ is 2.30258509, and its reciprocal is 0.43429448.

32. Show that the function e^{ax+b} can be written in the form ce^{ax}, where $c = e^b$.

33. Write the function $(4.6)^{2.8x}$ in the form e^{kx}.

34. Write the function $(0.8)^{1.2x}$ in the form e^{kx}.

35. Write the function $(2.5)^{3x}$ in the form e^{kx}.

36. It is desired to replace the function $(10)^{ax}$ by the equivalent function e^{kax}. What is the value of k?

37. If \$700 is invested at a rate of 3 per cent per annum compounded continuously, the compound amount at the end of t years is given by the formula

$$A = 700e^{0.03t}.$$

Make a graph showing how A increases with t. Find the amount at the end of 10 years.

38. Find the compound amount if \$300 is invested for 24 years at a rate of 2.5 per cent per annum compounded continuously, using the formula of Prob. 37.

39. Find the natural logarithm of each of the following numbers, using Table IV:

(a) 52.6.   (b) 4,285.   (c) 723.2.

(d) 0.386.   (e) 0.076.   (f) 0.00056.

40. In each of the following cases, find the number N whose natural logarithm is given:

(a) $\ln N = 2.4263.$ (b) $\ln N = 4.6175.$

(c) $\ln N = 6.2642 - 10.$ (d) $\ln N = 8.2785 - 10.$

11-6. *Boundary curves. Damped vibrations.* In Fig. 11-6 we have drawn lightly the graphs of $y = 3e^{-\frac{1}{4}x}$ and $y = \sin\frac{1}{2}\pi x$.

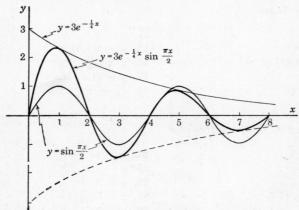

Figure 11-6

The latter curve has period 4, and there are therefore two complete cycles in the interval from $x = 0$ to $x = 8$. By multiplying the ordinates to these two curves for each value of x, we have obtained the graph (heavy curve) of

(1)
$$y = 3e^{-\frac{1}{4}x} \sin \frac{\pi x}{2}.$$

In connection with this multiplication of ordinates, the following facts should be observed.

1. At every point where the factor $\sin (\pi x/2) = 0$, the product is zero; hence the graph of (1) crosses the x-axis at $x = 0, 2, 4, 6, 8,$ . . . .

2. Since $\sin (\pi x/2)$ is never greater than 1, the product curve is never above the graph of $y = 3e^{-\frac{1}{4}x}$; at each point where $\sin (\pi x/2) = 1$, the product is *equal* to this other factor. In fact, the graph of (1) is tangent to the curve $y = 3e^{-\frac{1}{4}x}$ at $x = 1$, and 5.

3. At the points where $\sin (\pi x/2) = -1$, the product is equal numerically but opposite in sign to the other factor. Thus at the points where $x = 3$ and 7 the graph of (1) is tangent to the dotted curve whose equation is $y = -3e^{-\frac{1}{4}x}$. The two curves $y = \pm 3e^{-\frac{1}{4}x}$ therefore form *boundaries* between which the graph of (1) oscillates, its "amplitude" decreasing as x increases.

Figure 11-7

Figure 11-7 shows a weight W which is supported by a spring. If the weight is pulled down some additional distance and then released, it will oscillate up and down. It can be shown that if the resistance of the medium to the motion is proportional to the velocity, the equation governing the oscillations has the general form

$$y = Ae^{-kt} \sin (nt + \alpha)$$

where y is the vertical displacement of the weight (from its position of equilibrium) at time t, and the other letters represent constants whose values depend upon the stiffness of the spring, the viscosity of the medium, and the initial displacement and velocity of the weight. The curve shown in Fig. 11-6 is one of these "damped-vibration" curves. They are important not only in the study of mechanical vibrations in machines and structures but also in certain electrical-circuit phenomena.

The method of multiplication of ordinates is often valuable.

In the case of an equation like $y = x \cos x$, or $y = (1/x) \sin x$, or $y = xe^x$, one can usually visualize the general character of the graph by sketching the graphs of the separate factors and mentally multiplying the ordinates. Thus in Fig. 11-8 we have drawn the graphs of $y = x$ and $y = e^x$, and by multiplying the ordinates have obtained the graph of the equation

$$y = xe^x.$$

In connection with the use of this method observe that:

1. *Where both factors are positive or negative, the product is positive;*

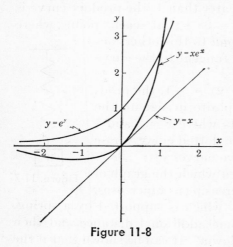

Figure 11-8

i.e., where both of the "factor" curves lie above or below the x-axis, the product curve is above. Where one is above and the other below, the product curve is below.

2. *Where either factor is zero, the product is zero if the other factor is finite.*

3. *Where either factor has the value 1, the product is equal to the other factor.* Thus in Fig. 11-8 the product curve crosses the graph of $y = e^x$ at $x = 1$ because at this point the other factor has the value 1.

4. *Where both factors are greater than 1 in absolute value, the absolute value of the product is larger than that of either factor; where the absolute value of one factor is larger than 1 and that of the other is smaller than 1, that of the product is between the two.* Thus in Fig. 11-8 the graph of $y = xe^x$ lies above that of either factor for $x > 1$ but lies between the two for $0 < x < 1$. Finally, *where both factors are less than 1 in absolute value, the absolute value of the product is less than that of either factor.* Thus in Fig. 11-8 the ordinates to the curve $y = xe^x$ in the interval $-1 < x < 0$ are smaller in absolute value than those to either the line $y = x$ or the curve $y = e^x$.

11-7. *The hyperbolic functions.* Certain combinations of the exponential functions e^x and e^{-x} occur sufficiently often in various scientific applications to make it desirable to assign names to them and tabulate their values. These functions are called *hyperbolic functions*. It can be shown that they are related to the equilateral hyperbola in somewhat the same way that the trigonometric functions are related to the circle, and they are accordingly given similar names. We shall not here discuss this relation but shall set up the definitions in an arbitrary way as follows:

$$\text{Hyperbolic sine } x \text{ (sinh } x) = \frac{e^x - e^{-x}}{2};$$

$$\text{Hyperbolic cosine } x \text{ (cosh } x) = \frac{e^x + e^{-x}}{2};$$

$$\text{Hyperbolic tangent } x \text{ (tanh } x) = \frac{e^x - e^{-x}}{e^x + e^{-x}}.$$

The hyperbolic cosecant (csch), secant (sech), and cotangent (coth) are defined, respectively, as the reciprocals of hyperbolic sine, cosine, and tangent. It should be emphasized that the hyperbolic functions are not new functions—they are simply names given to certain frequently occurring combinations of the exponential functions.

Table V, page 296, in this book gives the values of sinh x, cosh x, and tanh x, for values of x from 0 to 10. The corresponding graphs can be made from this table. The graphs of $y = \sinh x$ and $y = \cosh x$, which are shown in Fig. 11-9, could be made by drawing the separate graphs of $y = \frac{1}{2}e^x$ and $y = \frac{1}{2}e^{-x}$, and adding and subtracting the ordinates. The student should draw the graph of $y = \tanh x$.

It can be shown, using principles of mechanics, that a uniform cable supported at the ends hangs in a curve whose equation is of the form

$$y = \frac{a}{2} \left(e^{x/a} + e^{-x/a} \right)$$

where a is a constant whose value depends upon the amount of "sag" allowed. This curve is called a *catenary*, and it is easy to see that its equation can be written in the form

$$y = a \cosh \frac{x}{a}.$$

The graph of $y = \cosh x$ (Fig. 11-9) is then the catenary in which $a = 1$.

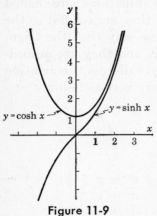

Figure 11-9

As indicated in the next set of exercises, there are relations between the hyperbolic functions that are quite similar to those between the trigonometric functions. Thus, corresponding to the relation $\cos^2 x + \sin^2 x = 1$, we have $\cosh^2 x - \sinh^2 x = 1$; corresponding to the formula $\sin 2x = 2 \sin x \cos x$, we have $\sinh 2x = 2 \sinh x \cosh x$. These relations may be proved by substituting for the hyperbolic functions the equivalent exponential expressions and carrying out the indicated operations. Thus to prove that $\cosh^2 x - \sinh^2 x = 1$, we proceed as follows:

$$\cosh^2 x - \sinh^2 x = \left(\frac{e^x + e^{-x}}{2}\right)^2 - \left(\frac{e^x - e^{-x}}{2}\right)^2$$
$$= \frac{e^{2x} + 2 + e^{-2x}}{4} - \frac{e^{2x} - 2 + e^{-2x}}{4}$$
$$= \tfrac{2}{4} + \tfrac{2}{4} = 1.$$

PROBLEMS

In each of the following cases, sketch the graph of the given equation, using the method of multiplication of ordinates:

1. $y = 3e^{-\frac{1}{4}x} \cos \frac{1}{2}\pi x$.
2. $y = 2e^{0.2t} \cos \frac{1}{2}\pi t$.
3. $y = 5e^{-0.1t} \sin \frac{1}{4}\pi t$.
4. $y = 5e^{-\frac{1}{2}x} \cos \pi x$.
5. $y = 3e^{x-1} \cos \frac{1}{2}\pi x$.
6. $y = 2e^{0.1x} \sin \frac{1}{4}\pi x$.
7. $y = 2e^{-0.2x} \cos \frac{1}{2}x$.
8. $y = 3e^{0.2x} \sin \frac{1}{2}x$.

9. Sketch the graph of the equation $y = \dfrac{2}{\sqrt{x}} \sin \frac{1}{2}\pi x$ over the interval $0 < x \leqq 8$.

10. Sketch the graph of the equation $y = \dfrac{2}{x} \cos \pi x$ over the interval $0 < x \leqq 4$.

11. Sketch the graph of the equation $y = \dfrac{x}{4} \sin \frac{1}{2}\pi x$ over the interval

$$-4 \leqq x \leqq 8.$$

12. Sketch the graph of the equation $y = 0.4x \cos \frac{1}{2}\pi x$ over the interval $-4 \leqq x \leqq 8$.

13. Sketch the graph of the equation $y = x \cdot 2^{-(\frac{1}{2}x)^2}$ over the interval

$$-4 \leqq x \leqq 4.$$

14. Sketch the graph of the equation $y = 2^{1-(\frac{1}{2}x)^2} \sin \frac{1}{2}\pi x$ over the interval $-4 \leqq x \leqq 4$.

15. Sketch the graph of the equation $y = 2e^{-(0.2t)^2} \cos \frac{1}{2}\pi t$ over the interval $-4 \leqq t \leqq 4$.

16. Prove that sinh x and tanh x are *odd* functions and that cosh x is an *even* function by showing that:

(*a*) sinh $(-x) = -$sinh x;

(*b*) cosh $(-x) =$ cosh x;

(*c*) tanh $(-x) = -$tanh x.

See Prob. 4, page 154.

In each of the following cases, use the definitions of the hyperbolic functions to prove that the given relation is an identity:

17. $\tanh^2 x + \mathrm{sech}^2 x = 1$.　　　　**18.** $\coth^2 x - \mathrm{csch}^2 x = 1$.

19. $\cosh x + \sinh x = e^x$.　　　　　　**20.** $\cosh x - \sinh x = e^{-x}$.

21. $\sinh 2x = 2 \sinh x \cosh x$.　　　　**22.** $\cosh 2x = \cosh^2 x + \sinh^2 x$.

23. $\tanh 2x = \dfrac{2 \tanh x}{1 + \tanh^2 x}$.　　**24.** $\coth 2x = \dfrac{1 + \coth^2 x}{2 \coth x}$.

25. $\sinh (x \pm y) = \sinh x \cosh y \pm \cosh x \sinh y$.

26. $\cosh (x \pm y) = \cosh x \cosh y \pm \sinh x \sinh y$.

27. $\tanh (x \pm y) = \dfrac{\tanh x \pm \tanh y}{1 \pm \tanh x \tanh y}$.

Sketch the graph of each of the following functions:

28. tanh x.　　　**29.** coth x.　　　**30.** sech x.　　　**31.** csch x.

32. Draw the catenary whose equation is $y = 5(e^{0.1x} + e^{-0.1x})$ over the interval $-10 \leqq x \leqq 10$.

33. Draw the catenary whose equation is $y = 2.5(e^{0.2x} + e^{-0.2x})$ over the interval $-8 \leqq x \leqq 8$.

34. In the equation $y = \dfrac{a}{2}(e^{x/a} + e^{-x/a})$, replace e by $10^{\log_{10} e}$ (which is of course equal to e by the definition of $\log_{10} e$). From this show that if 10 is used as the base for the exponential function, the equation of the catenary has the form

$$y = \frac{k}{2 \ln 10}(10^{x/k} + 10^{-x/k}).$$

35. Solve the equation $y = \frac{1}{2}(e^x - e^{-x})$ for x in terms of y. The resulting function of y is called the *inverse hyperbolic sine* of y.

36. Solve the equation $y = \frac{1}{2}(e^x + e^{-x})$ for x in terms of y. The resulting function of y is called the *inverse hyperbolic cosine* of y.

37. Solve the equation $y = (e^x - e^{-x})/(e^x + e^{-x})$ for x in terms of y. The resulting function of y is called the *inverse hyperbolic tangent* of y.

CHAPTER 12

PARAMETRIC EQUATIONS

12-1. *Introduction.* We have seen that we can define a curve in the xy-plane by means of an equation in the two variables x and y. The equation specifies the relation that holds between the two coordinates of any point P on the curve. Thus the equation $y^2 = 4x$ defines a curve. The curve consists of those points for which the square of the ordinate is equal to four times the abscissa.

Sometimes it is more convenient to define a curve by means of *two* equations which express the coordinates of the points on it as functions of a third variable. These equations may have the form

$$x = g(t), \qquad y = h(t).$$

The third variable (t in this case) is called a *parameter*, and the equations are called *parametric equations* of the curve. The direct relation between x and y would result from the operation of eliminating the parameter between these equations.

Consider, for example, the equations

$$(1) \qquad x = \tfrac{1}{2}t^2 - 2; \qquad y = \tfrac{1}{4}t^4 - \tfrac{7}{2}t^2.$$

If we put $t = 0$, we get $x = -2$ and $y = 0$; if we put $t = 1$, we get $x = -\tfrac{3}{2}$ and $y = -\tfrac{13}{4}$; if we put $t = 2$, we get $x = 0$ and $y = -10$, etc. In Fig. 12-1 we have plotted the corresponding points and drawn a smooth curve through them. The curve appears to resemble a portion of a parabola—not a complete parabola if t is restricted to the field of real numbers because x could not be less than -2.

In this simple case we can eliminate t between the two equations by solving the first one for t^2 in terms of x and substituting this for t^2 in the second. We thus get $t^2 = 2(x + 2)$; then

$$y = \tfrac{1}{4} \cdot 4(x + 2)^2 - \tfrac{7}{2} \cdot 2(x + 2),$$

or

(2) $$y = x^2 - 3x - 10.$$

Whenever x, y, and t satisfy the parametric equations (1), x and y must satisfy equation (2).   This means that every point defined by the parametric equations lies on the parabola $y = x^2 - 3x - 10$. It is easy to see that the parametric equations give the part of the

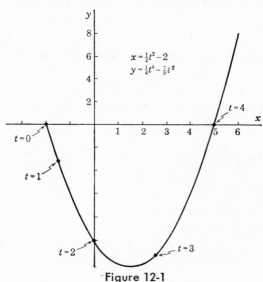

$x = \frac{1}{2}t^2 - 2$

$y = \frac{1}{4}t^4 - \frac{7}{2}t^2$

Figure 12-1

parabola for which $x \geqq -2$ for $t \geqq 0$.   This part is repeated for $t \leqq 0$.   If we let t take on values of the form bi, where b is real, we get the remainder of the parabola.

It should be observed that the value of t that is substituted into the parametric equations in order to get a corresponding pair of values of x and y does not itself appear on the graph.   In Fig. 12-1 we have indicated the values of t that yield certain points on the curve.

When the equation of a curve is given in the form $y = f(x)$ or $\phi(x,y) = 0$, various sets of parametric equations that define all or a part of the curve can be obtained easily.   Thus if we take the equation

$$y = x^2 - 3x - 10$$

and arbitrarily let $x = 2t - 1$, we find that $y = 4t^2 - 10t - 6$.

The equations

$$x = 2t - 1, \qquad y = 4t^2 - 10t - 6$$

then constitute a pair of parametric equations that define the curve. Similarly, if we let $x = \sin \theta$, we get

$$y = \sin^2 \theta - 3 \sin \theta - 10.$$

We thus have another pair of parametric equations—but in this case they define only the part of the parabola for which $|x| \leq 1$ because if θ is any real number then $-1 \leq \sin \theta \leq 1$.

12-2. Parametric equations of algebraic curves. It is sometimes easier to make the graph of an algebraic equation of higher degree from parametric equations than from the direct relation between x and y. Consider, for example, the equation

(1) $$x^4 - 3xy^2 + 2y^3 = 0.$$

It is easy to show that the graph is not symmetrical with respect to either axis or the origin. It has no horizontal or vertical asymptotes because the coefficients of the highest powers of both x and y are constants (see page 141). It goes through the origin, and the tangent lines to the graph at this point are $y = 0$ and $y = \frac{3}{2}x$. (These are found by striking out the term of fourth degree and considering the locus of the resulting equation,

$$2y^3 - 3xy^2 = 0;$$

see page 142.)

This information, while valuable, is hardly sufficient to enable us to sketch the graph. We may therefore try to obtain a few points on the curve. If we substitute values for x, we must in each case solve a cubic equation to find the corresponding values of y. If we substitute values for y, we have similar difficulties in solving for x.

We may obtain convenient parametric equations for the curve by letting $y = tx$. If we substitute tx for y in (1), and solve for x in terms of t, we get $x = t^2(3 - 2t)$. Then, since $y = tx$, we have $y = t^3(3 - 2t)$. The equations

(2) $$x = t^2(3 - 2t), \qquad y = t^3(3 - 2t)$$

then constitute a pair of parametric equations for the curve defined

by equation (1).   The graph is plotted from these equations in
Fig. 12-2.

It may be observed that the substitution used in getting the
parametric equations amounts to introducing a new variable t,
where $t = y/x$.   The value of t that corresponds to a given point
on the curve can therefore be interpreted as the slope of the line
joining that point to the origin.

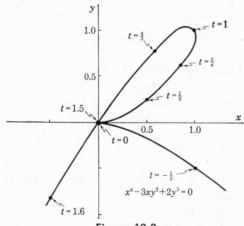

Figure 12-2

It should be observed also that while equation (1) may yield
three distinct real values of y, and consequently three points on
the curve, corresponding to a given value of x, the parametric
equations (2) yield a single pair of values of x and y, and consequently only one point on the curve, corresponding to a given
value of t.   A definite point on the curve is therefore determined
by specifying the value of t.

12-3. Path of a projectile.   Assume that a projectile is fired
with initial velocity v_0 ft. per second at an angle α with the horizontal.   Take the point at which the projectile is fired as the
origin, and choose coordinate axes as indicated in Fig. 12-3, the
x-axis being horizontal.

By using the fundamental principles of physics one can prove
that if the projectile is acted on only by the gravitational force
while it is in flight, its position at the end of t sec. is given by the
equations

$$x = (v_0 \cos \alpha)t, \qquad y = (v_0 \sin \alpha)t - \tfrac{1}{2}gt^2,$$

where g is a constant whose value is approximately $32(\text{ft./sec.}^2)$. These equations, which give the coordinates of the projectile at any time t while it is in flight, are parametric equations of its path.

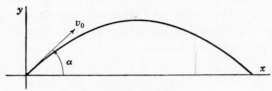

Figure 12-3

In order to obtain the relation that holds between x and y for any point of the path, we may eliminate t—by solving the first equation for t in terms of x and substituting this into the second. The result is

$$y = (\tan \alpha)x - \left(\frac{g}{2v_0{}^2 \cos^2 \alpha}\right)x^2.$$

This is an equation of the form $y = Ax - Bx^2$, and it of course represents a parabola.

The equations for the case in which the projectile is fired horizontally can be obtained from the above general case by putting $\alpha = 0$. The parametric equations for this case are then

$$x = v_0 t; \qquad y = -\tfrac{1}{2}gt^2.$$

These equations hold approximately in the case of a ball or stone that is thrown horizontally.

Example

A ball is pitched horizontally at a speed of 100 ft. per second. How far will it drop in a horizontal distance of 60 ft.?

Solution (Fig. 12-4)

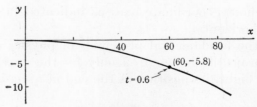

Figure 12-4

Since $v_0 = 100$ and g is approximately 32, we have the parametric equations

$$x = 100t; \qquad y = -16t^2.$$

If we put $x = 60$ in the first equation, we get $t = 0.6$. When we substitute 0.6 for t in the second equation, we get $y = -5.8$ ft. This means that the ball would have approximately the coordinates $(60, -5.8)$ when $t = 0.6$ sec.

PROBLEMS

In each of the following cases, plot the graph from the given parametric equations. Then eliminate the parameter, and, if possible, identify the curve.

1. $x = 4 - t; \quad y = 4t - t^2.$

2. $x = 2(t - 3); \quad y = 2t(t - 3).$

3. $x = 2 - 2\sqrt{1 + t}; \quad y = 2t - 2t\sqrt{1 + t}.$

4. $x = \sin \frac{1}{2}\pi t; \quad y = \cos^2 \frac{1}{2}\pi t.$

5. $x = 2 + \sin \frac{1}{4}\pi t; \quad y = 1 - \cos^2 \frac{1}{4}\pi t.$

6. $x = 2 + 2\cos t; \quad y = 1 - 3\sin^2 t.$

7. $x^2 = 16 \sin t; \quad y^2 = 16 \cos t.$

8. $x = 2\sqrt{1/t}\sqrt{1 - t}; \quad y = 2\sqrt{t}\sqrt{1 - t}.$

9. $x^2 = \sqrt{1/t}\sqrt{6 - t}; \quad y^2 = \sqrt{t}\sqrt{6 - t}.$

10. $x = 4 \cot t; \quad y = 4 \sin^2 t.$

11. By letting $x = ty$ show that the curve whose equation is $x^2 - 2y^3 - 8y^2 = 0$ has the parametric representation

$$y = \tfrac{1}{2}t^2 - 4, \qquad x = \tfrac{1}{2}t^3 - 4t.$$

Draw the graph from these equations.

12. By letting $y = tx$ show that the curve whose equation is $x^4 + y^3 = 4x^2y$ has the parametric representation

$$x = t(4 - t^2), \qquad y = t^2(4 - t^2).$$

Draw the graph from these equations.

13. By letting $y = tx$ show that the curve whose equation is $x^3 + y^3 = 3xy$ has the parametric representation

$$x = \frac{3t}{1 + t^3}, \qquad y = \frac{3t^2}{1 + t^3}.$$

Draw the graph from these equations.

14. By letting $y = tx$ show that the curve whose equation is

$$x^3 + xy^2 + 2y^2 - 6x^2 = 0$$

has the parametric representation

$$x = \frac{2(3 - t^2)}{1 + t^2}; \qquad y = \frac{2t(3 - t^2)}{1 + t^2}.$$

Draw the graph from these equations.

In each of the following cases, draw the graph from the parametric equations:

15. $x = t(4 - t^2)$; $y = t^2(4 - t^2)$.   **16.** $x = t(4 - t)$; $y = \frac{1}{8}t^2(9 - t^2)$.

17. $x = \frac{1}{8}t^3 + t$; $y = \frac{1}{8}t^3 - t$.   **18.** $x = 4 - 0.25t^2$; $y = 0.2t^3 - 1.8t$.

19. $x = 4t^3(2 - t)$; $y = 4t^2(2 - t)$.   **20.** $x = \dfrac{16t}{(1 + t^2)^2}$; $y = \dfrac{16t^2}{(1 + t^2)^2}$.

21. $x = \dfrac{4t^2 - 1}{1 - t^3}$; $y = \dfrac{4t^3 - t}{1 - t^3}$.

22. A baseball is thrown horizontally from a point 8 ft. above the ground with a speed of 140 ft. per second. Write parametric equations for its path, neglecting air resistance. Assuming the ground to be level, determine how far the ball will travel horizontally before striking it.

23. Assume that a baseball leaves the pitcher's hand at a point 5 ft. above the ground, and that it is thrown horizontally so that $\alpha = 0$. What is the minimum initial speed of the ball if it must be at least 6 in. above the ground when it passes over home plate, which is 60 ft. away?

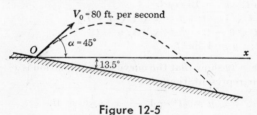

Figure 12-5

24. From a point O on the side of a hill, a ball is thrown as indicated in Fig. 12-5. Find the point at which it will strike the ground, air resistance being neglected.

12-4. *Parametric equations of the circle and ellipse.* Consider a circle with center at the origin and radius a as shown in Fig. 12-6.

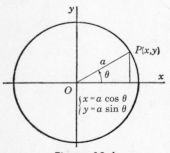

Figure 12-6

Let $P(x,y)$ be a point of the plane, and let θ be the angle xOP. It is clear that if and only if P lies on the circle we have the relations

$$x = a \cos \theta; \qquad y = a \sin \theta.$$

These are then parametric equations of the circle, θ being the parameter. The direct relation between x and y can of course be obtained by eliminating θ between these equations. This can be done readily by squaring both sides of each equation, and adding.

We thus have

$$x^2 = a^2 \cos^2 \theta; \qquad y^2 = a^2 \sin^2 \theta;$$
$$x^2 + y^2 = a^2(\cos^2 \theta + \sin^2 \theta);$$

or $\qquad\qquad x^2 + y^2 = a^2.$

The relation between x and y is often called the "rectangular equation" of the curve because it expresses the relation that holds between the two rectangular coordinates of any point on it.

Consider now the equations

$$x = a \cos \theta; \qquad y = b \sin \theta.$$

It is easy to show that they represent an ellipse whose semiaxes are a and b—for if we write them in the equivalent form

$$\frac{x}{a} = \cos \theta, \qquad \frac{y}{b} = \sin \theta,$$

and then square both sides of each equation and add, we get

$$\frac{x^2}{a^2} + \frac{y^2}{b^2} = 1.$$

From the parametric equations it can be shown that the ellipse can be constructed, point by point, as follows: Draw two concentric

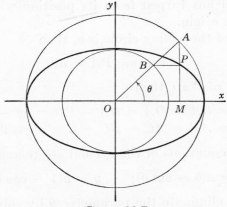

Figure 12-7

circles having radii a and b $(a > b)$ as shown in Fig. 12-7. These are called the *major* and *minor* auxiliary circles, respectively. To determine a point on the ellipse, draw a line through O at any angle θ with the positive x-axis, and cutting the major and minor auxiliary circles at A and B, respectively. Through A draw a line parallel to the y-axis, and through B draw a line parallel to the x-axis. These lines intersect at a point P which is a point on the ellipse; for if the coordinates of P are x and y, it is obvious that

$$x = OM = OA \cos \theta = a \cos \theta;$$
$$y = MP = OB \sin \theta = b \sin \theta.$$

12-5. The cycloid. *A cycloid is defined as the curve traced by a point **P** fixed on the circumference of a circle, when the circle rolls*

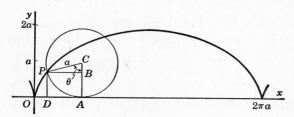

Figure 12-8

along a fixed line. The curve is shown in Fig. 12-8. Choosing the coordinate system as shown, we shall derive expressions for the coordinates of P in terms of the number of radians θ through which the wheel has turned from its position when this tracing point was at the origin.

If the radius of the rolling circle is a, then

$$OA = \text{arc } PA = a\theta.$$

The coordinates of P are then

$$x = OD = OA - DA = OA - PB = a\theta - a \sin \theta;$$
$$y = DP = AB = AC - BC = a - a \cos \theta.$$

The parametric equations of the cycloid are therefore

$$x = a(\theta - \sin \theta); \qquad y = a(1 - \cos \theta).$$

It is possible to eliminate the parameter θ by solving the second equation for $\cos \theta$ in terms of y and substituting this result into the first. The resulting rectangular equation is quite complicated, and for this reason one always uses the parametric equations when dealing with the cycloid.

12-6. *The involute.* A string is wound about the circumference of a circle, one end of the string being initially at A in Fig. 12-9. The string is then unwound while being held taut. *The curve traced by the end of the string as it unwinds is called the involute of the circle.* We can derive parametric equations for this curve as follows:

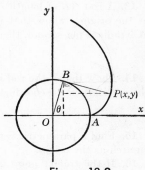

When the piece of string that originally lay along the arc AB has been unwound, the end of the string is at P where $PB \perp OB$; also, if θ is the angle (radians) subtended at O by arc AB, then

$$BP = \text{arc } AB = a\theta,$$

Figure 12-9

where $a = OB$ is the radius of the circle. If the coordinates of P are x and y, we then have

$$x = OB \cos \theta + BP \sin \theta = a \cos \theta + a\theta \sin \theta;$$
$$y = OB \sin \theta - BP \cos \theta = a \sin \theta - a\theta \cos \theta.$$

These equations give the coordinates of any point P on the curve in terms of the angle θ; the curve is accordingly defined by the parametric equations

$$x = a(\cos \theta + \theta \sin \theta); \qquad y = a(\sin \theta - \theta \cos \theta).$$

PROBLEMS

1. Show that the equations

$$x = h + a \cos \theta, \qquad y = k + a \sin \theta,$$

represent a circle of radius a with center at the point (h,k).

2. Show that the equations

$$x = h + a \cos \theta, \qquad y = k + b \sin \theta,$$

represent an ellipse with center at the point (h,k) and with semiaxes a and b.

In each of the following cases, sketch the curve represented by the given parametric equations. Also, eliminate the parameter, and thus find the "rectangular equation" of the curve.

3. $x = 1 + \cos \theta$; $y = 2 - \sin \theta$.   **4.** $x = 3 + 5 \sin \theta$; $y = 4 + 5 \cos \theta$.

5. $x = 2 \sin \theta$; $y = 2(1 + \cos \theta)$.   **6.** $x = 3 - 3 \cos \theta$; $y = 3 \sin \theta$.

7. $x = 3 \cos \theta - 2$; $y = 5 \sin \theta + 2$.

8. $x = 4(2 + \cos \theta)$; $y = 2 \sin \theta$.   **9.** $x = 3 \sin \theta$; $y = 1 + \cos \theta$.

10. $x = 6(1 - \sin \theta);$ $y = 3 \cos \theta.$ **11.** $x = 1 - 2\cos \theta;$ $y = \sin \theta - 2.$
12. $x = 5(1 + \sin \theta);$ $y = 2(1 - \cos \theta).$

13. A rod AB of length r rotates in the xy-plane about end A, which is fixed at the origin. Show that if B is initially on the x-axis, and if the rod rotates at ω radians per second, then the coordinates of B at the end of t sec. are

$$x = r \cos \omega t; \qquad y = r \sin \omega t.$$

14. Show that if the rod in Prob. 13 initially makes an angle of α radians with the x-axis, then the coordinates of B at the end of t sec. are

$$x = r \cos (\omega t + \alpha); \qquad y = r \sin (\omega t + \alpha).$$

15. Find a parametric representation of the cycloid using the highest point of an arch as the origin.

16. If the tracing point on the rolling circle in Sec. 12-5 is at a distance $b \neq a$ from the center, show that the equations of its path are

$$x = a\theta - b \sin \theta; \qquad y = a - b \cos \theta.$$

This curve is called a *prolate cycloid* if $b > a$, and a *curtate cycloid* if $b < a$.

17. Draw the curtate cycloid (see Prob. 16) for which $a = 8$, $b = 4$.

18. By eliminating the parameter θ from the equations

$$x = a(\theta - \sin \theta), \qquad y = a(1 - \cos \theta),$$

show that the rectangular equation of the cycloid with axes as shown in Fig. 12-8 is

$$x = a \arccos \frac{a - y}{a} \pm \sqrt{2ay - y^2}.$$

19. A circle of radius $\frac{1}{4}a$ rolls inside a circle of radius a as shown in Fig. 12-10.

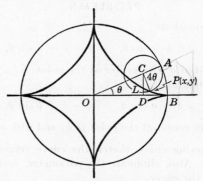

Figure 12-10

Show that the path traversed by a point P on the rolling circle is defined by the equations

$$x = a \cos^3 \theta, \qquad y = a \sin^3 \theta,$$

where θ is the angle shown.   This curve is called the *hypocycloid of four cusps*.
HINT: Arc AP = arc AB; hence $\angle ACP = 4\theta$.   Then,

$$x = OD + LP \qquad \text{and} \qquad y = DC - LC;$$

but $OD = OC \cos \theta = \frac{3}{4}a \cos \theta$, etc.   Observe that $\angle LCP = \frac{1}{2}\pi - 3\theta$.

20. The *hypocycloid* is the curve traced by a point fixed on the circumference
of a circle of radius b when this circle rolls on the *inside* of a circle of radius
a $(a > b)$.   Using a figure similar to Fig. 12-10 show that the equations of this
curve are

$$x = (a - b) \cos \theta + b \cos \frac{a - b}{b} \theta;$$

$$y = (a - b) \sin \theta - b \sin \frac{a - b}{b} \theta.$$

21. The *epicycloid* is the curve traced by a point fixed on the circumference of a
circle of radius b when this circle rolls on the *outside* of a circle of radius a.   Show
that parametric equations of this curve are

$$x = (a + b) \cos \theta - b \cos \frac{a + b}{b} \theta;$$

$$y = (a + b) \sin \theta - b \sin \frac{a + b}{b} \theta.$$

Use a figure similar to Fig. 12-10 but having the rolling circle on the outside of
the fixed circle.

22. A circle of radius a is drawn tangent to the x-axis at the origin and cutting
the y-axis at A (Fig. 12-11); the tangent to the circle at A is then drawn.

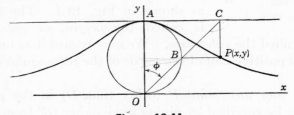

Figure 12-11

Through the origin O a secant line is drawn meeting the circle at B and the
tangent at C.   The horizontal line through B and the vertical line through C
meet at $P(x,y)$.   Show that the coordinates of P are

$$x = 2a \tan \phi, \qquad y = 2a \cos^2 \phi$$

where ϕ is the parameter shown in the figure.   The curve that is the locus of P
is called the *witch of Agnesi*.   By eliminating the parameter show that its rectangular equation is

$$y = \frac{8a^3}{x^2 + 4a^2}.$$

CHAPTER 13

POLAR COORDINATES

13-1. Introduction. The rectangular coordinate system in the plane is one in which we locate a point by specifying its directed distances from two fixed lines, namely, the x- and y-axes. We shall now consider a coordinate system in which we locate a point by specifying its distance and direction from a fixed point. One is essentially using this system when he says that a town B is 30 miles northeast of a certain town A—he is giving the distance and direction of B from A, instead of giving the distance east and the distance north.

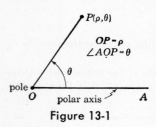

Figure 13-1

13-2. Polar coordinates. Let O be a fixed point in a plane, and let OA be a fixed "half line" in the plane through O as shown in Fig. 13-1. The fixed point is called the *origin*, or *pole*, and the line OA is called the *polar axis*. We may regard it as being identical with the positive half of the x-axis of the rectangular coordinate system.

Consider now any point P (other than O) in the plane. Its position can be specified by giving its distance OP from O and the angle that OP makes with OA. The length OP is called the *radius vector* of P and is denoted by the Greek letter ρ. The angle AOP is called the *vectorial angle* of P and is denoted by the Greek letter θ. The two numbers, ρ and θ, are called *polar coordinates* of P. They are usually written in the form (ρ,θ).

In plotting a point whose coordinates (ρ,θ) are given, we agree that if θ is a positive number we are to lay out an angle of θ radians in the counterclockwise sense measured from OA as the initial side. If θ is negative, the angle is to be measured in the clockwise sense. (It may of course be specified that the number θ is to be interpreted

194

as the number of degrees instead of the number of radians in angle AOP.)   For the present we agree that the number ρ must be a positive number when P does not coincide with O.   Finally, we agree to associate the origin with the coordinates $(0,\theta)$, where θ is any real number.

We thus have a coordinate system which associates a definite point of the plane with every ordered pair of real numbers (ρ,θ) provided that the first number is positive or zero.   In Fig. 13-2 we have plotted the points whose coordinates are $(4,\frac{1}{6}\pi)$, $(3,\pi)$, and $(2,-\frac{2}{3}\pi)$.

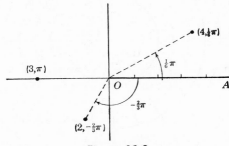

Figure 13-2

It will be recalled that the rectangular coordinate system gives us a one-to-one correspondence between the points of the plane and the ordered pairs of numbers (x,y); to each pair of coordinates there corresponds a definite point, and to each point there corresponds one and only one pair of coordinates.   In the case of polar coordinates the situation is somewhat different.   To a given pair of polar coordinates there corresponds a definite point of the plane (if the first number is not negative), but to a given point there correspond indefinitely many pairs of coordinates.   Thus the point with coordinates $(3,\pi)$ in Fig. 13-2 has also the coordinates $(3,-\pi)$, $(3,3\pi)$, and so on.   The situation is covered by saying that if a point P has coordinates (ρ,θ) then it has also the coordinates $(\rho,\theta + 2k\pi)$, where k is any integer.

Plotting in polar coordinates is facilitated by the use of polar coordinate paper.   This paper is ruled off in concentric circles and radial lines as indicated in Fig. 13-3.

It should be remarked that there are two systems of polar coordinates in common use.   The one that we have just described, in which ρ is never negative, is the one that is used in mathematical analysis—in the study of functions of a complex variable, for

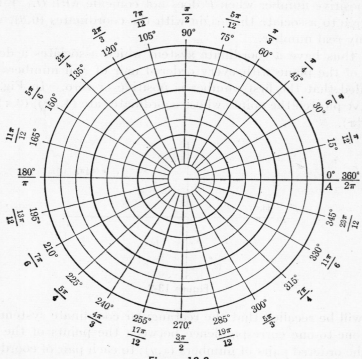

Figure 13-3

example. The other system is identical with this in case ρ is positive, but it permits the use of negative values of ρ. When the coordinates (ρ,θ) are given, and ρ is a negative number, the corresponding point is plotted as follows: *After laying out θ in the usual way, extend its terminal side through the origin and locate the point on this extension at a distance $|\rho|$ from the origin.* We have thus plotted the point $(-4,\frac{1}{4}\pi)$ in Fig. 13-4. This extension of the polar coordinate system amounts to taking the point with which we have associated the number pair (k,θ), where $k > 0$, and agreeing also to associate with it the number pair $(-k,\theta + \pi)$.

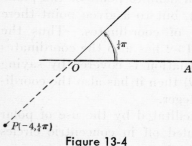

Figure 13-4

If we think only in terms of analytic geometry, we should perhaps be inclined to favor this extended system because it allows us to associate a point with every ordered pair of real numbers—and we might feel that something must be lost in the graphical representation of an equation $f(\rho,\theta) = 0$ if we can use only those number pairs satisfying it in which the first number is positive or zero.   On the other hand there are several disadvantages connected with its use, and in this chapter we shall assume in general the restriction that $\rho \geqq 0$.   In various places we shall indicate how the use of the extended polar coordinate system would affect the matter under discussion.

13-3. *Graphs in polar coordinates.*   The graph of an equation in polar coordinates is defined in essentially the same way as that of an equation in rectangular coordinates; *it is the locus of all points in the plane that have a pair of polar coordinates that satisfy the equation.*   The basic method of drawing the graph consists in making a table of corresponding values of ρ and θ, plotting the points, and drawing a curve through them.

Let us take, as a first example, the equation

$$\rho = \frac{8}{2 - \cos \theta}.$$

We may agree to let θ denote the number of degrees in the vectorial angle if we wish, and substitute values from 0 to 360° at intervals of 30°.   We thus obtain the following table:

θ	0°	30°	60°	90°	120°	150°	180°
ρ	8	7.1	5.3	4	3.2	2.8	2.7

θ	210°	240°	270°	300°	330°	360°
ρ	2.8	3.2	4	5.3	7.1	8

Upon plotting the points and connecting them we have the graph shown in Fig. 13-5.   The curve resembles an ellipse, and we shall see later that it is actually an ellipse—*with one focus at the origin.*

From the fact that cos θ varies only between -1 and $+1$ we could conclude immediately that ρ is never less than $2\frac{2}{3}$ or more than 8.   Also, from the periodic character of cos θ we know that the substitution of values greater than 360° for θ, or the substitution of negative values, will yield only a repetition of these same points. We have, therefore, the complete graph.

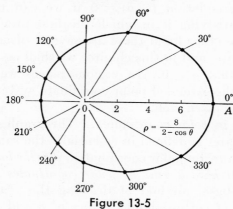

Figure 13-5

As a second example, consider the equation

$$\rho = 3 + 6 \cos \theta.$$

Corresponding to $\theta = 0°$ we have $\rho = 9$.   If we substitute 15°, 30°, 45°, and so on, up to 120°, for θ, we get successively smaller values for ρ—and corresponding to $\theta = 120°$ we have $\rho = 0$.   The corresponding points lie on the top part of the curve in Fig. 13-6. Now if we continue—and substitute 135°, 150°, and so on, for θ— we get negative values for ρ until we get to 240°, where we again have $\rho = 0$.   If we are using the system in which ρ cannot be negative, we discard these pairs of values and the interval 120° < θ < 240° becomes an "excluded interval."   If we plot them in accordance with the extension discussed above, we get the inside loop that is shown dotted in the figure.   Values of θ from 240 to 360° again yield positive values for ρ, and the corresponding points are those on the bottom half of the curve.   The graph thus consists of only the outer curve, or the outer curve and inner loop, depending upon which polar coordinate system we are using.

When we say that a certain curve is the graph of a given equation in polar coordinates, we mean that every point on this curve has at least one pair of coordinates that satisfies the equation, and that the equation is not satisfied by any pair of coordinates of any point that is not on this curve.　It is not necessary that *every* pair of coordinates of a point on the graph satisfy the equation.　Thus the point whose coordinates are $(3\pi,\pi)$ is on the graph of the equation $\rho = 3\theta$.　This point has also the coordinates $(3\pi,3\pi)$, $(3\pi,-\pi)$, etc., which do not satisfy the equation.

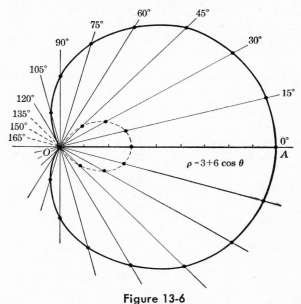

Figure 13-6

PROBLEMS

In each of the following cases plot the points whose polar coordinates are given. Find the corresponding rectangular coordinates for each point, assuming that the positive half of the x-axis coincides with the polar axis.

1. $A(2,\tfrac{1}{2}\pi)$; $B(5,\pi)$; $C(\sqrt{18}, \tfrac{3}{4}\pi)$.
2. $A(3,-\pi)$; $B(4,\tfrac{3}{4}\pi)$; $C(2,-\tfrac{1}{2}\pi)$.
3. $A(5,-\tfrac{3}{2}\pi)$; $B(4,0)$; $C(\sqrt{8},-\tfrac{3}{4}\pi)$.
4. $A(4,5\pi)$; $B(2,-2\pi)$; $C(6,\tfrac{5}{6}\pi)$.
5. $A(4,-\tfrac{2}{3}\pi)$; $B(6,-\tfrac{3}{2}\pi)$; $C(\sqrt{50},-\tfrac{5}{4}\pi)$.
6. $A(3,-3\pi)$; $B(4,-\tfrac{4}{3}\pi)$; $C(5,\tfrac{5}{3}\pi)$.

In each of the following cases the rectangular coordinates of three points are given.　Plot each point, and find two sets of polar coordinates for it (both with positive ρ), assuming that the polar axis coincides with the positive half of the x-axis.

7. $A(4,4)$; $B(-3,0)$; $C(0,-1)$.　　　8. $A(-2,2)$; $B(2,0)$; $C(-4,0)$.
9. $A(0,-3)$; $B(-2,-2)$; $C(0,1)$.　　10. $A(4,-4)$; $B(-2,0)$; $C(0,2)$.

11. The equations $x = a$ *constant* and $y = a$ *constant* are the families of lines parallel to the y-axis and x-axis, respectively. What is the corresponding situation regarding the equations $\rho = a$ *constant* and $\theta = a$ *constant?* In what way is this connected with the fact that rectangular coordinate paper is ruled in horizontal and vertical lines, and polar coordinate paper is ruled in concentric circles and radial lines?

12. Suppose that we should agree to restrict ρ by the requirement $\rho \geqq 0$ and to restrict θ to the interval $0 \leqq \theta < 2\pi$. Would we then have a one-to-one correspondence between the points of the plane and the number pairs (ρ, θ), or would one or more points still have more than one pair of coordinates?

In each of the following cases make a table of corresponding values of ρ and θ, and draw the graph. Assume the restriction that $\rho \geqq 0$.

13. $\rho = 4 - 2 \sin \theta$.　　　　　　**14.** $\rho = 3 + 2 \cos \theta$.

15. $\rho = 4 \cos \theta$.　　　　　　　**16.** $\rho = 3 \sin \theta$.

17. $\rho = 2(1 - \cos \theta)$.　　　　　**18.** $\rho = 3(1 + \sin \theta)$.

19. $\rho = 2 + 4 \sin \theta$.　　　　　**20.** $\rho = 4 \cos \theta - 2$.

21. $\rho = \dfrac{4}{1 + \sin \theta}$.　　　　　　**22.** $\rho = \dfrac{6}{2 - \cos \theta}$.

23. $\rho = \dfrac{9}{3 - 2 \sin \theta}$.　　　　　**24.** $\rho = \dfrac{8}{4 + 2 \sin \theta}$.

25. $\rho = \dfrac{6}{2 \cos \theta + 3}$.　　　　**26.** $\rho = \dfrac{4}{2 - \sin \theta}$.

27. $\rho = \dfrac{4}{\sin \theta + \cos \theta}$.　　　　**28.** $\rho = \dfrac{6}{\cos \theta + 2 \sin \theta}$.

29. Show that the graph of the equation $\rho = 6 \cos \theta$ is the same curve whether or not we allow ρ to be negative. Sketch the graph.

30. Show that the graph of the equation $\rho = -4 \sin \theta$ is the same curve whether or not we allow ρ to be negative. Sketch the graph.

31. Sketch the graph of the equation $\rho = 4 \sin \frac{1}{2}\theta$, using the restriction that $\rho \geqq 0$. In what way is the graph different if we allow ρ to be negative? Show that the equation is equivalent to the equation $\rho^2 = 8(1 - \cos \theta)$.

32. Draw the graph of the equation $\rho = 2 + 2 \sin \frac{1}{2}\theta$.

33. Draw the graph of the equation $\rho = 3 - 3 \cos \frac{1}{2}\theta$.

34. Draw the graph of the equation $\rho = 3 - 2 \sin \frac{1}{2}\theta$.

13-4. *Relations between polar and rectangular coordinates.*

We wish to determine the relations that exist between the polar coordinates (ρ, θ) and the corresponding rectangular coordinates (x, y) of any point P, it being assumed that the polar axis coincides with the positive half of the x-axis.

Let (ρ, θ) be polar coordinates of any point P other than the origin, and let us confine our attention at first to the case in which

$\rho > 0$. Then the definitions of the trigonometric functions, namely, $\cos \theta = x/\rho$ and $\sin \theta = y/\rho$, yield immediately the following relations (Fig. 13-7):

(1) $x = \varrho \cos \theta; \quad y = \varrho \sin \theta.$

If P is at the origin so that $\rho = 0$, these equations give $x = 0$ and $y = 0$, and thus apply in this case. Also, if we wish to associate

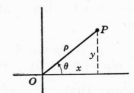

Figure 13-7

with P the number pair $(-\rho, \theta + \pi)$, these relations again hold; for

$(-\rho) \cos (\theta + \pi) = \rho \cos \theta \quad$ and $\quad (-\rho) \sin (\theta + \pi) = \rho \sin \theta.$

Finally, then, we can assert that if any pair of polar coordinates of a point are given, in either of the two systems, equations (1) give the rectangular coordinates of that point.

If the coordinates (x,y) of P are given, and we wish to determine a corresponding pair of polar coordinates (ρ, θ), we have immediately

(2) $\varrho^2 = x^2 + y^2.$

If we restrict ourselves to the system in which $\rho \geqq 0$, then

$$\rho = \sqrt{x^2 + y^2}.$$

With this choice of ρ, equations (1) determine $\sin \theta$ and $\cos \theta$, and thus determine a value of θ, say in the interval $0 \leqq \theta < 2\pi$. If we choose $\rho = -\sqrt{x^2 + y^2}$, equations (1) again determine a corresponding value of θ. Finally, if $x = 0$ and $y = 0$, equation (2) gives $\rho = 0$. Equations (1) do not in this case determine a value of θ. We have agreed that we may take any value of θ that we please, along with $\rho = 0$, as polar coordinates of the origin.

The above relations enable us to find the equation of a curve in polar coordinates when we know the equation in rectangular coordinates, and vice versa.   Consider, for example, the equation

$$x^2 + y^2 = 6x.$$

It is satisfied by the coordinates (x,y) of every point on the circle shown in Fig. 13-8.   If we think of the corresponding polar coordinates (ρ,θ) of each of these points, we know that $x^2 + y^2 = \rho^2$

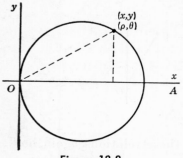

Figure 13-8

and $x = \rho \cos \theta$.   These polar coordinates must then satisfy the equation

$$\rho^2 = 6\rho \cos \theta$$

or $$\rho(\rho - 6 \cos \theta) = 0.$$

This means that any point whose rectangular coordinates satisfy the relation $x^2 + y^2 = 6x$ must have polar coordinates (ρ,θ) such that either $\rho = 0$ or $\rho = 6 \cos \theta$.   The only point satisfying the first of these conditions is the origin, and it is contained in the locus of the second.   We can therefore conclude that if the rectangular coordinates of a point satisfy the relation $x^2 + y^2 = 6x$, then the point has polar coordinates that satisfy the relation $\rho = 6 \cos \theta$.   Conversely, if a number pair (ρ,θ) satisfies the condition $\rho = 6 \cos \theta$, then it will satisfy the equation $\rho^2 = 6\rho \cos \theta$ and the corresponding rectangular coordinates will satisfy the equation $x^2 + y^2 = 6x$.   The locus of the equation $x^2 + y^2 = 6x$ is therefore identical with that of the equation $\rho = 6 \cos \theta$.

As a second example, consider the equation

$$\rho = \frac{3}{\sin \theta - 2}.$$

It is obvious that if ρ is restricted to nonnegative values, there is no graph.   In order to find the corresponding equation in rectangular coordinates, we write the given equation in the form $\rho \sin \theta - 3 = 2\rho$ and then replace $\rho \sin \theta$ by y and ρ by $\sqrt{x^2 + y^2}$.   The result is

$$y - 3 = 2 \sqrt{x^2 + y^2}.$$

This equation is not satisfied by any pair of real numbers, and so it has no graph.

If we do not make the restriction on ρ, we use $\pm \sqrt{x^2 + y^2}$ as the replacement for ρ and are thus led to consider all points (x,y) for which

$$y - 3 = \pm 2 \sqrt{x^2 + y^2}.$$

This is the corresponding equation in rectangular coordinates, but it can be put into a form in which we can identify the locus— for without changing the graph we may square both sides and then reduce the resulting equation to the following standard form:

$$\frac{x^2}{3} + \frac{(y + 1)^2}{4} = 1.$$

We thus see that the graph is an ellipse with center at $(0, -1)$—and we see that one focus is at the origin.

If we take this last equation and replace x by $\rho \cos \theta$ and y by $\rho \sin \theta$, we can show that every point whose coordinates (x,y) satisfy it must have a pair of polar coordinates such that either

$$\rho = \frac{3}{\sin \theta - 2} \qquad \text{or} \qquad \rho = \frac{3}{2 + \sin \theta}.$$

Without the restriction $\rho \geqq 0$, the graph of either of these equations is the ellipse. If the restriction is used, the first has no locus, but the locus of the second is the ellipse.

13-5. *Polar equations representing straight lines.* Consider the general equation of first degree in x and y, namely, $ax + by = c$. If $c \neq 0$, the line does not go through the origin. To find the corresponding equation in polar coordinates, we may replace x by $\rho \cos \theta$ and y by $\rho \sin \theta$. We thus get

$$a\rho \cos \theta + b\rho \sin \theta = c$$

or

$$\varrho = \frac{c}{a \cos \theta + b \sin \theta}.$$

The student may show that if the line does go through the origin, its equation in polar coordinates can be written in the form $\theta = k$, where k is a constant.

A special case is shown in Fig. 13-9. The line is parallel to the y-axis and has x-intercept a. Its equation in rectangular coordinates is $x = a$, and the corresponding equation in polar coordinates is

$$\varrho \cos \theta = a.$$

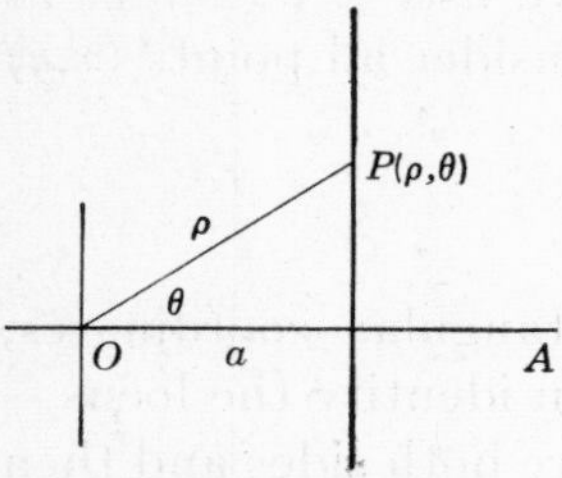

Similarly, if the line is parallel to the x-axis and has y-intercept b, its equation in rectangular coordinates is $y = b$ and that in polar coordinates is

$$\varrho \sin \theta = b.$$

Figure 13-9

13-6. *Polar equations representing circles.* It will be recalled that the standard equation of a circle with center at the point (h,k) and radius r is $(x - h)^2 + (y - k)^2 = r^2$. If we replace x by $\rho \cos \theta$ and y by $\rho \sin \theta$, we get

$$(\rho \cos \theta - h)^2 + (\rho \sin \theta - k)^2 = r^2.$$

When this equation is simplified, it can be written in the form

$$\varrho^2 - 2\varrho(h \cos \theta + k \sin \theta) = c,$$

where $c = r^2 - h^2 - k^2$. This polar equation of a circle in a

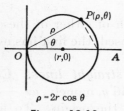

$\rho = 2r \cos \theta$

Figure 13-10

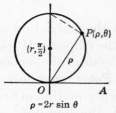

$\rho = 2r \sin \theta$

Figure 13-11

general position is not used very often, but certain special cases arise frequently. These are:

Center at origin, radius r: $\varrho = r$;
Center at $(r,0)$, radius r: $\varrho = 2r \cos \theta$;
Center at $(r,\tfrac{1}{2}\pi)$, radius r: $\varrho = 2r \sin \theta$.

The first of these needs no discussion. The student can derive the second and the third directly, using Figs. 13-10 and 13-11. They are of course special cases of the above general equation.

13-7. *Polar equations representing conic sections.* We could obtain polar equations of the parabola, ellipse, and hyperbola by taking the standard equations for these curves in rectangular coordinates and making the usual transformation.   It turns out, however, that we get simpler equations if we take a focus as the origin.   We therefore choose our coordinate system as indicated

in Fig. 13-12 and use the following definition of the conic section (page 136): *A parabola, ellipse, or hyperbola is the locus of all points in a plane whose undirected distance from a fixed point of the plane is equal to* **e** *times its undirected distance from a fixed line of the plane. The curve is a parabola if* **e = 1,**

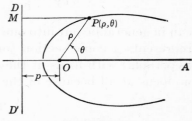

Figure 13-12

an ellipse if **0 < e < 1,** *and a hyperbola if* **e > 1.**   The fixed line is called a *directrix* of the curve, and the fixed point is a *focus.*

We restrict our attention to the coordinate system in which ρ is never negative, and we let p be a positive number representing the distance from the directrix DD' to the focus O.   Then the point $P(\rho,\theta)$ lies on the parabola, ellipse, or hyperbola if and only if

$$|OP| = e \cdot |MP|, \qquad \text{where } e > 0.$$

But $|OP| = \rho$, and $|MP| = p + \rho \cos \theta$.   The condition is then

$$\rho = e(p + \rho \cos \theta).$$

Upon solving this equation for ρ, we get the standard equation

$$\rho = \frac{ep}{1 - e \cos \theta}.$$

This equation represents an ellipse if **0 < e < 1,** a parabola if $e = 1$, and one of the two branches of a hyperbola if $e > 1$.

The student may show that if we take the directrix to the right of the pole instead of to the left as shown in the figure, the corresponding equation is

$$\rho = \frac{ep}{1 + e \cos \theta}.$$

Finally, if the directrix is taken parallel to the polar axis, the equation is

$$\rho = \frac{ep}{1 \pm e \sin \theta}.$$

The positive sign applies if the directrix is above the pole and the negative sign if below.

An equation of the form

$$\rho = \frac{k}{a \pm b \cos \theta \ (or \ \sin \theta)}$$

can in general be put into one of the above forms and it accordingly represents a conic section (or a branch of one in the case of the hyperbola) with focus at the origin. In special cases it may have no locus at all because of the restriction $\rho \geqq 0$.

Example 1

Identify and sketch the locus of the equation $\rho = \dfrac{8}{2 - \cos \theta}$.

Solution

We first divide numerator and denominator by 2 in order to obtain the standard form.

$$\rho = \frac{4}{1 - \frac{1}{2} \cos \theta}.$$

Since $e = \frac{1}{2}$, the equation represents an ellipse for which $ep = 4$ or $p = 8$. The graph is shown in Fig. 13-5.

Example 2

Identify and sketch the curve whose equation is $\rho = \dfrac{8}{5 + 5 \sin \theta}$.

Solution

If we divide numerator and denominator by 5, we get the equation

$$\rho = \frac{1.6}{1 + \sin \theta}.$$

In this case $e = 1$, and the equation represents a parabola. The graph is shown in Fig. 13-13.

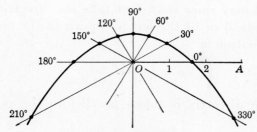

Figure 13-13

In making a rough sketch of a conic from an equation of the above form it is often sufficient, after identifying the curve, to plot only the points corresponding to $\theta = 0$, $\frac{1}{2}\pi$, π, and $\frac{3}{2}\pi$. The value of θ, if there is one, for which ρ "becomes infinite" can be found by equating the denominator of the right-hand member to zero and solving for θ. This gives the direction of the axis in the case of the parabola and the direction of the asymptotes in case of the hyperbola. It should be observed that the asymptotes to the hyperbola go through the *center* of the hyperbola, not through the origin. It is only their *directions* that are determined by equating the denominator to zero and solving for θ as suggested above.

PROBLEMS

In each of the following cases sketch the graph of the given equation. Find the corresponding equation for the curve in rectangular coordinates.

1. $\rho(\cos \theta + \sin \theta) = 3$.

2. $\rho(2 \cos \theta + 3 \sin \theta) = 8$.

3. $\rho = \dfrac{12}{2 \cos \theta - 3 \sin \theta}$.

4. $\rho = \dfrac{5}{\sin \theta - 2 \cos \theta}$.

5. $\rho \cos \theta + 4 = 0$.

6. $2 + \rho \sin \theta = 0$.

7. $6 + \rho(3 \sin \theta - \cos \theta) = 0$.

8. $\rho(4 \cos \theta + 5 \sin \theta) + 20 = 0$.

9. $\rho = 4 \cos \theta$.

10. $\rho = 5 \sin \theta$.

11. $\rho + 3 \sin \theta = 0$.

12. $\rho + 2 \cos \theta = 0$.

13. $\rho^2 - 6\rho \cos \theta + 4\rho \sin \theta = 48$.

14. $\rho = 8 \cos \theta + 6 \sin \theta$.

15. $\rho + 2 \cos \theta = 3 \sin \theta$.

16. $\rho^2 + 11 = 8\rho \cos \theta - 4\rho \sin \theta$.

17. $\rho^2 = 6\rho \sin \theta + 16$.

18. $\rho^2 = 4\rho \sin \theta + 12$.

19. $\rho = 5 \cos (\theta - \frac{1}{4}\pi)$.

20. $\rho + 2.8 \sin \left(\theta + \dfrac{\pi}{6} \right) = 0$.

In each of the following cases reduce the given equation to standard form and identify and sketch the curve. Find the corresponding equation in rectangular coordinates. (Consider both polar coordinate systems.)

21. $\rho = \dfrac{8}{2 + \sin \theta}$.

22. $\rho = \dfrac{12}{3 + 2 \cos \theta}$.

23. $\rho = \dfrac{4.8}{1.6 + 1.2 \cos \theta}$.

24. $\rho = \dfrac{6}{2 - \sin \theta}$.

25. $\rho = \dfrac{-6}{3 - 2 \sin \theta}$.

26. $\rho = \dfrac{7}{3 \cos \theta - 4}$.

27. $4\rho + 2\rho \cos \theta = 9$.

28. $6\rho - 4\rho \sin \theta = 9$.

29. $\rho + \rho \sin \theta = 4$.

30. $\rho(2 + 2 \cos \theta) = 7$.

31. $\rho = \dfrac{8}{3 + 3 \cos \theta}$.

32. $\rho = \dfrac{9}{2 - 2 \sin \theta}$.

33. $3\rho = \dfrac{8}{1 + \sin \theta}.$

34. $2\rho = \dfrac{9}{\cos \theta - 1}.$

35. $\rho = \dfrac{6}{2 - 3 \cos \theta}.$

36. $\rho = \dfrac{8}{4 + 3 \sin \theta}.$

37. $4\rho + 5\rho \cos \theta = 24.$

38. $3\rho + 6\rho \sin \theta = 16.$

39. $\rho = \dfrac{13}{1 - 2 \sin \theta}.$

40. $\rho = \dfrac{-8}{3 \cos \theta + 2}.$

41. Sketch the locus of all points (ρ, θ) which satisfy the equation

$$\rho \sin^2 \theta = 6 \cos \theta.$$

What is the corresponding equation in rectangular coordinates?

42. Sketch the locus of all points (ρ, θ) which satisfy the equation

$$\rho \sin^2 \theta = 4 \sin \theta.$$

What is the corresponding equation in rectangular coordinates?

43. Sketch the graph of the equation $\rho^2 = \dfrac{144}{9 \cos^2 \theta + 16 \sin^2 \theta}.$ What is the corresponding equation in rectangular coordinates?

44. Sketch the graph of the equation $\rho^2 = \dfrac{36}{4 - 13 \sin^2 \theta}.$ What is the corresponding equation in rectangular coordinates?

13-8. *Analysis of polar equations.* The problem of sketching the graph of a given equation in polar coordinates is often facilitated by an appropriate analysis of the equation. This analysis may include the determination of intercepts, tests for symmetry, and other items that were included in the discussion of equations in rectangular coordinates. The details of such tests will be left to the exercises.

Valuable information can frequently be obtained by noting the way in which ρ varies with θ as θ increases from 0 to 90°, 90 to 180°, 180 to 270°, etc. Consider, for example, the equation

$$\rho = 3 + 3 \cos \theta.$$

When $\theta = 0$, $\cos \theta = 1$ and $\rho = 6$. This is the largest value that ρ can have. Now as θ increases from 0 to 90°, $\cos \theta$ decreases from 1 to 0, and consequently ρ decreases from 6 to 3. As θ increases from 90 to 180°, $\cos \theta$ decreases from 0 to -1, and consequently ρ decreases from 3 to 0. The graph is thus tangent to the 180° line at the origin as shown in Fig. 13-14. As θ continues to increase from 180 to 360°, cos θ increases from -1 to 1, and consequently ρ increases from 0 to 6.

As a second example, consider the equation

$$\rho = 4 + 4 \sin \tfrac{1}{2}\theta.$$

When $\theta = 0$, $\sin \tfrac{1}{2}\theta = 0$ and $\rho = 4$. As θ increases from 0 to 180°, $\sin \tfrac{1}{2}\theta$ increases from 0 to 1 and consequently ρ increases from 4 to 8. As θ increases from 180 to 360°, $\sin \tfrac{1}{2}\theta$ decreases from 1 to 0 and therefore ρ decreases from 8 to 4. This gives the "outside" part of the graph (Fig. 13-15). Now as θ increases from 360 to 540°, $\sin \tfrac{1}{2}\theta$ decreases from 0 to -1 and therefore ρ decreases from 4 to 0—and finally, as θ increases from 540 to 720°, $\sin \tfrac{1}{2}\theta$ increases from -1 to 0 and ρ increases from 0 to 4.

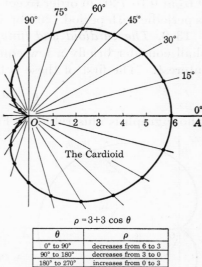

The Cardioid

$\rho = 3 + 3 \cos \theta$

θ	ρ
0° to 90°	decreases from 6 to 3
90° to 180°	decreases from 3 to 0
180° to 270°	increases from 0 to 3
270° to 360°	increases from 3 to 6

Figure 13-14

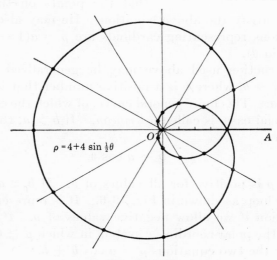

$\rho = 4 + 4 \sin \tfrac{1}{2}\theta$

Figure 13-15

This gives the "inner" part of the curve. It is because we are dealing with $\sin \frac{1}{2}\theta$ instead of $\sin \theta$ that we must consider values of θ from 0 to 720° in order to get the complete graph; that is, $\sin \frac{1}{2}\theta$ is periodic with period 720°, or 4π radians.

13-9. The cardioid and limaçon. In the next few sections we shall consider briefly a few equations whose graphs are of special interest. The first of these is the equation

$$\varrho = a + a \cos \theta$$

whose graph is illustrated by Fig. 13-14. Because of its heartlike

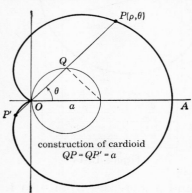

construction of cardioid
$QP = QP' = a$

Figure 13-16

shape this curve is called a *cardioid*. It is defined geometrically as follows: Draw a circle of diameter a (Fig. 13-16). From one end O of a diameter draw any line intersecting the circle at Q; on this line mark off two points P and P' such that

$$|QP| = |QP'| = a.$$

The locus of P and P' is the cardioid. The student may show that the points on the curve so constructed satisfy the above equation. He may also show that other equations representing cardioids are $\rho = a(1 - \cos \theta)$ and $\rho = a(1 \pm \sin \theta)$.

The construction used above may be generalized by making $|QP| = |QP'| = b$, where b is a positive number that is in general not equal to a. This more general curve, of which the cardioid is of course a special case, is called a *limaçon*. If $b > a$, the curve has the equation

$$\varrho = b + a \cos \theta.$$

In this case ρ is positive for all values of θ. If $b < a$, the curve has an inner loop as shown in Fig. 13-6. It is represented by the above equation if we allow negative values of ρ. If we restrict ourselves to the polar coordinate system in which $\rho \geqq 0$, the curve is defined by the two equations $\rho = a \cos \theta \pm b$.

13-10. *The rose curves.* The graphs of the equations

$$\varrho = a \cos n\theta \qquad \text{and} \qquad \varrho = a \sin n\theta,$$

where n is an integer, are called *rose curves.* They have the general shape illustrated by Fig. 13-17. If we use the polar coordinate system in which $\rho \geqq 0$, the graph has n "leaves." If we allow

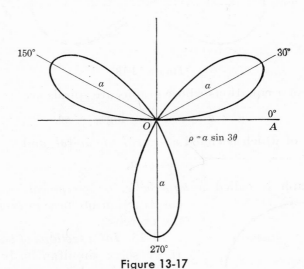

Figure 13-17

negative values of ρ, there are n leaves if n is odd and $2n$ leaves if n is even. Thus the graph of the equation $\rho = a \cos 2\theta$ has four leaves or two leaves depending upon whether or not we allow negative values of ρ.

13-11. *The lemniscate.* The locus of the equation

$$\varrho^2 = a^2 \cos 2\theta$$

is called a *lemniscate.* The graph is shown in Fig. 13-18. The equation $\rho^2 = a^2 \sin 2\theta$ of course represents the same curve in a different position relative to the polar axis.

13-12. *The spirals.* The polar equation that corresponds to the equation $y = ax$ in rectangular coordinates is

$$\varrho = a\theta.$$

Its graph is called a *spiral of Archimedes*. The curve is shown in Fig. 13-19 for the case in which $a > 0$.

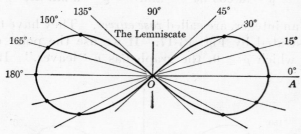

Figure 13-18

Other polar equations whose graphs are spirals are

$$\varrho = e^{a\theta} \qquad \text{or} \qquad \log \varrho = a\theta,$$

the graph of which is called a *logarithmic spiral*, and

$$\varrho\theta = a,$$

whose graph is called a *hyperbolic*, or *reciprocal*, *spiral*. The construction of these curves is left to the exercises.

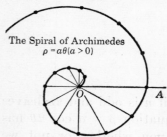

The Spiral of Archimedes
$\rho = a\theta (a > 0)$

Figure 13-19

13-13. *Intersections of polar curves.* If we solve simultaneously a pair of equations in polar coordinates, we find the number pairs (ρ,θ) that satisfy both equations. The corresponding points are of course points of intersection of the two graphs. This procedure may not yield all points of intersection for the following reason: We have seen that a given point has infinitely many pairs of polar coordinates, and we have agreed that a point is on the graph of a given equation if any one of its pairs of coordinates satisfies the equation. It is quite possible that a point of intersection of the graphs may have one or more pairs of coordinates that satisfy one of the two equations and other pairs that satisfy the other—but no pair that satisfies both.

Example

In order to solve the system

$$\rho = 2 \cos \theta,$$
$$\rho = 2 \sin \theta,$$

we first eliminate ρ and solve for θ. **We have**

$$2 \sin \theta = 2 \cos \theta,$$
$$\tan \theta = 1.$$

If we take $\theta = \frac{1}{4}\pi$ and substitute in either equation, we get $\rho = \sqrt{2}$. The curves then intersect at $(\sqrt{2}, \frac{1}{4}\pi)$. The graphs are shown in Fig. 13-20. They obviously also intersect at the origin. The number pair $(0,0)$ satisfies the second equation, and the pair $(0, \frac{1}{2}\pi)$ satisfies the first. The origin has no pair of coordinates that satisfies both equations. The student may verify that every pair of coordinates of the other point of intersection satisfies both equations.

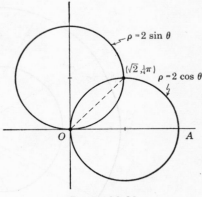

A given curve can have more than one equation in polar coordinates. For example, the equations

$$\rho = 4 + 4 \sin \tfrac{1}{2}\theta$$
and $$\rho = 4 - 4 \sin \tfrac{1}{2}\theta$$

Figure 13-20

represent the same curve. (The second equation was obtained from the first by replacing θ by $\theta + 2\pi$.) We may try to find the points of intersection of this curve with the curve whose equation is $\rho = 3 - 2 \cos \theta$ by solving either of the following systems:

$$\begin{cases} \rho = 4 + 4 \sin \tfrac{1}{2}\theta, \\ \rho = 3 - 2 \cos \theta. \end{cases} \qquad \begin{cases} \rho = 4 - 4 \sin \tfrac{1}{2}\theta, \\ \rho = 3 - 2 \cos \theta. \end{cases}$$

If we use the first system, and assume the restriction $\rho > 0$, then the value of θ at any point of intersection other than the origin must satisfy the relation

$$4 + 4 \sin \tfrac{1}{2}\theta = 3 - 2 \cos \theta$$
or $$4 \sin \tfrac{1}{2}\theta = -1 - 2 \cos \theta.$$

If we square both sides and then replace $\sin^2 \tfrac{1}{2}\theta$ by $\tfrac{1}{2}(1 - \cos \theta)$—using a well-known formula from trigonometry—we have

$$8(1 - \cos \theta) = 1 + 4 \cos \theta + 4 \cos^2 \theta.$$

This equation reduces to

$$4 \cos^2 \theta + 12 \cos \theta - 7 = 0$$
or $$(2 \cos \theta + 7)(2 \cos \theta - 1) = 0.$$

This means that θ must be such that $\cos \theta = \frac{1}{2}$. If we take $\theta = \frac{1}{3}\pi$, we get $\rho = 6$ from one equation and $\rho = 2$ from the other. If we take $\theta = \frac{1}{3}\pi + 2\pi$ or $\frac{7}{3}\pi$, we get $\rho = 2$ from each equation. Thus the number pair $(2, \frac{7}{3}\pi)$ satisfies both equations. Similarly, the pair $(2, -\frac{1}{3}\pi)$ satisfies both equations. These are coordinates

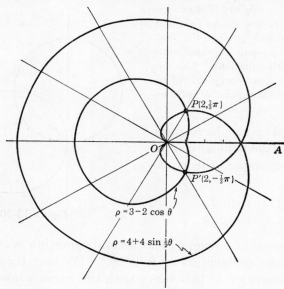

Figure 13-21

of the points P and P' of intersection shown in Fig. 13-21. The student should carry out the corresponding solution using the other pair of equations.

PROBLEMS

1. Show that the graph of an equation $\rho = f(\theta)$ is symmetrical with respect to the 0–180° line if the equation that results when θ is replaced by $-\theta$ has the same graph as the given equation. What is the corresponding statement regarding symmetry with respect to the 90–270° line?

In each of the following cases draw the graph of the given equation, assuming the restriction $\rho \geqq 0$:

2. $\rho = 1 + \cos \theta$.

3. $\rho = 2(1 - \sin \theta)$.

4. $\rho = 3 + 3 \sin \theta$.

5. $\rho = 3 - 3 \cos \theta$.

6. $\rho = 2 + \sin \theta$.

7. $\rho = 3 - 2 \sin \theta$.

8. $\rho = 4 + 3 \cos \theta$.

9. $\rho = 5 - 3 \cos \theta$.

10. $\rho = 2 - 4 \sin \theta$.

11. $\rho = 2 + 3 \cos \theta$.

12. $\rho = 3 + 5 \cos \theta$.

13. $\rho = 5 \cos \theta - 3$.

14. Draw the graph of the equation $\rho = 4 \sin \theta + 2$, using the coordinate system in which $\rho \geq 0$. Draw also the graph of the equation $\rho = 4 \sin \theta - 2$.

15. Describe the graph of the equation $\rho = 3 \sin \theta - 3$ if we use the coordinate system in which $\rho \geq 0$. Describe the graph also if we allow ρ to be negative.

16. Sketch the locus of all points (ρ,θ) for which $\rho = 6 \cos \theta \pm 3$, assuming the restriction $\rho \geq 0$.

In each of the following cases sketch the graph of the given equation, assuming the restriction $\rho \geq 0$:

17. $\rho = 4 \sin 3\theta$.   **18.** $\rho = 2 \cos 3\theta$.

19. $\rho = 3 \cos 2\theta$.   **20.** $\rho = 5 \sin 2\theta$.

21. $\rho = 3 \sin 5\theta$.   **22.** $\rho = \cos 5\theta$.

23. $\rho = \frac{1}{2}\theta$.   **24.** $\rho = 3\theta$.

25. $\rho = -2\theta$.   **26.** $\rho\theta = \pi$.

27. $\rho\theta = 5$.   **28.** $\rho = e^{\frac{1}{2}\theta}$.

29. $\rho^2 = 9 \cos 2\theta$.   **30.** $\rho^2 = 8 \sin 2\theta$.

31. Show that the transformation equations for rotation of axes in polar coordinates are $\rho = \rho'$ and $\theta = \theta' + \alpha$, where α is the angle through which the polar axis is to be rotated.

In each of the following cases sketch the two curves whose equations are given, and find coordinates of their points of intersection:

32. $\rho = 4 \sin \theta$; $\rho = 3 \cos \theta$.   **33.** $\rho \sin \theta = 3$; $\rho = 6$.

34. $\rho = 4 \sin \theta$; $\rho \sin \theta = 2$.   **35.** $\rho = 6 \cos \theta$; $\rho = 2(1 + \cos \theta)$.

36. $\rho = 2 \sin \theta$; $\rho = 2 + 4 \cos \theta$.   **37.** $\rho = \sin \theta$; $\rho = \sin 2\theta$.

38. $\rho = \cos 2\theta$; $\rho = 1 + \sin \theta$.   **39.** $\rho = 3 \cos \theta$; $\rho = 1 + \cos \theta$.

40. $\rho^2 = \sin 2\theta$; $\rho = \sin \theta$.

41. Show that the parametric equations

$$x = \frac{4(1 - 3t^2)}{(1 + t^2)^2}, \qquad y = \frac{4t(1 - 3t^2)}{(1 + t^2)^2}$$

define the rose curve whose polar equation is $\rho = 4 \cos 3\theta$.

42. Show that the parametric equations

$$x = \frac{at(3 - t^2)}{(1 + t^2)^2}, \qquad y = \frac{at^2(3 - t^2)}{(1 + t^2)^2}$$

define the rose curve whose polar equation is $\rho = a \sin 3\theta$.

43. A curve has the equation $x^2 - 2y^3 - 8y^2 = 0$ in rectangular coordinates. Find its equation in polar coordinates. Draw the graph from either equation.

44. A curve has the equation $x^4 - 3xy^2 + 2y^3 = 0$ in rectangular coordinates. Find its equation in polar coordinates, and draw the graph from this polar equation. Compare with Fig. 12-2.

CHAPTER 14

CURVE FITTING

14-1. *Introduction.* In various branches of science one often obtains a set of corresponding values of two variables by observation or experiment. It may then be important to find an equation that "fits" this table of values in a satisfactory way. Thus one might measure the atmospheric pressure at various altitudes in a given locality at a given time, and then try to devise an equation that would fit the observed data. Such an equation would express, at least in an approximate way, the atmospheric pressure as a function of the altitude.

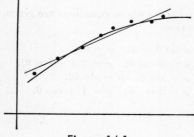

Figure 14-1

A given set of corresponding values of two variables can of course be plotted as points on rectangular coordinate paper. The problem then becomes that of finding the equation of a curve that passes through or near these points in such a way as to indicate their general trend. An equation, when determined in such a manner, is called an *empirical equation* between the variables. The process of finding it is called *curve fitting.*

There is of course no unique solution to the problem of fitting a curve to a given set of points. Both the straight line and the curve shown in Fig. 14-1 fit the given set of points in an approximate way, and it is obvious that other lines and curves could be drawn that might serve equally well.

The first problem in fitting a curve to a given set of data is to decide upon the type of curve to be employed. In some cases this is determined from theoretical considerations. When this is not the case, one may make the selection from considerations that appear later in this chapter. It is usually desirable to use the

216

simplest type of equation from which a reasonably good fit can be obtained.   The types to be considered in this chapter are

(1)	$y = ax + b$	linear type
(2)	$y = ax^2 + bx + c$	parabolic type
(3)	$y = ab^x$	exponential type
(4)	$y = ax^n$	power type

After the type of equation has been chosen, the remaining problem is to determine the values of the constants so that the equation fits the given data in a satisfactory way.   Thus if the given points lay approximately along a straight line, one would ordinarily choose the linear form $y = ax + b$ and proceed to determine a and b so as to secure a satisfactory fit.

We shall discuss two methods of evaluating the constants.   The first is the *method of average points*, and the second is the *method of least squares*.   The first is simpler and easier to apply, but the second ordinarily gives better results.

14-2. Definition of average point.   By the *average point* of a given group of points we shall mean *the point whose abscissa is the average of the abscissas of the group and whose ordinate is the average of the ordinates*.   If the coordinates of the given points are

$$(x_1,y_1),\ (x_2,y_2),\ (x_3,y_3),\ \cdots,\ (x_n,y_n),$$

and the coordinates of the average point for the group are (x_a,y_a), then

$$x_a = \frac{x_1 + x_2 + x_3 + \cdots + x_n}{n};$$

$$y_a = \frac{y_1 + y_2 + y_3 + \cdots + y_n}{n}.$$

14-3. Linear type.   Method of average points.   When the given points lie approximately along a line, as shown in Fig. 14-1, a linear equation that will fit the data reasonably well can be obtained by the method of average points as follows: First divide the given set of points into two groups, putting approximately the same number of points in each group.   Next, find the coordinates of the average point for each group, and take the line determined by these two points as the required line.

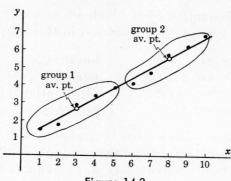

Figure 14-2

Example

Find the equation of a line that fits the points shown in Fig. 14-2, their coordinates being

x	1	2	3	4	5	6	7	8	9	10
y	1.48	1.76	2.78	3.32	3.86	4.15	4.75	5.66	6.18	6.86

Solution

We may take the first five points as group 1; the average point for this group has the coordinates

$$x_a = \frac{1 + 2 + 3 + 4 + 5}{5} = 3;$$

$$y_a = \frac{1.48 + 1.76 + 2.78 + 3.32 + 3.86}{5} = 2.64.$$

We then take the remaining five points as group 2; the coordinates of the average point for this group are

$$x'_a = \frac{6 + 7 + 8 + 9 + 10}{5} = 8;$$

$$y'_a = \frac{4.15 + 4.75 + 5.66 + 6.18 + 6.86}{5} = 5.52.$$

The slope of the line through these two average points is

$$\frac{5.52 - 2.64}{8 - 3} = 0.576;$$

and its equation is

$$y - 2.64 = 0.576(x - 3)$$

or
$$y = 0.576x + 0.912.$$

The result obtained by the above procedure depends, at least to some extent, upon the way in which we group the points. It is often necessary to choose the groups with care in order to obtain a good fit. It can be shown that the various choices of the groups result in lines all of which pass through the average point of the entire set.

14-4. Parabolic type. The method of average points can be applied in a similar way to the problem of fitting a parabola

$$y = ax^2 + bx + c$$

to a given set of points. In this case there are three constants to determine. One accordingly divides the given set of points into three groups, finds the average point of each group, and passes the parabola through these three points.

Example

Fit a parabola of the form $y = ax^2 + bx + c$ to the following data:

x	-2	-1	0	1	2	3	4	5	6	7	8
y	-3.5	0.4	2.5	4.2	5.8	6.6	7.8	8.0	8.6	7.6	6.2

Solution

We may take the first three points as group 1, the next four as group 2, and the last four as group 3. The coordinates of the corresponding average points are found to be

Group 1: $(-1, -0.2)$;
Group 2: $(2.5, 6.1)$;
Group 3: $(6.5, 7.6)$.

In order to pass the parabola through these three points, we substitute their coordinates for x and y in the equation $y = ax^2 + bx + c$ and obtain the following equations in a, b, and c:

$$\begin{cases} a - b + c = -0.2; \\ 6.25a + 2.5b + c = 6.1; \\ 42.25a + 6.5b + c = 7.6. \end{cases}$$

Solving these, we find that $a = -0.190$, $b = 2.085$,

$$c = 2.075.$$

The desired equation is then

$$y = -0.190x^2 + 2.085x + 2.075.$$

This curve and the given set of points are shown in Fig. 14-3. It is evident that a different choice of the groups might result in a parabola that differs appreciably from this one. One might conclude after studying the figure that a better fit

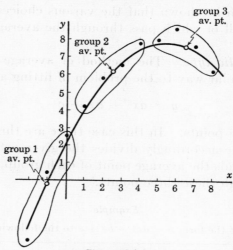

Figure 14-3

would probably be obtained by taking the first four points as group 1, the next four as group 2, and the last three as group 3.

14-5. Residuals. Criteria for goodness of fit. Let us assume that in Fig. 14-4 the curve $y = f(x)$ has been fitted to the points $P_1(x_1,y_1)$, $P_2(x_2,y_2)$, etc. We define the *residual* of any one of the given points, for this curve, to be the difference between the ordinate of the point and that of the corresponding point on the curve. Thus the residuals of the points P_1, P_2, and P_3 are, respectively,

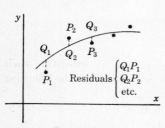

Figure 14-4

$$Q_1P_1 = y_1 - f(x_1);$$
$$Q_2P_2 = y_2 - f(x_2);$$
$$Q_3P_3 = y_3 - f(x_3).$$

The residual of a point is positive if the point is above the curve and negative if below.

In connection with the fitting of a curve to a given set of points we have spoken in a general way of securing a "good fit." By a good fitting curve we have meant a curve such that the absolute values of the residuals were small.

It can easily be shown that when one fits a straight line to a given set of points by the method of average points he obtains, whatever the choice of groups, a line for which *the algebraic sum of the residuals is zero.* This does not mean, however, that he necessarily has a good fit—for the residuals could all be numerically large, the positive ones balancing the negative ones. Thus if one has only two points, the best fitting line is the one passing through them. The perpendicular bisector of the segment joining them is also a line for which the algebraic sum of the residuals is zero, and this line would of course give a poor fit. It is evident then that we could not use the value of the algebraic sum of the residuals as a criterion of the goodness of fit.

If we should consider the *squares* of the residuals instead of the residuals themselves, we would be dealing with *positive quantities.* The sum of the squares of the residuals could not be zero (unless the curve actually passed through all the points), but one would obviously have a good fit if this sum were small. In fitting a curve of a specified type to a given set of points one might try to determine the constants so that this sum is as small as possible and regard the result as the best fitting curve of the type. In fact we now set up the following:

Definition. The best fitting curve of a given type is the one in which the constants are determined so that the sum of the squares of the residuals is a minimum.

The justification for calling this the best fitting curve of the type lies in the theory of probability and will not be discussed.

The best fitting curve cannot, in general, be found by the method of average points but requires the method of least squares which is given at the end of this chapter. The calculations involved in this latter method are much longer, and for this reason the method of average points is often used where the best fitting curve is not required.

PROBLEMS

In each of the following, fit a straight line to the given data by the method of average points using the subdivision indicated by the double bar. Compute the residuals at any three of the given points.

1.

x	2	4	6	8	10	12	14	16
y	6.4	7.1	8.0	9.1	9.8	10.8	11.6	12.2

2.

x	1.4	2.6	3.0	3.8	4.4	4.8	5.8	7	8.2
y	9.3	8.6	7.7	8.0	7.6	7.6	7.1	6.6	5.9

3.

x	−2	−1	0	1	2	3	4	5	6
y	−3.2	−2.5	−1.8	−1.3	−0.6	0.1	0.4	1.0	1.5

4. The resistance R (ohms) of a certain coil of copper wire at temperature T (degrees centigrade) was found by measurement to be as follows:

T	10.2°	19.8°	28.6°	39.8°	49.5°	58.4°	71.2°	80.5°	88.8°
R	13.12	13.54	14.08	14.72	15.06	15.58	16.24	16.66	17.24

Find the equation of a line to fit this data. Use the result to estimate the resistance at 45°.

5. The length L (inches) of a certain coiled steel spring under the action of a tensile pull was found to increase with the pull P (pounds) as shown below:

P	0	5	10	15	20	25	30	35	40	45
L	10.25	11.45	12.80	14.35	15.75	17.30	18.55	19.55	21.20	23.00

Find the equation of a straight line to fit this data. Use the result to estimate the length under a pull of 22 lb.

6. Show that every line for which the algebraic sum of the residuals is zero passes through the average point of the given set, and conversely. HINT: Let the given points be (x_1,y_1), (x_2,y_2), $\cdots$, (x_n,y_n). Assuming the equation $y = ax + b$ and equating to zero the sum of the residuals, we have

(1) $[y_1 - (ax_1 + b)] + [y_2 - (ax_2 + b)] + \cdots + [y_n - (ax_n + b)] = 0.$

Show that this reduces to

(2) $$\frac{y_1 + y_2 + \cdots + y_n}{n} = a\frac{x_1 + x_2 + \cdots + x_n}{n} + b$$

which means that the point

$$\left(\frac{x_1 + x_2 + \cdots + x_n}{n}, \frac{y_1 + y_2 + \cdots + y_n}{n}\right)$$

must be on the line if (1) is to be satisfied. Conversely, show that (1) follows from (2).

7. Fit a parabola of the form $y = ax^2 + bx + c$ to the following data:

x	0	1	2	3	4	5	6	7
y	-5.4	-5.2	-4.4	-2.8	-1.2	1.4	3.6	6.6

8. Fit a parabola of the form $y = ax^2 + bx + c$ to the following data:

x	-1	0	1	2	3	4	5	6
y	3.2	4.2	4.1	3.8	2.8	1.4	-1.1	-3.8

14-6. *The power type.* We consider now the problem of fitting an equation of the type

$$y = ax^n$$

to a given table of values of x and y. If we take the common logarithms of both members of the equation, we obtain

$$\log y = \log a + n \log x.$$

This is obviously a *linear* relation between $\log x$ and $\log y$, and if we let

$$\log x = u \quad \text{and} \quad \log y = v$$

it becomes

$$v = nu + \log a$$

where $\log a$ is a constant $(= L)$. It follows that *if the relation between x and y is of the form $y = ax^n$, the relation between $\log x$ and $\log y$ is linear.* We may then proceed as follows:

Step 1. Make a new table in which the entries are the logarithms of the numbers in the given table; denote these new entries by u and v where $u = \log x$ and $v = \log y$.

Step 2.   Plot the points (u,v) on rectangular coordinate paper.   If they tend to lie along a straight line, the equation $y = ax^n$ is applicable.

Step 3.   Fit a straight line $v = nu + L$ to this set of data, using the method of average points (or the method of least squares, which is discussed later).   The value of n in the required equation $y = ax^n$ is the coefficient of u in this linear equation, and the value of a can be found from the fact that $L = \log a$.

Example

Show that an equation of the form $y = ax^n$ is suitable for the data given below, and find proper values for a and n.

x	1	2	3	4	5	6	7	8
y	0.36	0.90	1.92	3.44	4.78	6.74	9.40	11.8

Solution

Taking the common logarithms of the given numbers, we construct the following table:

$u = \log x$	0.0000	0.3010	0.4771	0.6021	0.6990	0.7782	0.8451	0.9031
$v = \log y$	−0.4437	−0.0458	0.2833	0.5238	0.6794	0.8287	0.9731	1.0719

These points when plotted on rectangular coordinate paper tend to lie along a line as shown in Fig. 14-5. This means that an equation of the form $y = ax^n$ is applicable.

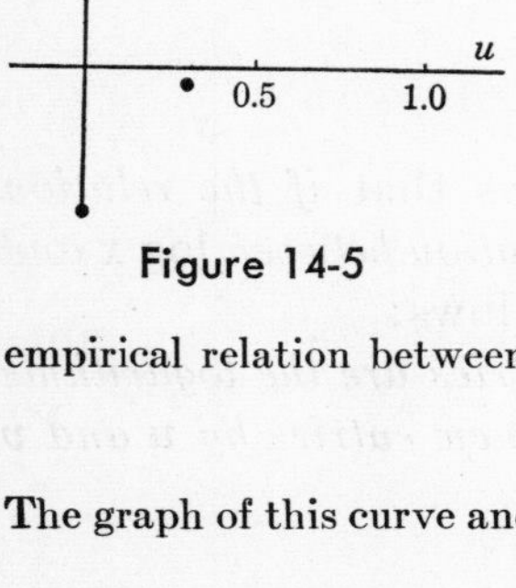

Figure 14-5

In order to fit a line to these points, we choose the first four as group 1 and the last four as group 2. The corresponding average points are $(0.3450, 0.0794)$ and $(0.8064, 0.8883)$; the line through these points has the equation

$$v = 1.753u - 0.5254.$$

This is of the form $v = nu + L$, where $n = 1.753$ and

$$L = \log a = -0.5254 = 9.4746 - 10;$$

from tables we find that $a = 0.2983$. The required empirical relation between x and y is then

$$y = 0.2983x^{1.753}.$$

The graph of this curve and the given points are shown in Fig. 14-6.

The test for applicability of the formula $y = ax^n$ can be made more quickly by plotting the given data on *logarithmic coordinate paper* instead of looking up the logarithms and using ordinary paper.

Logarithmic coordinate paper, as shown in Fig. 14-7, has its horizontal and vertical rulings not at distances of 1, 2, 3, etc., from the origin, but at distances of log 1, log 2, log 3, and so on. The sample shown has two "cycles," the first going from 1 to 10 and the second from 10 to 100. The next cycle to the right along the x-axis would go from 100 to 1,000; the next one to the left would go from 1 down to 0.1.

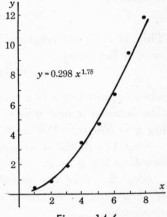

Figure 14-6

Plotting the given data directly on this paper is of course equivalent to plotting the logarithms on ordinary paper. If the points tend to lie on a line, an equation of the form $y = ax^n$ is applicable.

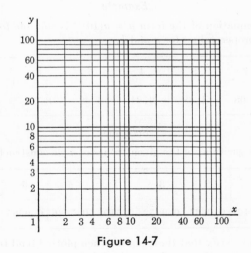

Figure 14-7

14-7. *The exponential type.* The problem of fitting an exponential equation of the form

$$y = a(10)^{kx}$$

to a given table of values of x and y is quite similar to that just discussed. We again take the common logarithms of both sides, obtaining

$$\log y = \log a + kx.$$

This is a *linear* relation between x and $\log y$, and if we let $\log y = v$, it becomes

$$v = kx + \log a,$$

where again $\log a$ is a constant $(= L)$. It follows that *if the relation between x and y is of the form y = a(10)^{kx}, that between x and $\log y$ is linear.* We may then proceed as follows:

Step 1. Make a new table in which the entries are x and $\log y$, denoting $\log y$ by v.

Step 2. Plot the points (x,v) on rectangular coordinate paper. If they tend to lie in a straight line, the equation y = a(10)^{kx} is applicable.

Step 3. Fit a straight line v = kx + L to this set of data, and then write down the required equation y = a(10)^{kx} after determining a from the relation L = $\log a$.

Example

Show that an equation of the form $y = a(10)^{kx}$ is suitable for the data given below, and find proper values for a and k.

x	1	2	3	4	5	6	7	8
y	0.72	1.08	1.68	3.24	5.28	8.64	13.8	22.6

Solution

By taking the logarithms of the given values of y we construct the table:

x	1	2	3	4	5	6	7	8
$v = \log y$	-0.1427	0.0334	0.2253	0.5106	0.7226	0.9365	1.1399	1.3541

The student may verify that these points when plotted tend to lie along a line. We fit a line to them in the usual way, obtaining

$$v = 0.2204x - 0.3944.$$

This is of the form $v = kx + L$, where $k = 0.2204$ and

$$L = \log a = -0.3944 = 9.6056 - 10.$$

From tables we find that $a = 0.4033$. The required empirical relation between x and y is then

$$y = 0.4033 \, (10)^{0.2204x}.$$

The graph of this equation and the given points are shown in Fig. 14-8.

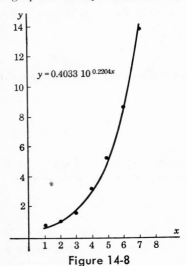

Figure 14-8

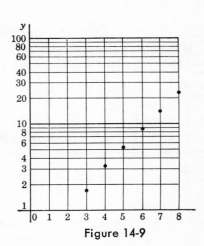

Figure 14-9

It is often convenient to use the exponential equation in the form $y = ae^{kx}$, where e is the base of natural logarithms. In the above example we may replace 10 by $e^{2.303}$ and thus transform the result into the form

$$y = 0.4033 \, (e^{2.303})^{0.2204x};$$

then, since $(e^m)^n = e^{mn}$, we obtain the result

$$y = 0.4033 e^{0.5076x}.$$

Of course the result can also be easily expressed in the general exponential form $y = ab^x$. Thus since

$$10^{0.2204x} = (10^{0.2204})^x = 1.661^x$$

the above result can be written in the form

$$y = 0.4033 \, (1.661)^x.$$

In practice it is usually desirable to use either 10 or e as the base.

The test for applicability of the formula $y = a(10)^{kx}$ can be made more quickly by plotting the given data directly on *semilogarithmic coordinate paper*, as is done in Fig. 14-9, instead of looking up the logarithms of the given values of y and using ordinary paper. As shown in the figure, this paper has uniformly spaced vertical rulings but logarithmically spaced horizontal rulings. Plotting the given points (x,y) on it is of course equivalent to plotting the points $(x, \log y)$ on ordinary paper. If the points tend to lie on a line, the equation $y = a(10)^{kx}$ (or ae^{kx}) is applicable.

PROBLEMS

In Probs. 1, 2, and 3, show that an equation of the form $y = ax^n$ is applicable, and find values for a and n.

1.

x	1	2	3	4	5	6	7	8
y	0.54	1.42	2.68	3.92	5.66	7.34	9.28	11.4

2.

x	2	4	6	8	10	12	14	16
y	3.6	5.5	7.1	8.3	9.4	10.5	11.5	12.4

3.

x	1	2	3	4	5	6
y	26.4	9.3	5.2	3.6	2.5	1.9

In Probs. 4, 5, and 6, show that an equation of the form $y = a(10)^{kx}$ is applicable, and find values for a and k. Express the final result also in the form $y = ae^{k'x}$.

4.

x	1	2	3	4	5	6
y	1.3	2.8	6.2	13.8	33.6	64.2

5.

x	0	1	2	3	4	5	6
y	42	26	16	10	7	4	3

6.

x	0	2	5	8	12	16
y	80	59	35	21	10	5

7. The time t (seconds) required for an object to fall a distance s (feet) was observed and the data recorded as shown below. Show that an equation of the form $t = as^n$ is applicable, and fit such an equation to the data.

s	5	10	15	20	25	30	35	40
t	0.58	0.84	1.03	1.19	1.34	1.47	1.60	1.71

8. In a certain chemical reaction it was found that out of an initial 60 grams of a certain substance the amount M remaining after t min. was as given below. Show that an equation of the form $M = a(10)^{kt}$ is applicable, and fit such an equation to the data. Express the result also in the form $M = ae^{k't}$.

t	0	3	6	9	12	15	18	21
M	60	38.2	24.4	15.6	9.9	6.4	4.1	2.6

9. The air resistance R (pounds) against an automobile was found to vary with the speed V (miles per hour) as shown below. Show that an equation of the form $R = aV^n$ is applicable, and find values for a and n.

V	10	20	30	40	50	60
R	8	29	72	128	197	274

10. The number N of bacteria per unit volume in a culture, at the end of t hr. was found to be as follows:

t	1	2	3	4	5	6	7	8
N	52	64	76	95	114	130	158	187

Show that the equation $N = a(10)^{kt}$ is applicable, and find values for a and k. Use the result to estimate the value of N when $t = 5.4$.

11. The pressure of a gas expanding adiabatically was found to vary with its volume as follows:

v	2.0	2.6	4.2	4.6	5.2	6.0
P	138	96	49	43	36	30

Show that a relation of the form $P = av^n$ is applicable, and determine a and n.

14-8. *Linear type. Method of least squares.*

It has been pointed out in previous sections that when one fits a straight line to a given set of data by the method of average points he obtains a line for which the algebraic sum of the residuals is zero. There are indefinitely many such lines; some of them give a good fit, and some do not. In accordance with the discussion on page 220, one may calculate the sum of the *squares* of the residuals and use the magnitude of this quantity as an indication of the goodness of fit.

The method of least squares gives the line for which *the sum of the squares of the residuals is a minimum.* There is only one such line for a given set of points, so the result does not depend upon any choice of groups. In this section we shall show how the equations for determining the constants are set up, reserving the proof for a later section. We shall use in this illustration the data from the example on page 218 in order that we may be able to compare the results. The data are as follows:

x	1	2	3	4	5	6	7	8	9	10
y	1.48	1.76	2.78	3.32	3.86	4.15	4.75	5.66	6.18	6.86

Assuming that $y = mx + b$, we write down two sets of equations: The first set, shown on the left below, is obtained by substituting the given coordinates for x and y in $y = mx + b$; the equations of the second set, shown on the right, are formed by multiplying both sides of each equation of the first set by the coefficient of m in it.

$$1.48 = m + b \qquad\qquad 1.48 = m + b$$
$$1.76 = 2m + b \qquad\qquad 3.52 = 4m + 2b$$
$$2.78 = 3m + b \qquad\qquad 8.34 = 9m + 3b$$
$$3.32 = 4m + b \qquad\quad 13.28 = 16m + 4b$$
$$3.86 = 5m + b \qquad\quad 19.30 = 25m + 5b$$
$$4.15 = 6m + b \qquad\quad 24.90 = 36m + 6b$$
$$4.75 = 7m + b \qquad\quad 33.25 = 49m + 7b$$
$$5.66 = 8m + b \qquad\quad 45.28 = 64m + 8b$$
$$6.18 = 9m + b \qquad\quad 55.62 = 81m + 9b$$
$$\underline{6.86 = 10m + b} \qquad \underline{68.60 = 100m + 10b}$$
$$\mathbf{40.80 = 55m + 10b} \qquad \mathbf{273.57 = 385m + 55b}$$

$$\left.\begin{array}{l} 40.80 = 55m + 10b \\ 273.57 = 385m + 55b \end{array}\right\} m = 0.596, \qquad b = 0.802.$$

We then add the two sets of equations, as indicated above, and solve the resulting two equations for m and b. In this case the best fitting line has the equation

$$y = 0.596x + 0.802.$$

If we divide both sides of the equation $40.80 = 55m + 10b$ (which was obtained by adding the group on the left above) by 10, we get

$$4.08 = 5.5m + b.$$

The average point of the given set is of course (5.5,4.08), and this equation states the condition that the line $y = mx + b$ pass through this point. It follows that the line $y = 0.596x + 0.802$, which we have called the *best fitting line*, is one of the many lines for which the algebraic sum of the residuals is zero—it is the one for which, at the same time, the sum of the squares of the residuals is as small as possible. The student should plot the given points, draw this line, and compare the result with Fig. 14-2, which was obtained for the same data by the method of average points.

14-9. The symbol Σ. In order to simplify the equations of the next section, we introduce the following notation: Given a set of data (x_1,y_1), (x_2,y_2), $\cdots$, (x_n,y_n), we shall denote the sum of all the x's by Σx and the sum of all the y's by Σy; that is,

$$\Sigma x \equiv x_1 + x_2 + \cdots + x_n,$$
$$\Sigma y \equiv y_1 + y_2 + \cdots + y_n.$$

Using this convenient notation, we may write the coordinates of the average point of the set as $(\Sigma x/n, \Sigma y/n)$.

Similarly, we shall denote the sum of the squares of the abscissas by Σx^2, the sum of the products of the abscissas by the corresponding ordinates by Σxy, etc.

14-10. *Derivation of equations for method of least squares.* If the points (x_1, y_1), (x_2, y_2), $\cdots$, (x_n, y_n) are fitted by the line $y = mx + b$, the residuals are

$$r_1 = y_1 - (mx_1 + b)$$
$$r_2 = y_2 - (mx_2 + b)$$
$$\cdots\cdots\cdots\cdots\cdots$$
$$r_n = y_n - (mx_n + b).$$

The squares of the residuals are

$$r_1{}^2 = y_1{}^2 - 2my_1x_1 - 2y_1b + m^2x_1{}^2 + 2mx_1b + b^2$$
$$r_2{}^2 = y_2{}^2 - 2my_2x_2 - 2y_2b + m^2x_2{}^2 + 2mx_2b + b^2$$
$$\cdots\cdots\cdots\cdots\cdots\cdots\cdots\cdots\cdots\cdots\cdots\cdots\cdots$$
$$r_n{}^2 = y_n{}^2 - 2my_nx_n - 2y_nb + m^2x_n{}^2 + 2mx_nb + b^2.$$

Adding these, and arranging the right-hand member in the form of a quadratic expression in b, we have

$$\Sigma r^2 = nb^2 + 2(m\Sigma x - \Sigma y)b + (m^2\Sigma x^2 - 2m\Sigma xy + \Sigma y^2).$$

If we should plot Σr^2 against b, the graph would be a parabola lying entirely above the b-axis (since Σr^2 is certainly positive); the parabola would open upward since the coefficient of b^2 is positive, and its minimum point would be at

$$b = -\frac{m\Sigma x - \Sigma y}{n}.^*$$

This implies that b and m must satisfy the relation

(1) $$\Sigma y = m\Sigma x + nb$$

in order that the sum of the squares of the residuals may be a minimum. Observe that this is precisely the equation obtained on page 231 by adding the equations in the left-hand column.

$*$ The graph of the equation $y = Ax^2 + Bx + C$ is a parabola with its axis parallel to the y-axis. If $A > 0$, it opens upward and has a minimum point (the vertex) at $x = -B/2A$.

Observe also that upon dividing both sides of the above equation by n we have

$$\frac{\Sigma y}{n} = m\, \frac{\Sigma x}{n} + b,$$

which is the condition that the average point of the group $(\Sigma x/n, \Sigma y/n)$ be on the line.

If we arrange the expression for the sum of the squares of the residuals in the form of a quadratic in m, we have

$$\Sigma r^2 = (\Sigma x^2)m^2 + 2(b\Sigma x - \Sigma xy)m + (\Sigma y^2 - 2b\Sigma y + nb^2).$$

For a minimum value of Σr^2 we must have

$$m = -\,\frac{b\Sigma x - \Sigma xy}{\Sigma x^2},$$

which implies that m and b must also satisfy the relation

$$\text{(2)} \qquad\qquad \Sigma xy = m\Sigma x^2 + b\Sigma x.$$

This is the equation obtained by adding the right-hand column on page 231. The two equations (1) and (2) determine uniquely the values of m and b in the equation $y = mx + b$ in order that Σr^2 shall be a minimum.

PROBLEMS

For each of the following sets of data find the best fitting straight line using the method of least squares. Plot the points, and draw the line.

1.

x	1	2	3	4	5	6
y	-2.9	-1.5	-0.4	1.2	2.5	3.5

2.

x	1	2	3	4	5	6	7
y	15.8	15.2	14.5	13.8	12.9	12.3	11.5

3.

x	0	3	6	9	12	15
y	2.4	4.0	5.8	7.8	9.3	11.2

4. The pressure P, in centimeters of mercury, of a fixed quantity of gas was found to vary with the centigrade temperature T, when its volume was held constant, as follows:

T	20	30	40	50	60	70	80
P	26.8	29.0	30.7	32.3	33.8	35.6	37.2

Express P in terms of T, using the method of least squares.

In each of the following problems the given data can be fitted by an equation of the form $y = ax^n$ or $y = a(10)^{kx}$. Determine which equation is applicable, and use the method of least squares to fit the data.

5.

x	1	2	3	4	5	6
y	2.5	7.7	15.2	24.8	35.2	48.0

6.

x	2	5	7	8	10	12
y	34	42	46	47	50	52

7.

x	1	2	3	4	5	6
y	3.96	5.92	9.18	13.7	20.8	31.6

8.

x	5	10	15	20	25	30
y	32	21	14	9	6	4

SOLID
ANALYTIC GEOMETRY

CHAPTER 15

PRELIMINARY DEFINITIONS AND FORMULAS

15-1. Rectangular coordinates in space. We now wish to extend our rectangular coordinate system to three dimensions. For this purpose we take three mutually perpendicular lines through a point O which we call the *origin*. These lines are called the x-, y-, and z-axes, respectively, and positive directions on them are chosen as indicated by the arrows in Fig. 15-1.

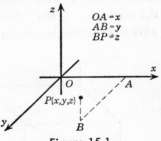

$OA = x$
$AB = y$
$BP = z$

$P(x,y,z)$

Figure 15-1

For the present we may regard the x- and y-axes as *horizontal* lines and thus think of their plane, which is called the *xy-plane*, as a horizontal plane. We may then regard the z-axis as a *vertical* line. The plane determined by the x- and z-axes is called the *xz-plane*, and that determined by the y- and z-axes is called the *yz-plane*. These *coordinate planes*, which intersect at the origin, may be visualized by thinking of the floor and two adjacent walls of a room. The floor is the xy-plane and the two walls are the xz- and yz-planes. The walls intersect along the vertical z-axis.

We locate a point P in space by giving its directed distances from the three coordinate planes. Its distance from the yz-plane, which is measured along or parallel to the x-axis, is its *x-coordinate*. Similar statements apply to the y- and z-coordinates. We write the coordinates of a point P in the order (x,y,z).

The coordinate planes divide space into eight octants which are characterized by the signs of the coordinates. The octant in which all three coordinates are positive is called the *first octant*. The

237

others are usually not numbered. In Fig. 15-2, A is in the first octant; B is in the octant in which the coordinates have the signs $(- + +)$.

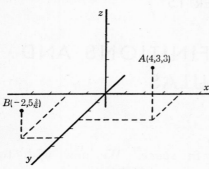

Figure 15-2

15-2. Construction of figures. One of the most difficult tasks confronting the student of solid analytic geometry is that of drawing the figures. There are several ways of doing this, but none of them is entirely satisfactory. The method that we shall employ is illustrated by Fig. 15-3. The x- and z-axes are perpendicular to each other. The y-axis makes an angle of 135° with each of these in this figure, but it may be drawn at some other angle. Equal units are used on the x- and z-axes, but the unit on the y-axis is only about 0.7 as long. This "foreshortening" of the dimensions along this axis decreases the amount of distortion.

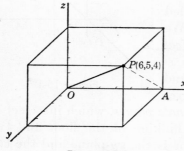

Figure 15-3

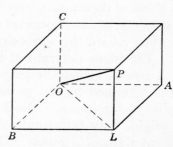

Figure 15-4

In the figure, we have plotted the point $P(6,5,4)$ and have drawn the rectangular box in which OP is a diagonal. Observe now that while OP is actually longer than OA in space it appears shorter in the figure. In space, the triangle OAP is a right triangle in which OP is the hypotenuse; the right angle is angle OAP. It is thus evident that the student must learn to visualize the actual space relations by thinking of the figure in space. Any representation of a three-dimensional object by a drawing made upon a flat sheet of paper is somewhat of a makeshift and is intended to serve only as an aid in visualizing the true relations in space.

15-3. The distance formula. Figure 15-4 represents a rectangular box whose edges are OA, OB, and OC. In order to find the length of a diagonal OP, we note that in right triangle OAL

$$\overline{OL}^2 = \overline{OA}^2 + \overline{AL}^2.$$

Then, since OP is the hypotenuse of right triangle OLP, we have

$$\overline{OP}^2 = \overline{OL}^2 + \overline{LP}^2$$
$$= \overline{OA}^2 + \overline{AL}^2 + \overline{LP}^2.$$

But $AL = OB$, and $LP = OC$. Hence we can say that

$$\overline{OP}^2 = \overline{OA}^2 + \overline{OB}^2 + \overline{OC}^2.$$

The square of the diagonal of a rectangular box is equal to the sum

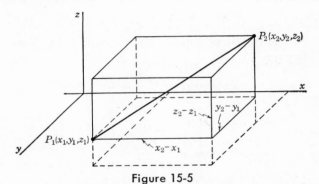

Figure 15-5

of the squares of its three edges. If O is the origin and P has coordinates (x,y,z), then $OA = x$, $OB = y$, and $OC = z$. The distance from O to P is then

$$OP = \sqrt{x^2 + y^2 + z^2}.$$

Now let $P_1(x_1,y_1,z_1)$ and $P_2(x_2,y_2,z_2)$ be any two points, and let it be required to find the undirected distance P_1P_2. As shown in Fig. 15-5, the segment P_1P_2 may be regarded as a diagonal of a rectangular box whose edges have the lengths $x_2 - x_1$, $y_2 - y_1$, and $z_2 - z_1$, respectively. Denoting the required undirected distance by d, we have immediately

$$\boldsymbol{d = \sqrt{(x_2 - x_1)^2 + (y_2 - y_1)^2 + (z_2 - z_1)^2}.}$$

15-4. *Direction angles and direction cosines of the radius vector OP.* The directed segment *OP* drawn from the origin to any point $P(x,y,z)$ is called the *radius vector* of *P*. If we denote its length by ρ, then

$$\varrho = OP = \sqrt{x^2 + y^2 + z^2}.$$

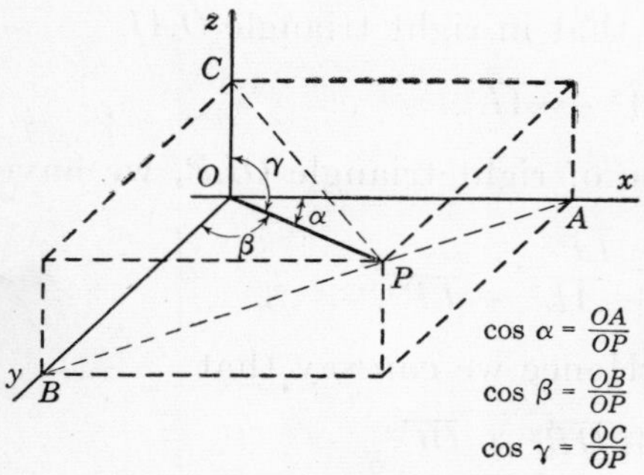

The angles α, β, and γ which *OP* makes with the positive directions on the *x*-, *y*-, and *z*-axes, respectively, are called the *direction angles* of *OP*. In Fig. 15-6 they are

$\cos \alpha = \frac{OA}{OP}$

$\cos \beta = \frac{OB}{OP}$

$\cos \gamma = \frac{OC}{OP}$

Figure 15-6

$\alpha = $ angle AOP;
$\beta = $ angle BOP;
$\gamma = $ angle COP.

Each of these is a positive angle not greater than 180°.

The cosines of the direction angles are called the *direction cosines* of *OP*. They are

$$\cos \alpha = \frac{OA}{OP} = \frac{x}{\rho};$$

$$\cos \beta = \frac{OB}{OP} = \frac{y}{\rho};$$

$$\cos \gamma = \frac{OC}{OP} = \frac{z}{\rho}.$$

If we square the direction cosines, and add, we have

$$\cos^2 \alpha + \cos^2 \beta + \cos^2 \gamma = \frac{x^2}{\rho^2} + \frac{y^2}{\rho^2} + \frac{z^2}{\rho^2}$$
$$= \frac{x^2 + y^2 + z^2}{\rho^2} = \frac{\rho^2}{\rho^2} = 1.$$

The sum of the squares of the direction cosines of OP is equal to one.

If *P* is in the first octant, its coordinates are all positive. In this case the direction cosines of *OP* are all positive, and its direction angles are all less than 90°. If *P* has one or more negative coordinates, the corresponding direction cosines are negative. The direction angles having negative cosines are between 90 and 180° (including the latter value).

Example

In Fig. 15-7, the point P has coordinates $(-3,5,4)$. The distance OP is

$$\rho = \sqrt{(-3)^2 + 5^2 + 4^2} = \sqrt{50} = 5\sqrt{2}.$$

The direction cosines and direction angles of OP are

$$\cos \alpha = \frac{x}{\rho} = \frac{-3}{5\sqrt{2}} = -0.42426; \qquad \alpha = 115°6'.$$

$$\cos \beta = \frac{y}{\rho} = \frac{5}{5\sqrt{2}} = 0.70711; \qquad \beta = 45°.$$

$$\cos \gamma = \frac{z}{\rho} = \frac{4}{5\sqrt{2}} = 0.56568; \qquad \gamma = 55°33'.$$

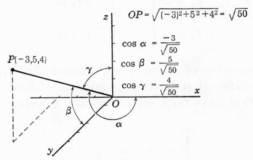

Figure 15-7

15-5. *Components of a force.* A force may be represented in magnitude and direction by an arrow or *vector*. The vector is drawn in the direction of the force, its length representing, to some convenient scale, the magnitude of the force.

In problems of mechanics it is frequently necessary to find the magnitudes of the components of a given force, in the directions of the coordinate axes. The procedure is illustrated by the following:

Example

A pull of 50 lb. is exerted in the direction determined by the line OP in Fig. 15-8. Find the components of this pull in the directions of the coordinate axes.

Solution

The 50-lb. force along OP is represented by the arrow or vector shown in the figure, its length representing 50 lb. to some scale. The required components are then represented by the lengths of the edges of the rectangular box drawn as shown. If the magnitude of the given force is F, and if the components are denoted by F_x, F_y, and F_z, respectively, then

$$F_x = F \cos \alpha; \qquad F_y = F \cos \beta; \qquad F_z = F \cos \gamma.$$

In this case the direction cosines of OP are found as follows:

$$OP = \sqrt{6^2 + 4^2 + 3^2} = \sqrt{61};$$

$$\cos \alpha = \frac{6}{\sqrt{61}}; \qquad \cos \beta = \frac{4}{\sqrt{61}}; \qquad \cos \gamma = \frac{3}{\sqrt{61}}.$$

The magnitudes of the components of the 50-lb. force are then

$$F_x = 50 \left(\frac{6}{\sqrt{61}} \right) = 38.4 \text{ lb.}$$

$$F_y = 50 \left(\frac{4}{\sqrt{61}} \right) = 25.6 \text{ lb.}$$

$$F_z = 50 \left(\frac{3}{\sqrt{61}} \right) = 19.2 \text{ lb.}$$

In various branches of science, one often deals with *vector quantities;* i.e., quantities that have not magnitude alone (such as temperature) but that have both *magnitude* and *direction*, such as force

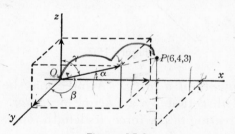

Figure 15-8

or velocity. Such quantities can be represented by vectors, and it is often necessary to compute the component of such a vector in a given direction.

PROBLEMS

1. In each of the following, plot the point P, and draw the radius vector OP; find its length, direction cosines, and direction angles:

(a) $P(2,2,4)$.   (b) $P(-12,-3,4)$.   (c) $P(4,-3,1)$.
(d) $P(5,5,-5)$.   (e) $P(-3,2,-6)$.   (f) $P(6,-3,-6)$.

2. For a certain radius vector OP, $\cos \alpha = \frac{2}{3}$ and $\cos \beta = \frac{1}{3}$. Find the two possible values for $\cos \gamma$, and draw the figure.

3. A line is drawn from the origin so as to make equal angles with the three coordinate axes. Find its direction cosines, and draw the line. HINT: The point $(1,1,1)$ is on the line.

4. Describe and sketch the locus of points (x,y,z) that satisfy the following conditions:

(a) $x = 4$.   (b) $x = 0$ and $z = 0$.   (c) $x = 3$ and $y = 4$.
(d) $z = x$.   (e) $x + y = 4$.   (f) $x + y = 4$ and $z = 0$.

5. Determine the coordinates of the point that is symmetrical with respect to the point $P(x,y,z)$ with respect to

(a) The origin.   (b) The xy-plane.   (c) The x-axis.

6. In each of the following, plot the given points, draw the line joining them, and compute its length:

(a) $A(2,6,1)$ $B(8,3,7)$.   (b) $P(-4,5,2)$ $Q(2,0,5)$.
(c) $M(-4,-3,2)$ $N(4,1,-6)$.

7. Draw each of the following triangles, and find the lengths of its sides:
(a) $A(0,4,1)$ $B(6,5,3)$ $C(10,0,6)$.
(b) $P(-3,-2,3)$ $Q(0,3,0)$ $R(4,0,0)$.

8. Draw each of the following triangles, and show that it is a right triangle:
(a) $A(2,6,2)$ $B(5,8,5)$ $C(8,2,6)$.
(b) $P(-4,-2,5)$ $Q(4,-1,8)$ $R(6,4,1)$.

9. Show that the coordinates of the mid-point of a segment

$$P_1(x_1,y_1,z_1)\ P_2(x_2,y_2,z_2)$$

are

$$\tfrac{1}{2}(x_1 + x_2),\qquad \tfrac{1}{2}(y_1 + y_2),\qquad \tfrac{1}{2}(z_1 + z_2).$$

10. Find the coordinates of the points that divide the segment $A(2,7,1)$ $B(8,-2,5)$ into three equal parts.

11. Find the equation of the surface all points of which are at a distance of 5 units from the origin. What is this surface?

12. Find the equation of the surface all points of which are at a distance of 5 units from the point $C(3,2,5)$. Describe the surface.

13. A point $P(x,y,z)$ moves so that its distance from $F(4,0,0)$ is always equal to its distance from the yz-plane. Find the equation of the surface on which it moves. Describe the surface, and try to sketch it.

14. A point $P(x,y,z)$ moves so that its distance from $A(2,5,1)$ is always equal to its distance from $B(8,1,6)$. Find the equation of the surface on which it moves, and describe the surface.

15. Find the equation of the locus of a point the sum of whose undirected distances from $(4,0,0)$ and $(-4,0,0)$ is equal to 10.

16. Find the coordinates of the point on the x-axis that is equidistant from $P(4,3,1)$ and $Q(-2,-6,2)$.

17. In each of the following, a force of the given magnitude acts away from the origin along the line OP.   Find its components along the axes.

(a) 100 lb.; $P(6,6,3)$.   (b) 70 lb.; $P(12,-4,-3)$.

(c) 60 lb.; $P(3,0,-4)$.   (d) 200 lb.; $P(-6,3,5)$.

18. Pulls of 27 lb. and 35 lb. are applied to the block as shown in Fig. 15-9. Find the total vertical pull, and also the resultant pulls in the x- and y-directions. What is the magnitude, and what are the direction angles, of a single force that would produce the same effect as these two forces?

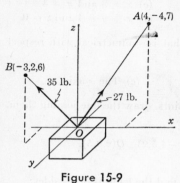

Figure 15-9

19. The same as Prob. 18 but with forces of 44 lb. and 20 lb. along OA and OB, respectively, the coordinates of A and B being $(9,6,2)$ and $(-8,6,0)$.

20. Forces of 44 lb., 35 lb., and 30 lb. act away from the origin along the lines OA, OB, and OC, respectively.   The coordinates of A, B, and C are $A(9,-2,-6)$, $B(-6,3,2)$, $C(3,4,0)$.   Find the algebraic sum of the components of these forces along each coordinate axis.   Find the magnitude and direction angles of the single force having these components.   This force is called the *resultant* of the given set of forces.

15-6. *Direction cosines of any directed line.*   Let l (Fig. 15-10) be any directed line in space.   The direction chosen as positive

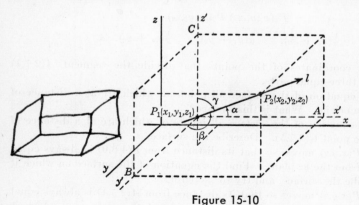

Figure 15-10

may be indicated by an arrowhead as shown in the figure.   We define the *direction angles* of l as follows:

Let $P_1(x_1,y_1,z_1)$ and $P_2(x_2,y_2,z_2)$ be any two points on l such that the directed segment P_1P_2 is positive.   Through P_1 draw lines P_1x', P_1y', and P_1z' parallel to, and in the positive directions of, the x-, y-, and z-axes, respectively.   Then the direction angles of l are α, β, and γ, where

$$\alpha = \text{angle } x'P_1P_2; \qquad \beta = \text{angle } y'P_1P_2; \qquad \gamma = \text{angle } z'P_1P_2.$$

Each of these is a positive angle not greater than $180°$.

The cosines of the above direction angles are called the *direction cosines* of the directed line l.   In order to compute their values we first find the distance P_1P_2 which we may denote by d:

$$d = \sqrt{(x_2 - x_1)^2 + (y_2 - y_1)^2 + (z_2 - z_1)^2}.$$

We then see from the figure that

$$\cos \alpha = \frac{P_1A}{P_1P_2} = \frac{x_2 - x_1}{d};$$

$$\cos \beta = \frac{P_1B}{P_1P_2} = \frac{y_2 - y_1}{d};$$

$$\cos \gamma = \frac{P_1C}{P_1P_2} = \frac{z_2 - z_1}{d}.$$

Since d is positive, each of the above direction cosines is positive or negative depending upon the sign of the numerator.   It should be observed that the effect of reversing the positive direction on the line is to change the signs of all the direction cosines—and to replace the direction angles by their supplements.

Finally, if we square the direction cosines, and add, we have the important relation

$$\cos^2 \alpha + \cos^2 \beta + \cos^2 \gamma = 1.$$

Example

Find the direction cosines of the line determined by the points $P_1(1, -2, 8)$ and $P_2(8, 2, 3)$ if the positive direction is from P_1 to P_2.

Solution (Fig. 15-11)

$$d = \sqrt{(8 - 1)^2 + [2 - (-2)]^2 + (3 - 8)^2}$$
$$= \sqrt{90} = 3\sqrt{10};$$

$$\cos \alpha = \frac{8 - 1}{3\sqrt{10}} = \frac{7\sqrt{10}}{30} = 0.73786;$$

$$\cos \beta = \frac{2 - (-2)}{3\sqrt{10}} = \frac{4\sqrt{10}}{30} = 0.42164;$$

$$\cos \gamma = \frac{3 - 8}{3\sqrt{10}} = \frac{-5\sqrt{10}}{30} = -0.52705.$$

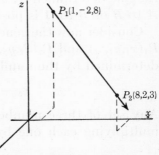

Figure 15-11

The value of cos γ is negative because γ is between 90 and 180°. If the positive direction had been from P_2 to P_1, the signs of the direction cosines would have been reversed.

15-7. Direction numbers. If a point moves from A to B along the line shown in Fig. 15-12, it moves 6 units in the positive x-direction, 3 units in the *negative* y-direction, and 2 units in the positive z-direction, as indicated by the dotted lines. The numbers 6, -3, and 2, written in the form

$$6: -3 : 2$$

may be used to define the *direction* of the line. They fix its direction by indicating that for every 6 units moved in the x-direction a

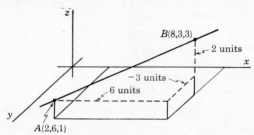

Figure 15-12

point traveling along the line must move -3 units in the y-direction and 2 units in the z-direction. Any set of three numbers proportional to these would serve equally well. Thus if the point moved 12 units in the x-direction, it would move -6 units in the y-direction and 4 units in the z-direction. The numbers $12: -6:4$ would then define the *same* direction. If the point travels from B to A, instead of from A to B, all the above distances have opposite signs; i.e., the numbers $-6: +3: -2$ also fix the direction of the line determined by A and B. We do not here specify whether A to B or B to A is positive.

Consider now the general case of a line determined by two points $P_1(x_1,y_1,z_1)$ and $P_2(x_2,y_2,z_2)$. The direction of the line in space is determined by the numbers

$$x_2 - x_1 : y_2 - y_1 : z_2 - z_1.$$

Any set of three numbers that could be obtained from these by multiplying each one by the same positive or negative constant

$k(\neq 0)$ would serve equally well in fixing the direction of the line. Any such set of numbers is called a set of *direction numbers* of the line.

In the plane, we have determined a line by specifying two points on it, or by giving one point and its direction (inclination or slope). In space, we may correspondingly fix a line by specifying two points on it, or by giving one point and a set of direction numbers.

Example

Draw the line passing through $A(-2,6,5)$ with direction numbers 2: -1: -1.

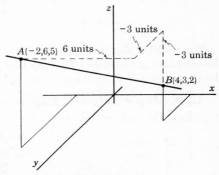

Solution (Fig. 15-13)

Starting at A, we may obtain another point on the line by going 2 units in the x-direction, -1 unit in the y-direction, and -1 unit in the z-direction. Or, if more convenient, we may use any multiple of these dis-tances. In the figure we have used

Figure 15-13

6, -3, and -3 units, respectively, thereby arriving at a point $B(4,3,2)$ which is on the required line.

It is obvious that any set of three numbers, not all zero, may be regarded in the above way as defining the direction of a line in space. They are proportional to the direction cosines in accord-ance with the following theorem, proof of which is left to the student:

Theorem.   *If a line has direction numbers $a:b:c$, its direction cosines are*

$$\cos \alpha = \frac{a}{\pm \sqrt{a^2 + b^2 + c^2}},$$

$$\cos \beta = \frac{b}{\pm \sqrt{a^2 + b^2 + c^2}},$$

$$\cos \gamma = \frac{c}{\pm \sqrt{a^2 + b^2 + c^2}},$$

where the signs of the denominators are all $+$ or all $-$, depending on which direction along the line is chosen as positive.

Example

The line shown in Fig. 15-12 has direction numbers $6: -3 : 2$. If the positive direction is from A to B, the corresponding direction cosines are

$$\cos \alpha = \frac{6}{+\sqrt{6^2 + (-3)^2 + 2^2}} = +\frac{6}{7};$$

$$\cos \beta = \frac{-3}{+7} = -\frac{3}{7};$$

$$\cos \gamma = \frac{2}{+7} = +\frac{2}{7}.$$

The positive sign was chosen for the radical because α and γ are obviously less than 90° and their cosines are therefore positive. If the positive direction had been from B to A, the negative sign would have been chosen.

15-8. *Angle between two directed lines.* Two lines drawn at random in space do not, in general, intersect. We, however, speak of the angle between such lines in accordance with the following:

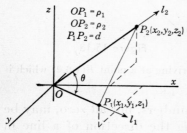

$OP_1 = \rho_1$
$OP_2 = \rho_2$
$P_1P_2 = d$
$P_2(x_2, y_2, z_2)$
$P_1(x_1, y_1, z_1)$

Figure 15-14

Definition. *The angle between two directed lines in space is equal to the angle between the positive directions of two lines that are parallel, respectively, to the given lines, have the same positive directions, and intersect at a point O.*

Without loss of generality we may take the point O in the above definition as the origin. The problem of finding the angle between any two directed lines in space then reduces to that of finding the angle θ between the positive directions of two lines l_1 and l_2 through the origin, as shown in Fig. 15-14. The cosine of this angle may be expressed in terms of the direction cosines of l_1 and l_2 as follows:

Choose a point $P_1(x_1, y_1, z_1)$ on l_1, and a point $P_2(x_2, y_2, z_2)$ on l_2; let $OP_1 = \rho_1$, $OP_2 = \rho_2$, and $P_1P_2 = d$. Then, using the cosine law, we have the relation

$$d^2 = \rho_1{}^2 + \rho_2{}^2 - 2\rho_1\rho_2 \cos \theta.$$

Solving this equation for $\cos \theta$, we have

$$\cos \theta = \frac{\rho_1{}^2 + \rho_2{}^2 - d^2}{2\rho_1\rho_2}.$$

But

$$\rho_1{}^2 = x_1{}^2 + y_1{}^2 + z_1{}^2; \qquad \rho_2{}^2 = x_2{}^2 + y_2{}^2 + z_2{}^2;$$
$$d^2 = (x_2 - x_1)^2 + (y_2 - y_1)^2 + (z_2 - z_1)^2.$$

Substituting these relations into the numerator of the above expression, and simplifying, we find that

$$\cos\theta = \frac{x_1 x_2 + y_1 y_2 + z_1 z_2}{\rho_1 \rho_2}$$
$$= \frac{x_1}{\rho_1}\frac{x_2}{\rho_2} + \frac{y_1}{\rho_1}\frac{y_2}{\rho_2} + \frac{z_1}{\rho_1}\frac{z_2}{\rho_2}.$$

Now, if the direction angles of l_1 are α_1, β_1, γ_1 and those of l_2 are α_2, β_2, γ_2, it is obvious that

$$\frac{x_1}{\rho_1} = \cos\alpha_1 \qquad \text{and} \qquad \frac{x_2}{\rho_2} = \cos\alpha_2;$$

$$\frac{y_1}{\rho_1} = \cos\beta_1 \qquad \text{and} \qquad \frac{y_2}{\rho_2} = \cos\beta_2;$$

$$\frac{z_1}{\rho_1} = \cos\gamma_1 \qquad \text{and} \qquad \frac{z_2}{\rho_2} = \cos\gamma_2.$$

Making these substitutions we finally have the result

$$\cos\theta = \cos\alpha_1 \cos\alpha_2 + \cos\beta_1 \cos\beta_2 + \cos\gamma_1 \cos\gamma_2.$$

Example

The directed line from $A(2,3,5)$ to $B(6,-2,2)$ has the direction cosines

$$\cos\alpha_1 = \frac{4}{\sqrt{50}}; \qquad \cos\beta_1 = \frac{-5}{\sqrt{50}}; \qquad \cos\gamma_1 = \frac{-3}{\sqrt{50}}.$$

The directed line from $C(-2,-2,8)$ to $D(4,1,6)$ has the direction cosines

$$\cos\alpha_2 = \frac{6}{7}; \qquad \cos\beta_2 = \frac{3}{7}; \qquad \cos\gamma_2 = \frac{-2}{7}.$$

The cosine of the angle θ between these lines is

$$\cos\theta = \left(\frac{4}{\sqrt{50}}\right)\left(\frac{6}{7}\right) + \left(-\frac{5}{\sqrt{50}}\right)\left(\frac{3}{7}\right) + \left(-\frac{3}{\sqrt{50}}\right)\left(-\frac{2}{7}\right)$$

$$= \frac{3\sqrt{2}}{14} = 0.30304.$$

$$\theta = 72°22'.$$

Two lines in space are mutually perpendicular if and only if $\theta = 90°$. Since $\cos 90° = 0$, the condition for perpendicularity of l_1 and l_2 is

$$\cos \alpha_1 \cos \alpha_2 + \cos \beta_1 \cos \beta_2 + \cos \gamma_1 \cos \gamma_2 = 0.$$

If, instead of the direction cosines of l_1 and l_2, we have their direction numbers $a_1:b_1:c_1$ and $a_2:b_2:c_2$, respectively, we may first compute the direction cosines and then use the above formula, or we may use directly the equivalent formula

$$\cos \theta = \pm \frac{a_1a_2 + b_1b_2 + c_1c_2}{\sqrt{a_1{}^2 + b_1{}^2 + c_1{}^2} \sqrt{a_2{}^2 + b_2{}^2 + c_2{}^2}}$$

The $+$ or $-$ sign is to be used depending on the choice of positive directions on l_1 and l_2. In terms of direction numbers the condition for perpendicularity becomes

$$a_1a_2 + b_1b_2 + c_1c_2 = 0.$$

Example

Two lines having direction numbers $2:6:-1$ and $4:-1:2$, respectively, are mutually perpendicular, because

$$(4) \cdot (2) + (-1) \cdot (6) + (2) \cdot (-1) = 0.$$

PROBLEMS

1. Draw each of the following lines, and find its direction numbers and direction cosines. The positive direction in each case is from the first given point to the second.

(a) $A(2,1,1)$ $B(6,6,4)$.   (b) $P(-2,3,4)$ $Q(0,1,3)$.
(c) $M(0,-3,2)$ $N(0,1,5)$.   (d) $C(-3,-2,-2)$ $D(6,0,3)$.
(e) $L(0,0,-2)$ $M(4,-4,0)$.   (f) $R(7,4,1)$ $S(1,-2,4)$.

2. In each of the following, a line is determined by the given point and direction numbers. In each case draw the line, and find its direction cosines, assuming the positive direction to be such that $\cos \gamma$ is positive.

(a) $A(2,5,1)$; $2:-2:1$.   (b) $A(-2,2,6)$; $6:3:-2$.
(c) $A(0,5,0)$; $4:-4:3$.   (d) $A(-4,0,-2)$; $2:0:1$.

3. Find the direction cosines of each of the coordinate axes.

4. Two of the direction angles of a certain line are $\alpha = 45°$ and $\beta = 60°$. Find its direction cosines if the positive direction is such that γ is an acute angle.

5. A line goes through $A(-4,6,1)$ and has direction numbers $2:-2:1$. What are the coordinates of the point where this line pierces the yz-plane? The xz-plane?

6. A line goes through $P(4,2,3)$ and has direction numbers $3:2:-1$. What are the coordinates of the point at which it pierces the xy-plane? The xz-plane?

7. A line goes through $P(4,7,2)$ and makes equal angles with the coordinate axes. What are the coordinates of the points at which it pierces the coordinate planes?

8. Find the cosine of the angle between the lines for which direction numbers are

(a) $2:1:-2$; $3:-6:2$.   (b) $7:4:4$; $6:-6:3$.

(c) $5:4:-3$; $1:-1:0$.   (d) $3:-1:-4$; $2:-3:1$.

9. Draw each of the following triangles, and show that it is a right triangle; compute the cosine of the angle at A:

(a) $A(2,7,1)$ $B(8,5,5)$ $C(7,3,4)$.

(b) $A(-2,3,2)$ $B(6,-3,4)$ $C(1,3,-1)$.

(c) $A(-4,-2,1)$ $B(5,-1,5)$ $C(8,4,-3)$.

10. A line l_1 is drawn from the origin to $P(4,-2,4)$, and from P a line l_2 is drawn so as to make equal angles with the coordinate axes. Draw the figure, and compute the angle between l_1 and l_2.

11. What relation must exist between the direction cosines of two lines if the lines are to be parallel?

12. A force of 42 lb. acts along the line AC as shown in Fig. 15-15. Find its component in the direction of AB. HINT: The required component is equal to $42 \cos \theta$.

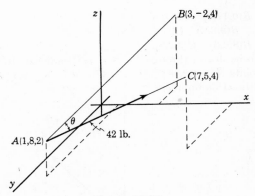

Figure 15-15

13. A force of 36 lb. acts along the line OP drawn from the origin to $P(7,4,4)$. Find the component of this force in the direction of a line making equal angles with the coordinate axes.

14. Show that the direction numbers $a:b:c$ of a line l that is perpendicular to each of two nonparallel lines l_1 and l_2 having direction numbers $a_1:b_1:c_1$ and $a_2:b_2:c_2$, respectively, are

$$a:b:c = \begin{vmatrix} b_1 & c_1 \\ b_2 & c_2 \end{vmatrix} : \begin{vmatrix} c_1 & a_1 \\ c_2 & a_2 \end{vmatrix} : \begin{vmatrix} a_1 & b_1 \\ a_2 & b_2 \end{vmatrix}$$

HINT: The condition that l is perpendicular to both l_1 and l_2 is that

$$aa_1 + bb_1 + cc_1 = 0$$

and $aa_2 + bb_2 + cc_2 = 0$. Solve these equations for a/c and b/c, using determinants.

15. Find the direction numbers of the radius vector that is perpendicular to the plane of OP and OQ in Fig. 15-16.

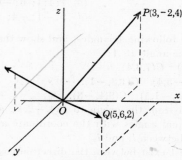

Figure 15-16

16. Draw each of the following triangles, and find the direction numbers of the normals to its plane. Draw the normal from the origin to the plane of the triangle.

(a) $A(8,0,0)$ $B(0,12,0)$ $C(0,0,8)$.

(b) $A(-5,0,0)$ $B(3,8,2)$ $C(-3,-4,8)$.

(c) $A(2,7,1)$ $B(8,2,3)$ $C(3,2,8)$.

17. A line is to be drawn through $P(3,4,4)$ perpendicular to the plane determined by the points $A(-4,2,-1)$ $B(2,-3,0)$ $C(-3,-3,5)$ as shown in Fig. 15-17. Find its direction numbers.

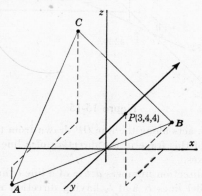

Figure 15-17

CHAPTER 16

PLANES AND LINES

16-1. Normal equation of a plane. A plane may be determined by specifying the length and direction of the normal ON drawn from the origin to the plane. In Fig. 16-1 let the directed length $ON = p$, and let the direction angles of ON be α, β, and γ.

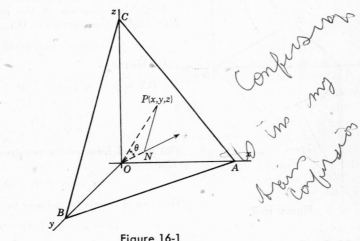

Figure 16-1

We wish now to determine the equation of the plane in terms of these data. For this purpose we let $P(x,y,z)$ be any point in the plane. We denote the directed length OP by ρ and let the direction angles of OP be α_1, β_1, and γ_1. Then, if θ is the angle between the directed segments OP and ON, the triangle OPN is a right triangle in which

$$OP \cos \theta = ON,$$

or

$$\rho \cos \theta = p.$$

Making use of the known formula for $\cos \theta$, we can write this in the form

253

$$\rho(\cos \alpha_1 \cos \alpha + \cos \beta_1 \cos \beta + \cos \gamma_1 \cos \gamma) = p.$$

Now since

$$\rho \cos \alpha_1 = x, \qquad \rho \cos \beta_1 = y, \qquad \text{and} \qquad \rho \cos \gamma_1 = z,$$

we have

(1) $$x \cos \alpha + y \cos \beta + z \cos \gamma = p.$$

This is called the *normal form* of the equation of a plane. It can be used for writing down the equation of a plane when the length and direction of its normal ON are known.

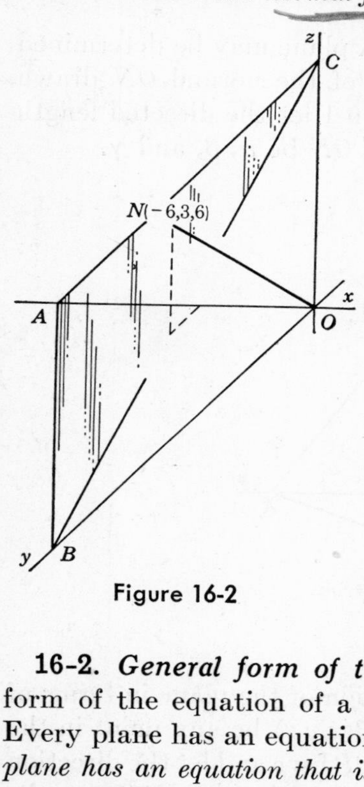

Example

Find the equation of the plane through $N(-6,3,6)$ perpendicular to ON.

Solution (Fig. 16-2)

In this case

$$ON = p = \sqrt{(-6)^2 + 3^2 + 6^2} = 9;$$
$$\cos \alpha = -\tfrac{2}{3};$$
$$\cos \beta = \tfrac{1}{3};$$
$$\cos \gamma = \tfrac{2}{3}.$$

The normal form of the required equation then

$$-\tfrac{2}{3}x + \tfrac{1}{3}y + \tfrac{2}{3}z = 9.$$

This can of course be reduced to

$$2x - y - 2z + 27 = 0.$$

Figure 16-2

16-2. General form of the equation of a plane. The normal form of the equation of a plane is of first degree in x, y, and z. Every plane has an equation of this form; so we can say that *every plane has an equation that is of first degree.* We can easily prove, conversely, that *every equation of first degree in x, y, and z represents a plane.* In fact we have the following:

Theorem: *The locus of every equation of the form*

(2) $$Ax + By + Cz + D = 0$$

in which A, B, and C are not all zero, is a plane. Furthermore, the normal to the plane has direction numbers $A:B:C$.

The proof is as follows: Without altering the locus of (2) we may divide by $\pm \sqrt{A^2 + B^2 + C^2}$, which is certainly not equal to zero. We thus obtain the equation

$$\frac{A}{\pm \sqrt{A^2 + B^2 + C^2}}\, x + \frac{B}{\pm \sqrt{A^2 + B^2 + C^2}}\, y$$
$$+ \frac{C}{\pm \sqrt{A^2 + B^2 + C^2}}\, z + \frac{D}{\pm \sqrt{A^2 + B^2 + C^2}} = 0.$$

Comparing this last equation with the normal form (1), we see that its locus, and hence that of (2), is a *plane* whose normal has the following direction cosines:

$$\cos \alpha = \frac{A}{\pm \sqrt{A^2 + B^2 + C^2}}$$
$$\cos \beta = \frac{B}{\pm \sqrt{A^2 + B^2 + C^2}}$$
$$\cos \gamma = \frac{C}{\pm \sqrt{A^2 + B^2 + C^2}}.$$

s that the numbers $A:B:C$ are direction numbers of the

e equation $Ax + By + Cz + D = 0$ is called the *general form* e equation of a plane. It can evidently be transformed into the normal form by dividing through by $\pm \sqrt{A^2 + B^2 + C^2}$. In doing this we choose the sign of the radical as follows: The distance from the origin to the plane is

$$p = \frac{-D}{\pm \sqrt{A^2 + B^2 + C^2}}.$$

In order that p may be positive, we may agree to take the sign of the radical opposite to that of D if $D \neq 0$. If $D = 0$, the plane goes through the origin and $p = 0$. In this case we agree to take the sign of the radical the same as that of C; this amounts to choosing the positive direction on the normal so that γ is an acute angle. If $C = D = 0$, then $p = 0$ and $\gamma = 90°$. In this case we choose the sign of the radical to agree with that of B, thus making β an acute angle.

16-3. Drawing the plane and its normal. The line in which a given plane intersects a coordinate plane is called the *trace* of the given plane on that coordinate plane. Thus the trace of the plane whose equation is

$$5x + 8y + 10z = 40$$

on the xy-plane is the line AB in Fig. 16-3. Its equation, found by putting $z = 0$ in the equation of the given plane, is

$$5x + 8y = 40.$$

The equations of the traces on the other coordinate planes are

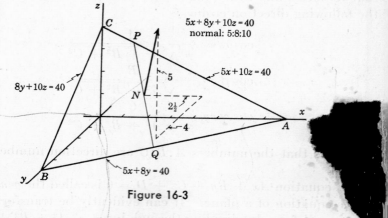

Figure 16-3

found similarly. In making a drawing it is often convenient to represent a plane in space by its traces as illustrated by the figure.

Let it now be required to select a random point on the plane and draw the normal to the plane through this point. If we draw a line from any point P on one trace to any point Q on another trace, the line PQ lies in the plane. If we choose a point N on PQ, this point will lie on the plane.

In order to draw the normal through N, we note that its direction numbers are $5:8:10$ (or any set of numbers proportional to these). In the figure we have obtained another point on the normal by going $2\frac{1}{2}$ units in the x-direction, 4 units in the y-direction, and 5 units in the z-direction, from N.

16-4. Plane parallel to one or more coordinate axes. The general equation of first degree in x, y, and z, is

$$Ax + By + Cz + D = 0,$$

in which A, B, and C are not all zero. We have seen that every such equation represents a plane whose normal has the direction numbers $A:B:C$. Suppose now that $C = 0$. In this case $\cos \gamma = 0$, $\gamma = 90°$, and the plane is parallel to the z-axis.

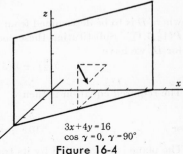

$3x + 4y = 16$
$\cos \gamma = 0$, $\gamma = 90°$
Figure 16-4

Example

The equation $3x + 4y = 16$ represents a plane parallel to the z-axis, and consequently perpendicular to the xy-plane, as shown in Fig. 16-4.

Similar considerations apply if A or $B = 0$. Discussion of the case in which two of the coefficients are zero is left to the student.

16-5. Plane through a point perpendicular to a line. One and only one plane can be passed through a given point perpendicular to a given line. Its equation can be found as illustrated by the following:

Example

Find the equation of the plane that passes through the point $P(1\frac{1}{2},5,1)$ and is perpendicular to the line $A(-1\frac{1}{2},-1,-1)$ $B(3\frac{1}{2},2,6\frac{1}{2})$.

Solution (Fig. 16-5)

Since the required plane is perpendicular to AB, *this line is a normal to the plane.*

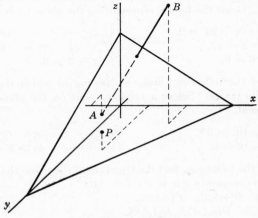

Figure 16-5

Its direction numbers can therefore be taken as the coefficients of x, y, and z, respectively, in the required equation. These direction numbers are $5:3:7\frac{1}{2}$.

The equation of the plane is then

$$5x + 3y + \tfrac{15}{2}z + D = 0,$$

where D is to be determined from the condition that the plane must pass through $P(1\frac{1}{2},5,1)$. Substituting these coordinates into the above equation, and solving for D, we have

$$5(\tfrac{3}{2}) + 3(5) + \tfrac{15}{2}(1) + D = 0;$$
$$D = -30.$$

The required equation is then

$$5x + 3y + \tfrac{15}{2}z - 30 = 0.$$

or

$$10x + 6y + 15z - 60 = 0.$$

The plane is represented by its traces in Fig. 16-5.

PROBLEMS

1. Write the equation of the plane for which

(a) $\alpha = 60°$, $\beta = 45°$, $\gamma = 60°$, $p = 4$.

(b) $\alpha = 135°$, $\beta = 45°$, $\gamma = 90°$, $p = 8$.

(c) $\alpha = 90°$, $\beta = 120°$, $\gamma = 30°$, $p = 6$.

2. In each of the following, plot the point P, and draw the radius vector OP. Then find the equation of the plane through P perpendicular to OP. Represent the plane in the drawing by its traces.

(a) $P(2,4,2)$.　　　　　(b) $P(-3,1,2)$.　　　　　(c) $P(-4,-3,0)$.

(d) $P(4,-2,1)$.　　　　　(e) $P(2,2,-2)$.　　　　　(f) $P(0,3,0)$.

3. Reduce each of the following equations to the normal form. Find the direction cosines of the normal to the plane, and find the distance of the plane from the origin. Draw the figure, representing the plane by its traces.

(a) $2x + 3y + 6z + 21 = 0$.　　　　(b) $2x - y + 2z = 12$.

(c) $8x + 4y - z = 27$.　　　　(d) $x - y - 2z = -6$.

(e) $x + 2z - 6 = 0$.　　　　(f) $y - 3 = 0$.

4. In each of the following, make a drawing in which the given plane is represented by its traces. Select a random point on the plane, and draw the normal at this point.

(a) $5x + 6y + 10z = 30$.　　　　(b) $3x - 2y + 2z - 12 = 0$.

(c) $3x - 4z + 12 = 0$.　　　　(d) $x - 2y - 4z + 8 = 0$.

5. In each of the following, find the equation of the plane that passes through the point P and is perpendicular to the line AB:

(a) $A(-2,1,1)$　$B(4,5,3)$;　$P(2,1,2)$.

(b) $A(-3,-2,5)$　$B(3,1,1)$;　$P(1,0,0)$.

(c) $A(1,5,2)$　$B(4,-1,5)$;　$P(2,2,2)$.

6. A plane is passed through the mid-point of the segment

$$A(-2,5,1) \quad B(6,1,5)$$

perpendicular to the line. Find its equation.

7. Find the coordinates of the point P on the segment $A(-2,-1,2)$ $B(7,5,5)$ that is two-thirds of the way from A to B. Find the equation of the plane through P perpendicular to AB.

8. Find the equation of the locus of points equidistant from the two points $A(-3,-2,-1)$ and $B(7,0,5)$.

9. Find the point on the y-axis that is equidistant from the two points $A(1,-4,4)$ and $B(7,6,2)$.

10. Find the center and radius of the sphere that passes through the points $A(10,-3,4)$, $B(11,7,-3)$, $C(-2,0,7)$, and $D(0,-4,5)$. HINT: The center is the point in space that is equidistant from A, B, C, and D. Hence, find the equations of the planes that are the perpendicular bisectors of segments AB, BC, and CD, and solve these equations simultaneously.

11. Show that the undirected distance from the plane

$$Ax + By + Cz + D = 0$$

to the point $P(x_1,y_1,z_1)$ is given by the formula

$$d = \frac{|Ax_1 + By_1 + Cz_1 + D|}{\sqrt{A^2 + B^2 + C^2}}.$$

12. In each of the following, find the distance from the given plane to the given point (see Prob. 11):

(a) $2x + 2y + z = 15$; $P(5,4,6)$.

(b) $2x - 3y + 6z - 18 = 0$; $P(1,-1,1)$.

(c) $4x - 5y - 3z + 24 = 0$; $P(-3,5,5)$.

13. Show that direction numbers of the line of intersection of the two planes

$$\begin{cases} A_1x + B_1y + C_1z + D_1 = 0 \\ A_2x + B_2y + C_2z + D_2 = 0 \end{cases}$$

are

$$\begin{vmatrix} B_1 & C_1 \\ B_2 & C_2 \end{vmatrix} : \begin{vmatrix} C_1 & A_1 \\ C_2 & A_2 \end{vmatrix} : \begin{vmatrix} A_1 & B_1 \\ A_2 & B_2 \end{vmatrix}$$

HINT: The line of intersection is perpendicular to the normals to both planes. Use Prob. 14, page 251.

14. Find the equation of the plane that passes through $P(1,3,2)$ and is perpendicular to the two planes $2x + y - z + 12 = 0$ and $x - y + z + 4 = 0$.

HINT: If a plane is perpendicular to each of two given planes, it is perpendicular to their line of intersection (see Prob. 13).

15. A plane is determined by the points $A(-3,7,-2)$, $B(8,1,3)$, and $P(4,6,1)$. A second plane is determined by A, B, and $Q(-3,7,2)$. A third plane passes through the point $R(2,3\frac{1}{2},-1)$ and is perpendicular to the first two planes. What is its equation?

16-6. *Plane determined by three points.* Of the four constants in the equation

$$Ax + By + Cz + D = 0$$

only three are *essential;* for we may divide through by any one (whose value is not zero) and thus reduce the number to three. Thus if $A \neq 0$, the above equation may be written in the form

$$x + by + cz + d = 0$$

where $\qquad b = \dfrac{B}{A}, \qquad c = \dfrac{C}{A}, \qquad$ and $\qquad d = \dfrac{D}{A}.$

Since the equation contains three essential constants, the plane is determined by three independent conditions. One such set of conditions is the requirement that the plane shall pass through three given points, not all on the same line. A procedure for finding the equation of the plane from these data is illustrated by the following:

Example

Find the equation of the plane passing through the points $(-1,2,4)$, $(3,3,\frac{1}{2})$, and $(4,1,1\frac{1}{2})$.

Solution

Assuming that the plane determined by these points is such that $A \neq 0$ in the equation $Ax + By + Cz + D = 0$, we may write its equation in the form

$$x + by + cz + d = 0.$$

Substituting the coordinates of the given points for x, y, and z, we obtain the following three equations in b, c, and d:

$$\begin{cases} -1 + 2b + 4c + d = 0 \\ 3 + 3b + \tfrac{1}{2}c + d = 0 \\ 4 + b + \tfrac{3}{2}c + d = 0. \end{cases}$$

Solving these, we find that

$$b = \tfrac{5}{4}; \qquad c = \tfrac{3}{2}; \qquad d = -\tfrac{15}{2}.$$

The required equation is then

$$x + \tfrac{5}{4}y + \tfrac{3}{2}z - \tfrac{15}{2} = 0$$

or $\qquad\qquad 4x + 5y + 6z - 30 = 0.$

If the plane determined by the three points had been parallel to x-axis (so that $A = 0$), the above set of equations would have been inconsistent. In this case we might have divided through by B or

C.　Since A, B, and C are not all zero, we can always divide by one of them.

16-7. Intercept equation of a plane. The *intercept* of a plane on a coordinate axis is the directed distance from the origin to the point of intersection of the plane and the axis. The plane shown in Fig. 16-6 has intercepts a, b, and c, on the x-, y-, and z-axes, respectively. The student may show that if none of the intercepts is zero the plane has the equation

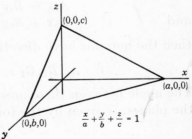

Figure 16-6

$$\frac{x}{a} + \frac{y}{b} + \frac{z}{c} = 1.$$

This is called the *intercept form* of the equation. It corresponds to the intercept form of the equation of a line that was studied in Chap. 3.

16-8. Angle between two planes. Let two planes intersect along a line as shown in Fig. 16-7. There are two supplementary

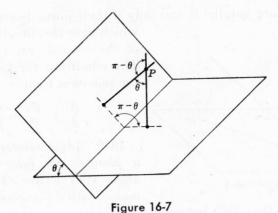

Figure 16-7

angles of intersection, θ and $\pi - \theta$. *These angles are equal, respectively, to the two angles between the normals drawn to the planes from any point P in space.* The problem of finding the angle between two planes thus reduces to that of finding the angle between two lines, namely, their normals. If the equations of the planes are

$$A_1x + B_1y + C_1z + D_1 = 0$$

and
$$A_2x + B_2y + C_2z + D_2 = 0,$$

then the normals have direction numbers

$$A_1:B_1:C_1 \quad \text{and} \quad A_2:B_2:C_2.$$

The angle between these normals, and consequently that between the planes, is given by the formula (Sec. 15-8)

$$\cos \theta = \pm \frac{A_1A_2 + B_1B_2 + C_1C_2}{\sqrt{A_1{}^2 + B_1{}^2 + C_1{}^2}\sqrt{A_2{}^2 + B_2{}^2 + C_2{}^2}}.$$

If positive directions are chosen on the normals, we may, if we wish, define the angle between the planes as that between the positive directions of the normals and choose the sign in the above formula accordingly. If we prefer, we may agree to choose the sign in each case so as to make cos θ positive; in this case the formula gives the cosine of the acute angle.

The planes are mutually perpendicular if and only if cos $\theta = 0$. Hence the condition for perpendicularity of the planes is

$$A_1A_2 + B_1B_2 + C_1C_2 = 0.$$

The planes are parallel if and only if their normals are parallel, in which case the direction numbers of the normals are proportional. The condition for parallelism of the planes is then

$$\frac{A_1}{A_2} = \frac{B_1}{B_2} = \frac{C_1}{C_2}.$$

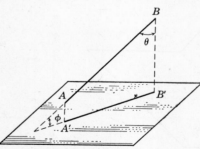

Figure 16-8

16-9. *Angle between a line and a plane.* We may define the angle that a line AB in space makes with a plane as the angle ϕ (not greater than 90°) between AB and its projection $A'B'$ on the plane. As shown in Fig. 16-8, this angle is the complement of the acute angle θ between the line AB and the normal to the plane.

Let the direction numbers of AB be $a_1:b_1:c_1$ and those of the normal to the plane be $a_2:b_2:c_2$. Then since

$$\sin \phi = \cos \theta,$$

we have

$$\sin \phi = \pm \frac{a_1 a_2 + b_1 b_2 + c_1 c_2}{\sqrt{a_1^2 + b_1^2 + c_1^2} \sqrt{a_2^2 + b_2^2 + c_2^2}}.$$

The sign is to be chosen so that $\sin \phi$ is positive. This stipulation is of course equivalent to saying that $\sin \phi$ is equal to the *absolute value* of the right-hand member of the above equation.

PROBLEMS

1. In each of the following, find the equation of the plane determined by P, Q, and R; find the intercepts of the plane on the axes and draw the figure:
  (a) $P(4,2,3)$ $Q(1,1,5)$ $R(2,6,2)$.
  (b) $P(-1,1,\frac{7}{3})$ $Q(\frac{3}{2},8,1)$ $R(-3,4,0)$.
  (c) $P(3,2,0)$ $Q(1,0,-5)$ $R(4,2,1)$.

2. A plane passes through the points $(3,1,7)$ and $(-3,-2,3)$ and has its x-intercept equal to three times its z-intercept. What is its equation?

3. A plane has its y-intercept equal to -4 and passes through the points $(5,1,5)$ and $(-1,-2,4)$. What is its equation?

4. A plane passes through the points $(-3,5,4)$ and $(8,-4,-2)$ and is perpendicular to the plane $2x - y - z = 3$. Find its equation.

5. The x- and z-intercepts of a plane are -4 and 6, respectively. The plane is perpendicular to the plane $x + 2y - 2z = 12$. What is its equation?

6. Find the acute angle between the two given planes.
  (a) $2x - y + 2z - 10 = 0$; $4x + y + z - 7 = 0$.
  (b) $5x + 3y - 4z + 14 = 0$; $x - 4y - z + 12 = 0$.
  (c) $3x + 4y = 16$; $4y - 2z = 5$.

7. One corner of the rectangular block shown in Fig. 16-9 is cut off by a plane passing through A, B, and C. What angle does this plane make with the horizontal top plane (BCD) of the block?

8. The base of a right pyramid 12 in. high is a rectangle 8 in. long and 6 in.

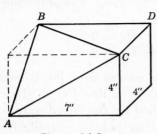

Figure 16-9

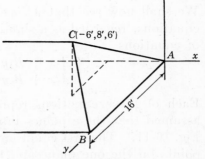

Figure 16-10

wide. Compute the dihedral angle between two of its faces.

9. One end of a roof has the construction shown in Fig. 16-10. Compute the angle between the planes that intersect along BC.

10. A plane passes through the point $P(-4, -2, 3)$ and is parallel to the plane $3x + y - 2z = 5$. Find its equation.

11. For what value of k are the planes $x - 6y + 8z - 4 = 0$ and

$$4x + ky + z - 7 = 0$$

mutually perpendicular?

12. In each of the following, find the angle that the line PQ makes with the given plane:

(a) $P(-2, 3, 1)$ $Q(4, 6, 7)$; $x + 4y + z - 10 = 0$.
(b) $P(6, 8, 5)$ $Q(-4, 3, 0)$; $2x - 4y + 4z - 11 = 0$.
(c) $P(3, 5, -2)$ $Q(0, 0, 2)$; $8x - 4y + z + 16 = 0$.

13. A line segment is to be drawn from $P(10, 4, 4)$ to a point Q on the z-axis. PQ is to be parallel to the plane $2x + 3y + 4z = 30$. What are the coordinates of Q?

16-10. *Equations of a line in space. General form.* We have seen that the locus of any linear equation in x, y, and z is a plane.

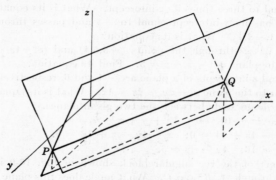

Figure 16-11

We shall now see that a *line* in space can be defined by *two* such equations, regarded as a simultaneous system. Consider the pair of equations

$$\begin{cases} A_1x + B_1y + C_1z + D_1 = 0 \\ A_2x + B_2y + C_2z + D_2 = 0. \end{cases}$$

Each of these equations represents a plane, and let it now be assumed that these planes intersect along a line PQ as shown in Fig. 16-11. The first equation is satisfied by the coordinates of all points on the one plane and by no other points. Similarly, the second is satisfied by the coordinates of all points on the other plane and by no other points. It is immediately evident that *the line of intersection of the planes is the locus of all points whose coordi-*

nates satisfy **both** *equations.* The *two* equations therefore *define* this line.

In order to make the graph of the line, we may locate two points on it as follows: Substitute any convenient value for z into the two equations, and then solve them simultaneously for the corresponding values of x and y. This of course gives the coordinates of one point on the line. Obtain a second point in the same way, using a different value for z. The line can then be drawn through the two points.

Example

Draw the line defined by the equations

$$\begin{cases} 3x - 2y + z - 8 = 0 \\ 2x - 2y - z + 2 = 0. \end{cases}$$

Solution

Putting $z = 2$, we obtain the equations $3x - 2y = 6$ and $x - y = 0$. Solving these, we find $x = 6$, $y = 6$. Putting $z = 4$, we similarly find $x = 2$, $y = 1$. Two points on the line are then $(6,6,2)$ and $(2,1,4)$. The line is shown in Fig. 16-12.

It is obvious that we could have substituted arbitrary values for x or y instead of for z. In particular, we could have put $y = 0$, thus locating the point where the line pierces the xz-plane; or we could have put $x = 0$ to find the point where it pierces the yz-plane.

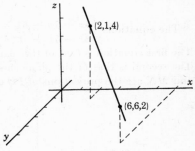

Figure 16-12

Two equations of the type discussed above constitute the *general form* of the equations of a line. Other forms in which the equations may be given are discussed in the following sections.

16-11. *The projection form.* Let a line l be defined by the two equations

(1) $$A_1x + B_1y + C_1z + D_1 = 0$$
(2) $$A_2x + B_2y + C_2z + D_2 = 0.$$

Each of these equations represents a plane through l as indicated in Fig. 16-11, where l is the line PQ. Consider now the equation

(3) $$(A_1x + B_1y + C_1z + D_1) + k(A_2x + B_2y + C_2z + D_2) = 0,$$

where k is any constant.   This equation represents a plane because it is of first degree.   Furthermore, it is satisfied by the coordinates of every point on line l because for every such point the quantities in both parentheses are equal to zero.   Hence, for every value of k, (3) represents a plane through the line l.   It is the equation of the *family* of planes through l, one of these planes corresponding to each value assigned to k.

Suppose now that k is chosen in (3) so as to eliminate z.   The resulting equation in x and y is that of the plane through l perpendicular to the xy-plane.   Similarly, if k is chosen so as to eliminate x or y from (3), the resulting equation in y or z or in x and z is that of the plane through l perpendicular to the yz- or xz-plane, respectively.   These planes are called the *projecting planes* of the line l on the coordinate planes.   It is often convenient to define a line by giving the equations of two of its projecting planes instead of two general planes.

Example

The equations $\begin{cases} 4x + 7y - 64 = 0 \\ 2x - 7z + 3 = 0 \end{cases}$ define the line PQ shown in Fig. 16-13.
The first equation is that of the plane through PQ perpendicular to the xy-plane. The second is that of the plane through PQ perpendicular to the xz-plane. ST and MN are the projections of PQ on these coordinate planes.

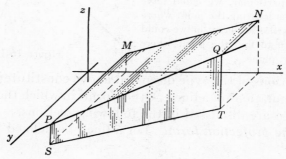

Figure 16-13

The above equations are called the *projection form* of the equations of a line.   If the equations of a line are given in the general form, the corresponding projection form can be obtained as illustrated by the following:

Example

A line is defined by the equations

$$\begin{cases} x + 5y + 6z = 10 \\ 3x + y - 2z = 4. \end{cases}$$

If we eliminate z by multiplying both sides of the second equation by 3, and adding, we obtain the equation $10x + 8y = 22$, or

$$5x + 4y - 11 = 0.$$

If we similarly eliminate y we get $7x - 8z - 5 = 0$. The equations

$$\begin{cases} 5x + 4y - 11 = 0 \\ 7x - 8z - 5 = 0 \end{cases}$$

then constitute the projection form of the equations of the line. (We could of course have eliminated x and used the resulting equation in y and z together with either of the above two.)

16-12. The symmetric form. A line may be determined by specifying the coordinates of two points on it, or by giving one point on it and its direction cosines or direction numbers. From such data its equations can easily be written down in the *symmetric form*, which we shall now derive.

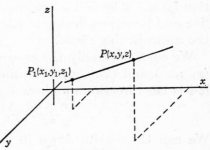

Figure 16-14

Let $P_1(x_1,y_1,z_1)$ be one point on a line l (Fig. 16-14) whose direction angles are α, β, and γ. Let $P(x,y,z)$ be any other point on the line, and denote the directed distance P_1P by d. Then

$$\cos \alpha = \frac{x - x_1}{d}; \qquad \cos \beta = \frac{y - y_1}{d}; \qquad \cos \gamma = \frac{z - z_1}{d}.$$

If we solve each of these equations for d, and equate the values so obtained, we have the equations

$$\frac{x - x_1}{\cos \alpha} = \frac{y - y_1}{\cos \beta} = \frac{z - z_1}{\cos \gamma}.$$

These equations constitute the *symmetric form* of the equations of a line. They can be used for writing down the equations when the coordinates of one point on the line, and its direction cosines, are known (provided, of course, that none of the direction cosines is zero).

The above equalities still hold if we multiply all the denominators by any nonzero constant. *We may thus replace the direction cosines by a set of direction numbers.* The equations of the line through the point (x_1, y_1, z_1) with direction numbers $a:b:c$ are then

$$\frac{x - x_1}{a} = \frac{y - y_1}{b} = \frac{z - z_1}{c}.$$

This is also called the *symmetric* form. It is of course equivalent to the two equations

$$\frac{x - x_1}{a} = \frac{y - y_1}{b}; \qquad \frac{x - x_1}{a} = \frac{z - z_1}{c}.$$

These equations, when simplified, obviously constitute the projection form. The first is the equation of the plane that contains the line and is perpendicular to the xy-plane. The second represents the xz-projecting plane.

We consider finally the case of a line determined by two points (x_1, y_1, z_1) and (x_2, y_2, z_2). To find its equations, we first note that it has the direction numbers

$$x_2 - x_1 : y_2 - y_1 : z_2 - z_1.$$

We can then write down its equations in the above symmetric form.

Example

Find the symmetric and projection equations of the line through $A(2,2,4)$ and $B(8, 6\frac{1}{2}, 2\frac{1}{2})$.

Solution (Fig. 16-15)

Direction numbers of the line are $6 : 4\frac{1}{2} : -1\frac{1}{2}$ or $4 : 3 : -1$. The symmetric equations are then

$$\frac{x - 2}{4} = \frac{y - 2}{3} = \frac{z - 4}{-1}.$$

The equation $\dfrac{x - 2}{4} = \dfrac{y - 2}{3}$ reduces to $3x - 4y + 2 = 0$; the equation

$$\frac{x - 2}{4} = \frac{z - 4}{-1}$$

reduces to $x + 4z - 18 = 0$.   The projection form of the equations is then

$$\begin{cases} 3x - 4y + 2 = 0 \\ x + 4z - 18 = 0. \end{cases}$$

These equations represent the two projecting planes shown in the figure.

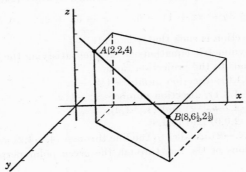

Figure 16-15

16-13. *The parametric form.* If we let t denote the value of each of the three fractions in the symmetric form, we may write

$$\frac{x - x_1}{a} = t; \qquad \frac{y - y_1}{b} = t; \qquad \frac{z - z_1}{c} = t.$$

Solving these equations for x, y, and z, respectively, we obtain the equations

$$x = x_1 + at; \qquad y = y_1 + bt; \qquad z = z_1 + ct.$$

These are *parametric equations* of the line, t being the parameter.

Example

The equations

$$x = 2 + 4t, \qquad y = 2 + 3t, \qquad z = 4 - t$$

represent the line shown in Fig. 16-15. We may obtain the coordinates of a point on the line by assigning any value to t. Thus if we let $t = -1$ we find that $x = -2$, $y = -1$, $z = 5$. This point is on the line.

PROBLEMS

1. Locate two points on the line defined by the given pair of equations, and draw the line.

(*a*) $x + 3y + z = 18$; $2x + y - 3z = 6$.

(*b*) $x - y + z - 2 = 0$; $8x - 9y + 4z + 10 = 0$.

2. Find the points where the line defined by the given equations pierces the xy- and xz-planes; draw the line through these points.

(a) $6x - y + 3z = 18$; $2x - 3y - 3z + 10 = 0$.

(b) $x + y - z = 2$; $x + 3y + z = 10$.

(c) $2x + 6y - 6z = 35$; $x - 4y + 8z + 21 = 0$.

3. Find the direction cosines of the line defined by the equations

$$2x - 3y - 2z + 11 = 0, \qquad x - 6y + 2z + 10 = 0,$$

if the positive direction is such that γ is acute.

4. Write the symmetric equations of the line satisfying the given conditions; reduce the equations to the projection form.

(a) Through $(2,1,6)$; direction numbers $4:3:-2$.

(b) Through $(-1,8,1)$; direction numbers $2:-1:2$.

(c) Through $(-2,-5,-2)$ and $(4,-1,2)$.

(d) Through $(-2,0,0)$ and $(4,5,3)$.

(e) Through $(6,2,-2)$ parallel to the line through $(4,-4,2)$ and $(1,-2,-1)$.

5. Find equations of the line through the given point perpendicular to the given plane.

(a) $A(8,10,8)$; $x + y + 2z = 6$.

(b) $P(2,1,4)$; $4x - 3y + 2z = 12$.

6. What angle does the line $\dfrac{x-4}{7} = \dfrac{y-1}{4} = \dfrac{z+3}{4}$ make with the plane $x - 2y - 2z = 8$?

7. Show that the lines $\dfrac{x+5}{3} = \dfrac{y-7}{4} = \dfrac{z+2}{2}$ and $\dfrac{x-3}{6} = \dfrac{y+5}{-5} = \dfrac{z-2}{1}$ are mutually perpendicular.

8. A line is drawn through $P(0,4,0)$ with direction numbers $6:4:5$. Write its equations. Another line is to be drawn from P to a point A on the z-axis, and this second line is to be perpendicular to the first. Find the coordinates of A.

9. Find the angle between the lines

$$\frac{x-2}{4} = \frac{y-1}{7} = \frac{z}{-4} \qquad \text{and} \qquad \frac{x}{3} = \frac{y-1}{4} = \frac{z+4}{-5}.$$

10. At what point does the line $\dfrac{2x-9}{6} = \dfrac{y-3}{1} = \dfrac{z-5}{4}$ pierce the plane $2x + 3y + 3z - 12 = 0$?

11. Draw the line whose parametric equations are $x = 2 - 3t$, $y = 1 + 4t$, $z = 6 - t$. Find its projection equations.

12. A line is drawn from $A(3,-1,4)$ to meet the line $x = 4t + 1$, $y = 6 - t$, $z = 1 + t$ at right angles. Find the point of intersection.

13. Compute the shortest distance from $P(7,2,3)$ to the line

$$A(2,3,1) \qquad B(6,-4,5).$$

HINT: In Fig. 16-16, $PL = AP \sin \theta$.

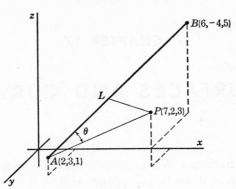

Figure 16-16

14. Compute the shortest distance from $P(0,4,0)$ to the line that passes through $A(2,1,6)$ and has direction numbers $6:2:-3$.

15. At a point on the plane $2x + 3y + 6z = 18$ a force of 70 lb. is applied along the line whose projection equations are $3x - 4y + 2 = 0, 3x - 6z + 2 = 0$. Compute the component of the force normal to the plane (see Fig. 16-17).

16. Find the equation of the plane through $P(-4,6,1)$ perpendicular to the line whose projection equations are $x - 2z + 2 = 0$ and $2y + z + 5 = 0$.

17. Find the equation of the plane that passes through the point $(2,-3,4)$ and contains the line whose projection equations are

$$2x - y - 3 = 0,$$
$$x + 3z - 6 = 0.$$

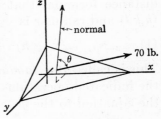

Figure 16-17

HINT: First write the equation of the family of planes containing the line.

18. Find the equation of the plane that passes through the origin and contains the line $\dfrac{x + 1}{3} = \dfrac{2y + 3}{4} = \dfrac{z + 6}{-2}$.

19. Show that the lines

$$\frac{x - 1}{3} = \frac{y + 2}{5} = \frac{z + 6}{13} \quad \text{and} \quad \frac{x - 4}{9} = \frac{y - 3}{5} = \frac{z - 7}{4}$$

determine a plane and find its equation.

20. Show that the lines

$$\frac{x + 2}{2} = \frac{y - 1}{-3} = \frac{z + 5}{4} \quad \text{and} \quad \frac{x - 3}{1} = \frac{2y + 5}{-3} = \frac{z + 3}{2}$$

are parallel, and find the equation of the plane determined by them.

CHAPTER 17

SURFACES AND CURVES

17-1. *Introduction.* We have seen that the locus of an equation of first degree in x, y, and z is a plane, and that two such equations may define a line. In the present chapter we shall study the loci of several equations of higher degree. We shall find that the locus of a single such equation is, in general, a surface. Two equations, each representing a surface, will be used to define a curve in space, namely, the curve of intersection.

17-2. *The sphere.* The student can easily show, by using the distance formula, that the equation of a sphere with center at (h,k,l) and radius r is

$$(1) \qquad (x - h)^2 + (y - k)^2 + (z - l)^2 = r^2.$$

This is called the *standard equation* of the sphere. By performing the indicated operations on the left-hand member, one can reduce the equation to the *general form*

$$(2) \qquad x^2 + y^2 + z^2 + Gx + Hy + Iz + K = 0.$$

Conversely, any equation of the form (2) can be transformed into form (1) by completing the squares. Such an equation therefore represents a sphere, a point sphere, or no locus, depending upon whether the constant that constitutes the right-hand member when the equation has been put into form (1) is positive, zero, or negative. The situation is entirely analogous to that of the circle.

17-3. *Cylindrical surfaces.* A surface generated by a line which moves so that it is always parallel to a fixed line and always intersects a fixed curve is called a *cylindrical surface* or *cylinder*. Any position of the generating line is called an *element* of the cylinder, and the fixed curve is called a *directrix*.

Consider now the equation

$$y^2 = 4x.$$

In the xy-plane the graph of this equation is the parabola shown in Fig. 17-1. Now let a cylindrical surface be generated by a line which moves so that it always intersects this parabola and remains parallel to the z-axis. It is easy to show that the equation $y^2 = 4x$ is satisfied by the coordinates of every point on this surface. Thus, let $P(x,y,z)$ be any point on the surface, and let $P'(x,y,0)$ be the projection of P on the xy-plane. Then, if the coordinates of P' satisfy the equation $y^2 = 4x$, those of P must do likewise because

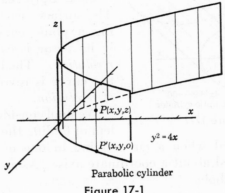

Parabolic cylinder

Figure 17-1

both points have the same x- and y-coordinates. Conversely, every point whose coordinates satisfy the equation lies on the cylindrical surface. *The equation $y^2 = 4x$ is then the equation of the surface.*

Observe that the parabola in the xy-plane is the locus of points whose coordinates satisfy the *two* equations $y^2 = 4x$ and $z = 0$. This is the *trace* of the surface in the xy-plane. The upper parabola shown in the figure is the section of the surface cut by a plane parallel to the xy-plane and 4 units above it. All points on this parabola satisfy the two equations $y^2 = 4x$ and $z = 4$.

By applying the above method of reasoning to the general case of an equation $\phi(x,y) = 0$ we may prove the following:

Theorem. If an equation that represents a surface does not contain the variable z, then the surface is a cylinder with elements parallel to the z-axis. Its directrix is the curve in the xy-plane which is the locus of the given equation.

Similarly, if the variable x (or y) is absent, the locus is a cylindrical surface whose elements are parallel to the x- (or y-) axis.

Example

In the xz-plane the locus of the equation

$$4x^2 + 9z^2 = 36$$

is an ellipse. In space, the locus of this equation is the *elliptic cylinder* having this ellipse as its directrix, and having its elements parallel to the y-axis (see Fig. 17-2).

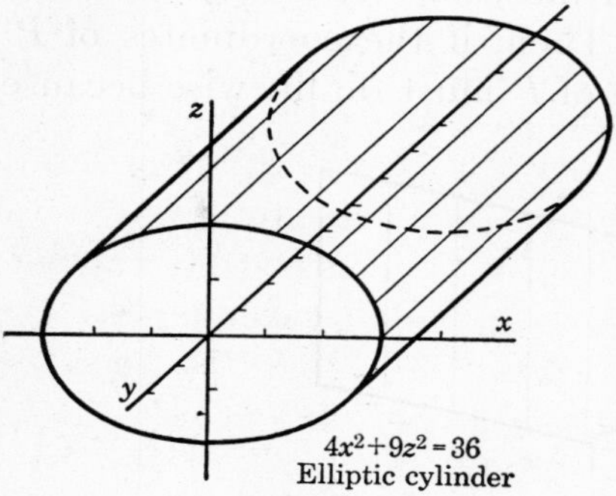

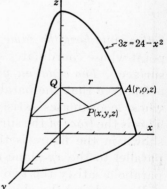

$4x^2+9z^2=36$
Elliptic cylinder

Figure 17-2

17-4. Surfaces of revolution.

The surface generated by revolving a plane curve about a line in its plane is called a *surface of revolution*. The line about which the curve is revolved is the *axis of revolution*.

We shall consider now the problem of finding the equation of the surface generated when a curve lying in one of the coordinate planes is revolved about a coordinate axis. As an example, let us revolve the parabola

$$3z = 24 - x^2$$

about the z-axis and find the equation of the surface thus generated. As shown in Fig. 17-3, any point such as A travels in a circle of radius $r = QA$. For any point P on this circle we have immediately

$$x^2 + y^2 = r^2.$$

The coordinates (r,z) must satisfy the equation

$$3z = 24 - r^2;$$

hence $$r^2 = 24 - 3z.$$

$3z=24-x^2$

$A(r,o,z)$

$P(x,y,z)$

Figure 17-3

Substituting this for r^2 in the above equation, we have

$$x^2 + y^2 = 24 - 3z.$$

This is the equation of the surface. It may be observed that our procedure for finding it amounts to replacing x in the equation of the given curve by $\sqrt{x^2 + y^2}$. The surface is called a *paraboloid of revolution*. The figure shows only one-fourth of the part lying above the xy-plane.

17-5. Sections parallel to a coordinate plane. Let us take the equation

$$x^2 + y^2 = 24 - 3z$$

and put $z = 3$. The resulting equation is $x^2 + y^2 = 15$. This is the equation of the curve cut from the surface by the plane $z = 3$. In this case the section is the circle with center at Q in Fig. 17-3.

In order to determine the nature of the surface defined by a given equation in x, y, and z, it is often necessary to study the sections cut from it by planes parallel to the coordinate planes. As indicated above, *the equations of sections parallel to the* **xy-plane** *may be found by putting* $z = k$ *in the equation of the surface*. Thus if we put $z = k$ in the equation $x^2 + y^2 = 24 - 3z$, we have

$$x^2 + y^2 = 24 - 3k.$$

It is clear that these sections are circles of radius $\sqrt{24 - 3k}$.

Similarly, if we put $x = k$, we have the equation

$$y^2 = 24 - 3z - k^2.$$

Thus the sections of the surface cut by planes parallel to the yz-plane are parabolas. In particular the trace in the yz-plane is the parabola $y^2 = 24 - 3z$. If one recalls that the shape of the parabola $z = ay^2 + by + c$ is completely determined by the value of a alone, he can immediately conclude that the above sections are all *congruent* parabolas.

Sections parallel to the xz-plane can be investigated similarly by putting $y = k$.

PROBLEMS

1. Find the equation of the sphere satisfying the following conditions:

(a) Center at $(4, -2, 1)$, radius 6.

(b) Center at $(2, 0, 0)$, radius 2.

(c) Having the points $(-4, 5, 1)$ and $(4, 1, 7)$ as ends of a diameter.

(d) Center at $(4, 2, 5)$ and tangent to the xy-plane.

2. Show that the center and radius of the sphere represented by equation (2) are, respectively,

Center $(-\tfrac{1}{2}G, -\tfrac{1}{2}H, -\tfrac{1}{2}I)$; radius $= \tfrac{1}{2}\sqrt{G^2 + H^2 + I^2 - 4K}$.

What are the conditions under which the equation represents a sphere, a point sphere, and no locus, respectively?

3. Find the equation of the plane that is tangent to the sphere

$$x^2 + y^2 + z^2 - 4x + 6y - 4z - 32 = 0$$

at $(8, -1, 5)$. HINT: The tangent plane is perpendicular to the radius.

4. A sphere has its center at $(0,4,0)$, and it passes through the point $(7,0,4)$. Write the equation of its tangent plane and normal line at this point. (The normal line is the line perpendicular to the tangent plane.)

5. Sketch the following cylindrical surfaces:

(a) $y^2 + z^2 = 25$.   (b) $x^2 + y^2 = 8x$.   (c) $x^2 + z = 4$.

(d) $xy + 4 = 0$.   (e) $z = e^{-x^2}$.   (f) $y + \log z = 0$.

In each of the following problems the equations of a curve lying in one of the coordinate planes are given. Find the equation of the surface generated when the curve is revolved about the specified coordinate axis. Draw the figure.

6. $x^2 = 4z$, $y = 0$; z-axis.   **7.** $x^2 + z^2 = a^2$, $y = 0$; x-axis.

8. $z = 4x$, $y = 0$; z-axis.   **9.** $y = 2x$, $z = 0$; y-axis.

10. $z^2 + 1 = x$, $y = 0$; x-axis.   **11.** $\dfrac{x^2}{25} + \dfrac{z^2}{9} = 1$, $y = 0$; z-axis.

12. $\dfrac{x^2}{a^2} + \dfrac{y^2}{b^2} = 1$, $z = 0$; x-axis.   **13.** $z = e^{-x^2}$, $y = 0$; z-axis.

14. $z = \sin x$, $y = 0$; x-axis.

In each of the following problems determine the nature of the curves cut from the given surface by planes parallel to the coordinate planes. Determine in each case whether or not the given surface could be generated by revolving a curve about one of the coordinate axes.

15. $x^2 + 2y^2 + 2z^2 = 16$.   **16.** $4x^2 + 4y^2 - z^2 = 0$.

17. $2x^2 + 3y^2 + 4z^2 = 12$.   **18.** $x^2 + z^2 - y = 4$.

17-6. Quadric surfaces.

The locus of an equation of second degree in x, y, and z is called a *quadric surface*. One such surface is the sphere which we have already considered. In the following sections we shall discuss briefly the *standard equations* of several other quadric surfaces.

17-7. The ellipsoid. The surface defined by the equation

$$\frac{x^2}{a^2} + \frac{y^2}{b^2} + \frac{z^2}{c^2} = 1$$

is called an *ellipsoid* (Fig. 17-4). It has certain obvious properties of symmetry, and its sections parallel to the coordinate planes are ellipses.

If any two of the three constants a, b, and c, are equal, the surface is an ellipsoid of revolution, which is sometimes called a *spheroid*. If $a = b = c$, the surface is a sphere.

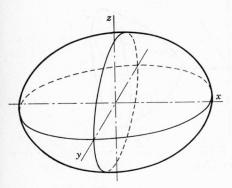

Ellipsoid: $\frac{x^2}{a^2} + \frac{y^2}{b^2} + \frac{z^2}{c^2} = 1$

Figure 17-4

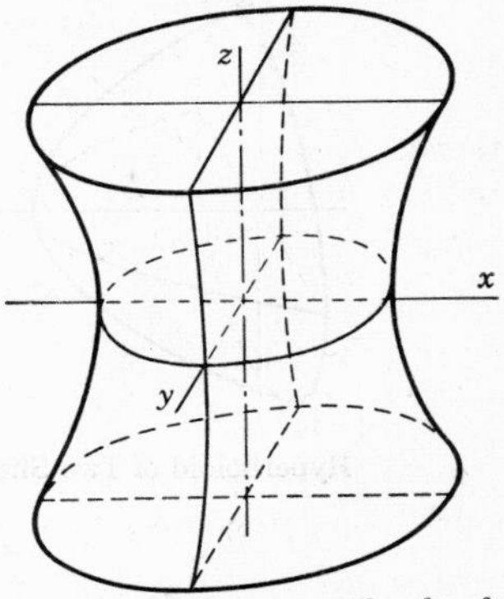

Hyperboloid of One Sheet: $\frac{x^2}{a^2} + \frac{y^2}{b^2} - \frac{z^2}{c^2} = 1$

Figure 17-5

17-8. *The hyperboloid of one sheet.* The surface defined by the equation

$$\frac{x^2}{a^2} + \frac{y^2}{b^2} - \frac{z^2}{c^2} = 1$$

is called a *hyperboloid of one sheet* (Fig. 17-5). Its trace in the xy-plane is the ellipse $\frac{x^2}{a^2} + \frac{y^2}{b^2} = 1$. Sections parallel to the xy-plane are also ellipses, while those parallel to the other two coordinate planes are hyperbolas. If $a = b$, the surface is a hyperboloid of revolution, the sections parallel to the xy-plane being circles.

17-9. *The hyperboloid of two sheets.* The locus of the equation

$$\frac{x^2}{a^2} - \frac{y^2}{b^2} - \frac{z^2}{c^2} = 1$$

is called a *hyperboloid of two sheets* (Fig. 17-6). It is evident from the equation that sections parallel to the xy- and xz-planes are hyperbolas. The trace in the yz-plane is the "imaginary ellipse" $\frac{y^2}{b^2} + \frac{z^2}{c^2} = -1$. The section cut by the plane $x = a$ is a "point ellipse," while for $|x| > a$ the corresponding sections are ellipses. If $b = c$, these ellipses are circles and the surface is a hyperboloid of revolution.

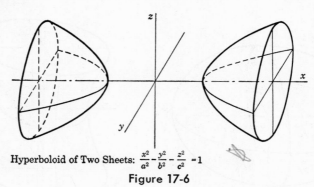

Hyperboloid of Two Sheets: $\dfrac{x^2}{a^2} - \dfrac{y^2}{b^2} - \dfrac{z^2}{c^2} = 1$

Figure 17-6

17-10. *The elliptic paraboloid.* The surface defined by the equation

$$\frac{x^2}{a^2} + \frac{y^2}{b^2} = z$$

is an *elliptic paraboloid* (Fig. 17-7). Sections parallel to and above the xy-plane are ellipses. Sections parallel to the other coordinate planes are parabolas. If $a = b$, the elliptic sections are circles and the surface is a paraboloid of revolution.

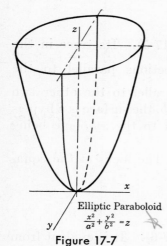

Elliptic Paraboloid
$\dfrac{x^2}{a^2} + \dfrac{y^2}{b^2} = z$

Figure 17-7

17-11. *The hyperbolic paraboloid.* The surface whose equation is

$$\frac{x^2}{a^2} - \frac{y^2}{b^2} = z$$

is called a *hyperbolic paraboloid* (Fig. 17-8). Its trace in the xy-plane consists of the two lines $\dfrac{x^2}{a^2} - \dfrac{y^2}{b^2} = 0$; sections parallel to and above the xy-plane are hyperbolas with transverse axes parallel to the x-axis; sections parallel to and below the xy-plane are hyperbolas with transverse axes parallel to the y-axis.

Sections parallel to the other two coordinate planes are parabolas. Those parallel to the xz-plane open upward, while those parallel to the yz-plane open downward.

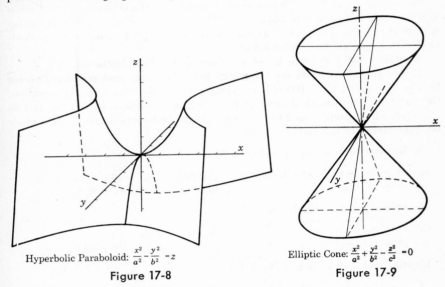

Hyperbolic Paraboloid: $\dfrac{x^2}{a^2} - \dfrac{y^2}{b^2} = z$

Figure 17-8

Elliptic Cone: $\dfrac{x^2}{a^2} + \dfrac{y^2}{b^2} - \dfrac{z^2}{c^2} = 0$

Figure 17-9

17-12. The elliptic cone.   The locus of the equation

$$\frac{x^2}{a^2} + \frac{y^2}{b^2} - \frac{z^2}{c^2} = 0$$

is an *elliptic cone* (Fig. 17-9). Its trace in the xy-plane is the "point ellipse" $\dfrac{x^2}{a^2} + \dfrac{y^2}{b^2} = 0$. Sections parallel to the xy-plane are ellipses. Its trace in each of the other two coordinate planes is a pair of lines through the origin; sections parallel to these coordinate planes are hyperbolas.

If $a = b$, the elliptic sections are circles and the surface is a *circular cone*. It could be generated by revolving a line having the equations $z = mx$, $y = 0$ about the z-axis.

PROBLEMS

1. The point that is symmetrical to $P(x,y,z)$ with respect to the xy-plane has the coordinate $(x,y,-z)$. It follows that if the equation of a surface is unaltered when z is replaced by $-z$, the surface is symmetrical with respect to the xy-plane. State corresponding tests for symmetry with respect to the other coordinate planes. Which quadric surfaces are symmetrical with respect to all three coordinate planes?

2. The point that is symmetrical to $P(x,y,z)$ with respect to the x-axis has the coordinates $(x, -y, -z)$. It follows that if the equation of a surface is unaltered when y and z are replaced by $-y$ and $-z$, respectively, the surface is symmetrical with respect to the x-axis. State corresponding tests for symmetry with respect to the other coordinate axes. Is the hyperbolic paraboloid symmetrical with respect to one of the axes?

3. State a test for symmetry of a surface with respect to the origin.

4. Are the above tests for symmetry both necessary and sufficient, or are they merely sufficient? HINT: If replacing z by $-z$ does not alter the equation, the surface is symmetrical with respect to the xy-plane. Hence the test is *sufficient*. But if replacing z by $-z$ *does* change the equation, might the surface be symmetrical to the xy-plane anyway?

5. Identify each of the following surfaces:

(a) $x^2 - 3y^2 - z^2 + 4 = 0$.
(c) $x^2 + y^2 = z^2$.

(b) $9x^2 + 16z^2 - 36y = 0$.
(d) $3x^2 + 4y^2 + 6z = 0$.

6. Identify each of the following surfaces:

(a) $x^2 + 3y^2 = z^2$.
(c) $x^2 = 4(z - y^2)$.

(b) $4x^2 = 25(y^2 + z)$.
(d) $x^2 + 6(y^2 + z^2) = 24$.

Identify and sketch each of the following surfaces:

7. $z = x^2 + y^2$.
9. $z + 8 = 2(x^2 + y^2)$.
11. $4x^2 - y = 4 - z^2$.
13. $2y^2 + 4z^2 = x^2$.
15. $4x^2 + 4y^2 - z^2 = 16$.
17. $y^2 + z^2 = x^2 + 4$.
19. $y^2 + z^2 = 2(x^2 - 8)$.
21. $x^2 + 2y^2 = 4(4 - z^2)$.
23. $2x^2 + 4y^2 + z^2 = 16$.
25. $x^2 - 2y^2 = 2z$.

8. $x^2 + 4y^2 + 4z = 0$.
10. $y^2 + z^2 = 8 - x$.
12. $4x^2 + 4y^2 - z^2 = 0$.
14. $y^2 - 9x^2 = 4z^2$.
16. $2x^2 + 3y^2 - 4z^2 = 24$.
18. $x^2 - 2y^2 - z^2 = 4$.
20. $2x^2 + y^2 = 16 - 2z^2$.
22. $x^2 + 5y^2 + 5z^2 = 25$.
24. $x^2 + 4y^2 + 4z^2 = 8x$.
26. $x^2 - y^2 = 4z$.

27. Discuss the sections of the hyperboloid $\dfrac{x^2}{a^2} + \dfrac{y^2}{b^2} - \dfrac{z^2}{c^2} = 1$ made by the plane $x = k$. Show in particular that the transverse axis of this hyperbola is parallel to the y-axis for $|k| < a$ but parallel to the z-axis for $|k| > a$. Discuss the case in which $k = a$.

17-13. *Curves in space.* Consider the two equations

$$\begin{cases} x^2 + y^2 - 4z = 0 \\ x - y + 2z = 12. \end{cases}$$

The locus of the first equation is a paraboloid, while that of the second is a plane that intersects the paraboloid in a curve. The points whose coordinates satisfy *both* equations are those lying on this curve. We may therefore regard the above pair of equations as the equations of this curve in space.

We may project this space curve onto the xy-plane by dropping a perpendicular from each point of the curve to the plane. These perpendiculars or projectors form a cylindrical surface whose equation is obtained by eliminating z between the given equations. In the above case, the equation of this *projecting cylinder* is

$$x^2 + y^2 + 2x - 2y - 24 = 0.$$

The projecting cylinders on the xz- and yz-planes can be obtained similarly by eliminating y and x, respectively. A curve in space is often defined by giving the equations of two of its projecting cylinders. This corresponds to our method of defining a line in space by giving the equations of two of its projecting planes.

17-14. Parametric equations of a curve in space. We have already seen that the line through (x_1, y_1, z_1) with the direction numbers $a:b:c$ has the parametric equations

$$x = x_1 + at, \qquad y = y_1 + bt, \qquad z = z_1 + ct.$$

In each of these equations the right-hand member is a *linear* function of t.

In general, the three equations

$$x = f_1(t), \qquad y = f_2(t), \qquad z = f_3(t),$$

are parametric equations of a *curve* in space, t being the parameter. The result of eliminating t between the first two equations is the xy-projecting cylinder of the curve, and the other projecting cylinders are similarly obtained.

As an example, consider the equations

$$x = 4 \cos t, \qquad y = 4 \sin t, \qquad z = \tfrac{2}{3}t.$$

When $t = 0$, we have $x = 4$, $y = 0$, $z = 0$. These are the coordinates of point A in Fig. 17-10. If we let $t = \tfrac{1}{2}\pi$, we have $x = 0$, $y = 4$, $z = \tfrac{1}{3}\pi$. The corresponding point is B in the figure. By continuing in this manner we may plot the curve as shown.

If we eliminate t between the first two of the given equations, we have the relation

$$x^2 + y^2 = 16.$$

Since the x- and y-coordinates of every point on the curve satisfy this equation, the curve must lie upon this cylinder. It is called

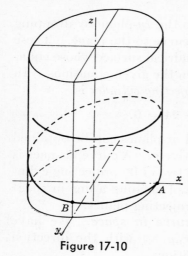

a *helix*, and its parametric equations have the general form

$$x = a \cos t, \qquad y = a \sin t, \qquad z = bt.$$

The thread on a bolt, or the handrailing on a circular staircase, is a curve of this kind.

17-15. Cylindrical coordinates. In our study of plane analytic geometry we saw that some types of curves have simpler equations in polar than in rectangular coordinates. Similarly, some of the problems of space geometry can be handled more easily by means of coordinate systems other than the rectangular one that we have

Figure 17-10

been using. In this section, and in the following one, we shall discuss briefly the *cylindrical* and *spherical* coordinate systems. Both of these systems are of great value in the study of more advanced topics in mathematics.

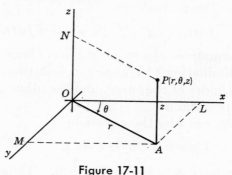

Figure 17-11

Let P be a point in space whose rectangular coordinates are (x,y,z), and let A be the foot of the perpendicular from P to the xy-plane. Let (r,θ) be the polar coordinates in the xy-plane of the point A.* Then the three numbers (r,θ,z) are called the *cylindrical coordinates* of P.

* We use (r,θ) instead of (ρ,θ) here because we still wish to denote the radius vector OP by ρ.

The relations that enable one to change the equation of a surface from rectangular to cylindrical coordinates are easily seen from Fig. 17-11 to be

$$x = r \cos \theta; \qquad y = r \sin \theta; \qquad z = z.$$

Those for making the reverse transformation are equally obvious.

Example

The equation $x^2 + y^2 - z^2 = 0$, which represents a circular cone, becomes $r^2 - z^2 = 0$ or $z = \pm r$ in cylindrical coordinates. Similarly, the equation $x^2 + y^2 + z^2 = 16$ becomes $r^2 + z^2 = 16$.

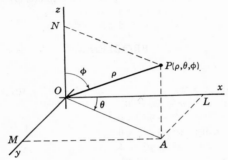

Figure 17-12

17-16. Spherical coordinates. Let P be a point in space whose rectangular coordinates are (x,y,z), and let A be the foot of the perpendicular from P to the xy-plane. Then, as shown in Fig. 17-12, let

$$OP = \varrho, \qquad \text{angle } LOA = \theta, \qquad \text{angle } NOP = \phi.$$

The three numbers (ρ,θ,ϕ) are the *spherical coordinates* of P. This coordinate system is similar to that used in locating points on the earth's surface by means of longitude and latitude. The angle θ corresponds to the longitude and ϕ to the colatitude, the latitude being the angle AOP.

In the spherical coordinate system, θ may have any positive or negative value; ϕ is identical with the direction angle γ and is restricted to positive values not greater than π. It is customary to restrict ρ to positive values, but if we wish, we may agree to interpret negative values of ρ as we did in dealing with polar coordinates in the plane.

The relations that enable one to transform the equation of a surface from rectangular to spherical coordinates are easily found.

Noting that $OA = NP = \rho \sin \phi$, while $ON = \rho \cos \phi$, we deduce immediately that

$$x = \rho \sin \phi \cos \theta;$$
$$y = \rho \sin \phi \sin \theta;$$
$$z = \rho \cos \phi.$$

Example

The equation $x^2 + y^2 = 4z$ represents a paraboloid of revolution. Upon making the above substitutions for x, y, and z, we obtain the equation of this surface in spherical coordinates as follows:

$$\rho^2 \sin^2 \phi \ (\cos^2 \theta + \sin^2 \theta) = 4\rho \cos \phi;$$
$$\rho \sin^2 \phi = 4 \cos \phi;$$
$$\rho = 4 \cos \phi \csc^2 \phi.$$

PROBLEMS

Draw the following curves:

1. $x^2 + y^2 = 25$; $\quad z = x$.
2. $x^2 + y^2 = 10x$; $\quad z = \frac{1}{2}x$.
3. $2z = x^2 + y^2$; $\quad x - y + 2z = 6$.
4. $x^2 + y^2 + z^2 = 25$; $\quad x^2 + y^2 = 9$.
5. $x^2 + y^2 + z^2 = 36$; $\quad x^2 + y^2 = 6x$.
6. $x^2 + y^2 + z^2 = 32$; $\quad x^2 + y^2 = 4z$.
7. $x^2 + y^2 + z^2 = 25$; $\quad 9z^2 = 16(x^2 + y^2)$.
8. $x = 5 \cos t$; $\quad y = 5 \sin t$; $\quad z = t$.
9. $x = 5 \sin t$; $\quad y = 4 \cos t$; $\quad z = \frac{1}{2}t$.
10. $x = t - 4$; $\quad y = t$; $\quad z = \frac{1}{2}t^2$.
11. $x = 4 \cos^2 t$; $\quad y = 4 \sin^2 t$; $\quad z = t^2$.
12. $x = 4 \cos t$; $\quad y = 4 \sin t$; $\quad z = 8 \sin t$.

Transform each of the following equations into both cylindrical and spherical coordinates; sketch the locus:

13. $x^2 + y^2 = 6$.
14. $x^2 + y^2 = 8xy$.
15. $xy = 2$.
16. $x^2 + y^2 - \frac{1}{2}z^2 = 0$.
17. $x^2 + y^2 + z^2 = 16$.
18. $x^2 + y^2 + z^2 = 6z$.
19. $x^2 - y^2 - 2z^2 = 4$.
20. $4z = x^2 - y^2$.

21. Derive a formula for the distance between two points in terms of their spherical coordinates.

22. Describe the locus in spherical coordinates of each of the following equations: $\rho = k$; $\theta = k$; $\phi = k$.

23. Describe the locus in spherical coordinates of each of the following equations: $\rho \sin \phi = k$; $\rho \cos \phi = k$.

24. Write the equations expressing the cylindrical coordinates, r, θ, and z in terms of ρ, θ, and ϕ.

25. Which one or ones of the three systems of space coordinates establishes a one-to-one correspondence between points of space and triplets of numbers?

NUMERICAL TABLES

ANALYTIC GEOMETRY

TABLE I. COMMON LOGARITHMS

N	0	1	2	3	4	5	6	7	8	9
10	0000	0043	0086	0128	0170	0212	0253	0294	0334	0374
11	0414	0453	0492	0531	0569	0607	0645	0682	0719	0755
12	0792	0828	0864	0899	0934	0969	1004	1038	1072	1106
13	1139	1173	1206	1239	1271	1303	1335	1367	1399	1430
14	1461	1492	1523	1553	1584	1614	1644	1673	1703	1732
15	1761	1790	1818	1847	1875	1903	1931	1959	1987	2014
16	2041	2068	2095	2122	2148	2175	2201	2227	2253	2279
17	2304	2330	2355	2380	2405	2430	2455	2480	2504	2529
18	2553	2577	2601	2625	2648	2672	2695	2718	2742	2765
19	2788	2810	2833	2856	2878	2900	2923	2945	2967	2989
20	3010	3032	3054	3075	3096	3118	3139	3160	3181	3201
21	3222	3243	3263	3284	3304	3324	3345	3365	3385	3404
22	3424	3444	3464	3483	3502	3522	3541	3560	3579	3598
23	3617	3636	3655	3674	3692	3711	3729	3747	3766	3784
24	3802	3820	3838	3856	3874	3892	3909	3927	3945	3962
25	3979	3997	4014	4031	4048	4065	4082	4099	4116,	4133
26	4150	4166	4183	4200	4216	4232	4249	4265	4281	4298
27	4314	4330	4346	4362	4378	4393	4409	4425	4440	4456
28	4472	4487	4502	4518	4533	4548	4564	4579	4594	4609
29	4624	4639	4654	4669	4683	4698	4713	4728	4742	4757
30	4771	4786	4800	4814	4829	4843	4857	4871	4886	4900
31	4914	4928	4942	4955	4969	4983	4997	5011	5024	5038
32	5051	5065	5079	5092	5105	5119	5132	5145	5159	5172
33	5185	5198	5211	5224	5237	5250	5263	5276	5289	5302
34	5315	5328	5340	5353	5366	5378	5391	5403	5416	5428
35	5441	5453	5465	5478	5490	5502	5514	5527	5539	5551
36	5563	5575	5587	5599	5611	5623	5635	5647	5658	5670
37	5682	5694	5705	5717	5729	5740	5752	5763	5775	5786
38	5798	5809	5821	5832	5843	5855	5866	5877	5888	5899
39	5911	5922	5933	5944	5955	5966	5977	5988	5999	6010
40	6021	6031	6042	6053	6064	6075	6085	6096	6107	6117
41	6128	6138	6149	6160	6170	6180	6191	6201	6212	6222
42	6232	6243	6253	6263	6274	6284	6294	6304	6314	6325
43	6335	6345	6355	6365	6375	6385	6395	6405	6415	6425
44	6435	6444	6454	6464	6474	6484	6493	6503	6513	6522
45	6532	6542	6551	6561	6571	6580	6590	6599	6609	6618
46	6628	6637	6646	6656	6665	6675	6684	6693	6702	6712
47	6721	6730	6739	6749	6758	6767	6776	6785	6794	6803
48	6812	6821	6830	6839	6848	6857	6866	6875	6884	6893
49	6902	6911	6920	6928	6937	6946	6955	6964	6972	6981
50	6990	6998	7007	7016	7024	7033	7042	7050	7059	7067
51	7076	7084	7093	7101	7110	7118	7126	7135	7143	7152
52	7160	7168	7177	7185	7193	7202	7210	7218	7226	7235
53	7243	7251	7259	7267	7275	7284	7292	7300	7308	7316
54	7324	7332	7340	7348	7356	7364	7372	7380	7388	7396
N	0	1	2	3	4	5	6	7	8	9

TABLE I. COMMON LOGARITHMS (*Continued*)

N	0	1	2	3	4	5	6	7	8	9
55	7404	7412	7419	7427	7435	7443	7451	7459	7466	7474
56	7482	7490	7497	7505	7513	7520	7528	7536	7543	7551
57	7559	7566	7574	7582	7589	7597	7604	7612	7619	7627
58	7634	7642	7649	7657	7664	7672	7679	7686	7694	7701
59	7709	7716	7723	7731	7738	7745	7752	7760	7767	7774
60	7782	7789	7796	7803	7810	7818	7825	7832	7839	7846
61	7853	7860	7868	7875	7882	7889	7896	7903	7910	7917
62	7924	7931	7938	7945	7952	7959	7966	7973	7980	7987
63	7993	8000	8007	8014	8021	8028	8035	8041	8048	8055
64	8062	8069	8075	8082	8089	8096	8102	8109	8116	8122
65	8129	8136	8142	8149	8156	8162	8169	8176	8182	8189
66	8195	8202	8209	8215	8222	8228	8235	8241	8248	8254
67	8261	8267	8274	8280	8287	8293	8299	8306	8312	8319
68	8325	8331	8338	8344	8351	8357	8363	8370	8376	8382
69	8388	8395	8401	8407	8414	8420	8426	8432	8439	8445
70	8451	8457	8463	8470	8476	8482	8488	8494	8500	8506
71	8513	8519	8525	8531	8537	8543	8549	8555	8561	8567
72	8573	8579	8585	8591	8597	8603	8609	8615	8621	8627
73	8633	8639	8645	8651	8657	8663	8669	8675	8681	8686
74	8692	8698	8704	8710	8716	8722	8727	8733	8739	8745
75	8751	8756	8762	8768	8774	8779	8785	8791	8797	8802
76	8808	8814	8820	8825	8831	8837	8842	8848	8854	8859
77	8865	8871	8876	8882	8887	8893	8899	8904	8910	8915
78	8921	8927	8932	8938	8943	8949	8954	8960	8965	8971
79	8976	8982	8987	8993	8998	9004	9009	9015	9020	9025
80	9031	9036	9042	9047	9053	9058	9063	9069	9074	9079
81	9085	9090	9096	9101	9106	9112	9117	9122	9128	9133
82	9138	9143	9149	9154	9159	9165	9170	9175	9180	9186
83	9191	9196	9201	9206	9212	9217	9222	9227	9232	9238
84	9243	9248	9253	9258	9263	9269	9274	9279	9284	9289
85	9294	9299	9304	9309	9315	9320	9325	9330	9335	9340
86	9345	9350	9355	9360	9365	9370	9375	9380	9385	9390
87	9395	9400	9405	9410	9415	9420	9425	9430	9435	9440
88	9445	9450	9455	9460	9465	9469	9474	9479	9484	9489
89	9494	9499	9504	9509	9513	9518	9523	9528	9533	9538
90	9542	9547	9552	9557	9562	9566	9571	9576	9581	9586
91	9590	9595	9600	9605	9609	9614	9619	9624	9628	9633
92	9638	9643	9647	9652	9657	9661	9666	9671	9675	9680
93	9685	9689	9694	9699	9703	9708	9713	9717	9722	9727
94	9731	9736	9741	9745	9750	9754	9759	9763	9768	9773
95	9777	9782	9786	9791	9795	9800	9805	9809	9814	9818
96	9823	9827	9832	9836	9841	9845	9850	9854	9859	9863
97	9868	9872	9877	9881	9886	9890	9894	9899	9903	9908
98	9912	9917	9921	9926	9930	9934	9939	9943	9948	9952
99	9956	9961	9965	9969	9974	9978	9983	9987	9991	9996
N	0	1	2	3	4	5	6	7	8	9

TABLE II. TRIGONOMETRIC FUNCTIONS

Angles	Sines		Cosines		Tangents		Cotangents		Angles
	Nat.	Log.	Nat.	Log.	Nat.	Log.	Nat.	Log.	
0° 00′	.0000	∞	1.0000	0.0000	.0000	∞	∞	∞	90° 00′
10	.0029	7.4637	1.0000	0000	.0029	7.4637	343.77	2.5363	50
20	.0058	7648	1.0000	0000	.0058	7648	171.89	2352	40
30	.0087	9408	1.0000	0000	.0087	9409	114.59	0591	30
40	.0116	8.0658	.9999	0000	.0116	8.0658	85.940	1.9342	20
50	.0145	1627	.9999	0000	.0145	1627	68.750	8373	10
1° 00′	.0175	8.2419	.9998	9.9999	.0175	8.2419	57.290	1.7581	89° 00′
10	.0204	3088	.9998	9999	.0204	3089	49.104	6911	50
20	.0233	3668	.9997	9999	.0233	3669	42.964	6331	40
30	.0262	4179	.9997	9999	.0262	4181	38.188	5819	30
40	.0291	4637	.9996	9998	.0291	4638	34.368	5362	20
50	.0320	5050	.9995	9998	.0320	5053	31.242	4947	10
2° 00′	.0349	8.5428	.9994	9.9997	.0349	8.5431	28.636	1.4569	88° 00′
10	.0378	5776	.9993	9997	.0378	5779	26.432	4221	50
20	.0407	6097	.9992	9996	.0407	6101	24.542	3899	40
30	.0436	6397	.9990	9996	.0437	6401	22.904	3599	30
40	.0465	6677	.9989	9995	.0466	6682	21.470	3318	20
50	.0494	6940	.9988	9995	.0495	6945	20.206	3055	10
3° 00′	.0523	8.7188	.9986	9.9994	.0524	8.7194	19.081	1.2806	87° 00′
10	.0552	7423	.9985	9993	.0553	7429	18.075	2571	50
20	.0581	7645	.9983	9993	.0582	7652	17.169	2348	40
30	.0610	7857	.9981	9992	.0612	7865	16.350	2135	30
40	.0640	8059	.9980	9991	.0641	8067	15.605	1933	20
50	.0669	8251	.9978	9990	.0670	8261	14.924	1739	10
4° 00′	.0698	8.8436	.9976	9.9989	.0699	8.8446	14.301	1.1554	86° 00′
10	.0727	8613	.9974	9989	.0729	8624	13.727	1376	50
20	.0756	8783	.9971	9988	.0758	8795	13.197	1205	40
30	.0785	8946	.9969	9987	.0787	8960	12.706	1040	30
40	.0814	9104	.9967	9986	.0816	9118	12.251	0882	20
50	.0843	9256	.9964	9985	.0846	9272	11.826	0728	10
5° 00′	.0872	8.9403	.9962	9.9983	.0875	8.9420	11.430	1.0580	85° 00′
10	.0901	9545	.9959	9982	.0904	9563	11.059	0437	50
20	.0929	9682	.9957	9981	.0934	9701	10.712	0299	40
30	.0958	9816	.9954	9980	.0963	9836	10.385	0164	30
40	.0987	9945	.9951	9979	.0992	9966	10.078	0034	20
50	.1016	9.0070	.9948	9977	.1022	9.0093	9.7882	0.9907	10
6° 00′	.1045	9.0192	.9945	9.9976	.1051	9.0216	9.5144	0.9784	84° 00′
10	.1074	0311	.9942	9975	.1080	0336	9.2553	9664	50
20	.1103	0426	.9939	9973	.1110	0453	9.0098	9547	40
30	.1132	0539	.9936	9972	.1139	0567	8.7769	9433	30
40	.1161	0648	.9932	9971	.1169	0678	8.5555	9322	20
50	.1190	0755	.9929	9969	.1198	0786	8.3450	9214	10
7° 00′	.1219	9.0859	.9925	9.9968	.1228	9.0891	8.1443	0.9109	83° 00′
10	.1248	0961	.9922	9966	.1257	0995	7.9530	9005	50
20	.1276	1060	.9918	9964	.1287	1096	7.7704	8904	40
30	.1305	1157	.9914	9963	.1317	1194	7.5958	8806	30
40	.1334	1252	.9911	9961	.1346	1291	7.4287	8709	20
50	.1363	1345	.9907	9959	.1376	1385	7.2687	8615	10
8° 00′	.1392	9.1436	.9903	9.9958	.1405	9.1478	7.1154	0.8522	82° 00′
10	.1421	1525	.9899	9956	.1435	1569	6.9682	8431	50
20	.1449	1612	.9894	9954	.1465	1658	6.8269	8342	40
30	.1478	1697	.9890	9952	.1495	1745	6.6912	8255	30
40	.1507	1781	.9886	9950	.1524	1831	6.5606	8169	20
50	.1536	1863	.9881	9948	.1554	1915	6.4348	8085	10
9° 00′	.1564	9.1943	.9877	9.9946	.1584	9.1997	6.3138	0.8003	81° 00′
	Nat.	Log.	Nat.	Log.	Nat.	Log.	Nat.	Log.	
Angles	Cosines		Sines		Cotangents		Tangents		Angles

TABLE II. TRIGONOMETRIC FUNCTIONS (*Continued*)

Angles	Sines		Cosines		Tangents		Cotangents		Angles
	Nat.	Log.	Nat.	Log.	Nat.	Log.	Nat.	Log.	
9° 00′	.1564	9.1943	.9877	9.9946	.1584	9.1997	6.3138	0.8003	81° 00′
10	.1593	2022	.9872	9944	.1614	2078	6.1970	7922	50
20	.1622	2100	.9868	9942	.1644	2158	6.0844	7842	40
30	.1650	2176	.9863	9940	.1673	2236	5.9758	7764	30
40	.1679	2251	.9858	9938	.1703	2313	5.8708	7687	20
50	.1708	2324	.9853	9936	.1733	2389	5.7694	7611	10
10° 00′	.1736	9.2397	.9848	9.9934	.1763	9.2463	5.6713	0.7537	80° 00′
10	.1765	2468	.9843	9931	.1793	2536	5.5764	7464	50
20	.1794	2538	.9838	9929	.1823	2609	5.4845	7391	40
30	.1822	2606	.9833	9927	.1853	2680	5.3955	7320	30
40	.1851	2674	.9827	9924	.1883	2750	5.3093	7250	20
50	.1880	2740	.9822	9922	.1914	2819	5.2257	7181	10
11° 00′	.1908	9.2806	.9816	9.9919	.1944	9.2887	5.1446	0.7113	79° 00′
10	.1937	2870	.9811	9917	.1974	2953	5.0658	7047	50
20	.1965	2934	.9805	9914	.2004	3020	4.9894	6980	40
30	.1994	2997	.9799	9912	.2035	3085	4.9152	6915	30
40	.2022	3058	.9793	9909	.2065	3149	4.8430	6851	20
50	.2051	3119	.9787	9907	.2095	3212	4.7729	6788	10
12° 00′	.2079	9.3179	.9781	9.9904	.2126	9.3275	4.7046	0.6725	78° 00′
10	.2108	3238	.9775	9901	.2156	3336	4.6382	6664	50
20	.2136	3296	.9769	9899	.2186	3397	4.5736	6603	40
30	.2164	3353	.9763	9896	.2217	3458	4.5107	6542	30
40	.2193	3410	.9757	9893	.2247	3517	4.4494	6483	20
50	.2221	3466	.9750	9890	.2278	3576	4.3897	6424	10
13° 00′	.2250	9.3521	.9744	9.9887	.2309	9.3634	4.3315	0.6366	77° 00′
10	.2278	3575	.9737	9884	.2339	3691	4.2747	6309	50
20	.2306	3629	.9730	9881	.2370	3748	4.2193	6252	40
30	.2334	3682	.9724	9878	.2401	3804	4.1653	6196	30
40	.2363	3734	.9717	9875	.2432	3859	4.1126	6141	20
50	.2391	3786	.9710	9872	.2462	3914	4.0611	6086	10
14° 00′	.2419	9.3837	.9703	9.9869	.2493	9.3968	4.0108	0.6032	76° 00′
10	.2447	3887	.9696	9866	.2524	4021	3.9617	5979	50
20	.2476	3937	.9689	9863	.2555	4074	3.9136	5926	40
30	.2504	3986	.9681	9859	.2586	4127	3.8667	5873	30
40	.2532	4035	.9674	9856	.2617	4178	3.8208	5822	20
50	.2560	4083	.9667	9853	.2648	4230	3.7760	5770	10
15° 00′	.2588	9.4130	.9659	9.9849	.2679	9.4281	3.7321	0.5719	75° 00′
10	.2616	4177	.9652	9846	.2711	4331	3.6891	5669	50
20	.2644	4223	.9644	9843	.2742	4381	3.6470	5619	40
30	.2672	4269	.9636	9839	.2773	4430	3.6059	5570	30
40	.2700	4314	.9628	9836	.2805	4479	3.5656	5521	20
50	.2728	4359	.9621	9832	.2836	4527	3.5261	5473	10
16° 00′	.2756	9.4403	.9613	9.9828	.2867	9.4575	3.4874	0.5425	74° 00′
10	.2784	4447	.9605	9825	.2899	4622	3.4495	5378	50
20	.2812	4491	.9596	9821	.2931	4669	3.4124	5331	40
30	.2840	4533	.9588	9817	.2962	4716	3.3759	5284	30
40	.2868	4576	.9580	9814	.2994	4762	3.3402	5238	20
50	.2896	4618	.9572	9810	.3026	4808	3.3052	5192	10
17° 00′	.2924	9.4659	.9563	9.9806	.3057	9.4853	3.2709	0.5147	73° 00′
10	.2952	4700	.9555	9802	.3089	4898	3.2371	5102	50
20	.2979	4741	.9546	9798	.3121	4943	3.2041	5057	40
30	.3007	4781	.9537	9794	.3153	4987	3.1716	5013	30
40	.3035	4821	.9528	9790	.3185	5031	3.1397	4969	20
50	.3062	4861	.9520	9786	.3217	5075	3.1084	4925	10
18° 00′	.3090	9.4900	.9511	9.9782	.3249	9.5118	3.0777	0.4882	72° 00′
	Nat.	Log.	Nat.	Log.	Nat.	Log.	Nat.	Log.	
Angles	Cosines		Sines		Cotangents		Tangents		Angles

Table II. Trigonometric Functions (Continued)

Angles	Sines Nat.	Log.	Cosines Nat.	Log.	Tangents Nat.	Log.	Cotangents Nat.	Log.	Angles
18° 00'	.3090	9.4900	.9511	9.9782	.3249	9.5118	3.0777	0.4882	72° 00'
10	.3118	4939	.9502	9778	.3281	5161	3.0475	4839	50
20	.3145	4977	.9492	9774	.3314	5203	3.0178	4797	40
30	.3173	5015	.9483	9770	.3346	5245	2.9887	4755	30
40	.3201	5052	.9474	9765	.3378	5287	2.9600	4713	20
50	.3228	5090	.9465	9761	.3411	5329	2.9319	4671	10
19° 00'	.3256	9.5126	.9455	9.9757	.3443	9.5370	2.9042	0.4630	71° 00'
10	.3283	5163	.9446	9752	.3476	5411	2.8770	4589	50
20	.3311	5199	.9436	9748	.3508	5451	2.8502	4549	40
30	.3338	5235	.9426	9743	.3541	5491	2.8239	4509	30
40	.3365	5270	.9417	9739	.3574	5531	2.7980	4469	20
50	.3393	5306	.9407	9734	.3607	5571	2.7725	4429	10
20° 00'	.3420	9.5341	.9397	9.9730	.3640	9.5611	2.7475	0.4389	70° 00'
10	.3448	5375	.9387	9725	.3673	5650	2.7228	4350	50
20	.3475	5409	.9377	9721	.3706	5689	2.6985	4311	40
30	.3502	5443	.9367	9716	.3739	5727	2.6746	4273	30
40	.3529	5477	.9356	9711	.3772	5766	2.6511	4234	20
50	.3557	5510	.9346	9706	.3805	5804	2.6279	4196	10
21° 00'	.3584	9.5543	.9336	9.9702	.3839	9.5842	2.6051	0.4158	69° 00'
10	.3611	5576	.9325	9697	.3872	5879	2.5826	4121	50
20	.3638	5609	.9315	9692	.3906	5917	2.5605	4083	40
30	.3665	5641	.9304	9687	.3939	5954	2.5386	4046	30
40	.3692	5673	.9293	9682	.3973	5991	2.5172	4009	20
50	.3719	5704	.9283	9677	.4006	6028	2.4960	3972	10
22° 00'	.3746	9.5736	.9272	9.9672	.4040	9.6064	2.4751	0.3936	68° 00'
10	.3773	5767	.9261	9667	.4074	6100	2.4545	3900	50
20	.3800	5798	.9250	9661	.4108	6136	2.4342	3864	40
30	.3827	5828	.9239	9656	.4142	6172	2.4142	3828	30
40	.3854	5859	.9228	9651	.4176	6208	2.3945	3792	20
50	.3881	5889	.9216	9646	.4210	6243	2.3750	3757	10
23° 00'	.3907	9.5919	.9205	9.9640	.4245	9.6279	2.3559	0.3721	67° 00'
10	.3934	5948	.9194	9635	.4279	6314	2.3369	3686	50
20	.3961	5978	.9182	9629	.4314	6348	2.3183	3652	40
30	.3987	6007	.9171	9624	.4348	6383	2.2998	3617	30
40	.4014	6036	.9159	9618	.4383	6417	2.2817	3583	20
50	.4041	6065	.9147	9613	.4417	6452	2.2637	3548	10
24° 00'	.4067	9.6093	.9135	9.9607	.4452	9.6486	2.2460	0.3514	66° 00'
10	.4094	6121	.9124	9602	.4487	6520	2.2286	3480	50
20	.4120	6149	.9112	9596	.4522	6553	2.2113	3447	40
30	.4147	6177	.9100	9590	.4557	6587	2.1943	3413	30
40	.4173	6205	.9088	9584	.4592	6620	2.1775	3380	20
50	.4200	6232	.9075	9579	.4628	6654	2.1609	3346	10
25° 00'	.4226	9.6259	.9063	9.9573	.4663	9.6687	2.1445	0.3313	65° 00'
10	.4253	6286	.9051	9567	.4699	6720	2.1283	3280	50
20	.4279	6313	.9038	9561	.4734	6752	2.1123	3248	40
30	.4305	6340	.9026	9555	.4770	6785	2.0965	3215	30
40	.4331	6366	.9013	9549	.4806	6817	2.0809	3183	20
50	.4358	6392	.9001	9543	.4841	6850	2.0655	3150	10
26° 00'	.4384	9.6418	.8988	9.9537	.4877	9.6882	2.0503	0.3118	64° 00'
10	.4410	6444	.8975	9530	.4913	6914	2.0353	3086	50
20	.4436	6470	.8962	9524	.4950	6946	2.0204	3054	40
30	.4462	6495	.8949	9518	.4986	6977	2.0057	3023	30
40	.4488	6521	.8936	9512	.5022	7009	1.9912	2991	20
50	.4514	6546	.8923	9505	.5059	7040	1.9768	2960	10
27° 00'	.4540	9.6570	.8910	9.9499	.5095	9.7072	1.9626	0.2928	63° 00'
	Nat.	Log.	Nat.	Log.	Nat.	Log.	Nat.	Log.	
Angles	Cosines		Sines		Cotangents		Tangents		Angles

TABLE II. TRIGONOMETRIC FUNCTIONS (*Continued*)

Angles	Sines		Cosines		Tangents		Cotangents		Angles
	Nat.	Log.	Nat.	Log.	Nat.	Log.	Nat.	Log.	
27° 00'	.4540	9.6570	.8910	9.9499	.5095	9.7072	1.9626	0.2928	63° 00'
10	.4566	6595	.8897	9492	.5132	7103	1.9486	2897	50
20	.4592	6620	.8884	9486	.5169	7134	1.9347	2366	40
30	.4617	6644	.8870	9479	.5206	7165	1.9210	2335	30
40	.4643	6668	.8857	9473	.5243	7196	1.9074	2804	20
50	.4669	6692	.8843	9466	.5280	7226	1.8940	2774	10
28° 00'	.4695	9.6716	.8829	9.9459	.5317	9.7257	1.8807	0.2743	62° 00'
10	.4720	6740	.8816	9453	.5354	7287	1.8676	2713	50
20	.4746	6763	.8802	9446	.5392	7317	1.8546	2683	40
30	.4772	6787	.8788	9439	.5430	7348	1.8418	2652	30
40	.4797	6810	.8774	9432	.5467	7378	1.8291	2622	20
50	.4823	6833	.8760	9425	.5505	7408	1.8165	2592	10
29° 00'	.4848	9.6856	.8746	9.9418	.5543	9.7438	1.8040	0.2562	61° 00'
10	.4874	6878	.8732	9411	.5581	7467	1.7917	2533	50
20	.4899	6901	.8718	9404	.5619	7497	1.7796	2503	40
30	.4924	6923	.8704	9397	.5658	7526	1.7675	2474	30
40	.4950	6946	.8689	9390	.5696	7556	1.7556	2444	20
50	.4975	6968	.8675	9383	.5735	7585	1.7437	2415	10
30° 00'	.5000	9.6990	.8660	9.9375	.5774	9.7614	1.7321	0.2386	60° 00'
10	.5025	7012	.8646	9368	.5812	7644	1.7205	2356	50
20	.5050	7033	.8631	9361	.5851	7673	1.7090	2327	40
30	.5075	7055	.8616	9353	.5890	7701	1.6977	2299	30
40	.5100	7076	.8601	9346	.5930	7730	1.6864	2270	20
50	.5125	7097	.8587	9338	.5969	7759	1.6753	2241	10
31° 00'	.5150	9.7118	.8572	9.9331	.6009	9.7788	1.6643	0.2212	59° 00'
10	.5175	7139	.8557	9323	.6048	7816	1.6534	2184	50
20	.5200	7160	.8542	9315	.6088	7845	1.6426	2155	40
30	.5225	7181	.8526	9308	.6128	7873	1.6319	2127	30
40	.5250	7201	.8511	9300	.6168	7902	1.6212	2098	20
50	.5275	7222	.8496	9292	.6208	7930	1.6107	2070	10
32° 00'	.5299	9.7242	.8480	9.9284	.6249	9.7958	1.6003	0.2042	58° 00'
10	.5324	7262	.8465	9276	.6289	7986	1.5900	2014	50
20	.5348	7282	.8450	9268	.6330	8014	1.5798	1986	40
30	.5373	7302	.8434	9260	.6371	8042	1.5697	1958	30
40	.5398	7322	.8418	9252	.6412	8070	1.5597	1930	20
50	.5422	7342	.8403	9244	.6453	8097	1.5497	1903	10
33° 00'	.5446	9.7361	.8387	9.9236	.6494	9.8125	1.5399	0.1875	57° 00'
10	.5471	7380	.8371	9228	.6536	8153	1.5301	1847	50
20	.5495	7400	.8355	9219	.6577	8180	1.5204	1820	40
30	.5519	7419	.8339	9211	.6619	8208	1.5108	1792	30
40	.5544	7438	.8323	9203	.6661	8235	1.5013	1765	20
50	.5568	7457	.8307	9194	.6703	8263	1.4919	1737	10
34° 00'	.5592	9.7476	.8290	9.9186	.6745	9.8290	1.4826	0.1710	56° 00'
10	.5616	7494	.8274	9177	.6787	8317	1.4733	1683	50
20	.5640	7513	.8258	9169	.6830	8344	1.4641	1656	40
30	.5664	7531	.8241	9160	.6873	8371	1.4550	1629	30
40	.5688	7550	.8225	9151	.6916	8398	1.4460	1602	20
50	.5712	7568	.8208	9142	.6959	8425	1.4370	1575	10
35° 00'	.5736	9.7586	.8192	9.9134	.7002	9.8452	1.4281	0.1548	55° 00'
10	.5760	7604	.8175	9125	.7046	8479	1.4193	1521	50
20	.5783	7622	.8158	9116	.7089	8506	1.4106	1494	40
30	.5807	7640	.8141	9107	.7133	8533	1.4019	1467	30
40	.5831	7657	.8124	9098	.7177	8559	1.3934	1441	20
50	.5854	7675	.8107	9089	.7221	8586	1.3848	1414	10
36° 00'	.5878	9.7692	.8090	9.9080	.7265	9.8613	1.3764	0.1387	54° 00'
	Nat.	Log.	Nat.	Log.	Nat.	Log.	Nat.	Log.	
Angles	Cosines		Sines		Cotangents		Tangents		Angles

TABLE II. TRIGONOMETRIC FUNCTIONS (Continued)

Angles	Sines		Cosines		Tangents		Cotangents		Angles
	Nat.	Log.	Nat.	Log.	Nat.	Log.	Nat.	Log.	
36° 00′	.5878	9.7692	.8090	9.9080	.7265	9.8613	1.3764	0.1387	54° 00′
10	.5901	7710	.8073	9070	.7310	8639	1.3680	1361	50
20	.5925	7727	.8056	9061	.7355	8666	1.3597	1334	40
30	.5948	7744	.8039	9052	.7400	8692	1.3514	1308	30
40	.5972	7761	.8021	9042	.7445	8718	1.3432	1282	20
50	.5995	7778	.8004	9033	.7490	8745	1.3351	1255	10
37° 00′	.6018	9.7795	.7986	9.9023	.7536	9.8771	1.3270	0.1229	53° 00′
10	.6041	7811	.7969	9014	.7581	8797	1.3190	1203	50
20	.6065	7828	.7951	9004	.7627	8824	1.3111	1176	40
30	.6088	7844	.7934	8995	.7673	8850	1.3032	1150	30
40	.6111	7861	.7916	8985	.7720	8876	1.2954	1124	20
50	.6134	7877	.7898	8975	.7766	8902	1.2876	1098	10
38° 00′	.6157	9.7893	.7880	9.8965	.7813	9.8928	1.2790	0.1072	52° 00′
10	.6180	7910	.7862	8955	.7860	8954	1.2723	1046	50
20	.6202	7926	.7844	8945	.7907	8980	1.2647	1020	40
30	.6225	7941	.7826	8935	.7954	9006	1.2572	0994	30
40	.6248	7957	.7808	8925	.8002	9032	1.2497	0968	20
50	.6271	7973	.7790	8915	.8050	9058	1.2423	0942	10
39° 00′	.6293	9.7989	.7771	9.8905	.8098	9.9084	1.2349	0.0916	51° 00′
10	.6316	8004	.7753	8895	.8146	9110	1.2276	0890	50
20	.6338	8020	.7735	8884	.8195	9135	1.2203	0865	40
30	.6361	8035	.7716	8874	.8243	9161	1.2131	0839	30
40	.6383	8050	.7698	8864	.8292	9187	1.2059	0813	20
50	.6406	8066	.7679	8853	.8342	9212	1.1988	0788	10
40° 00′	.6428	9.8081	.7660	9.8843	.8391	9.9238	1.1918	0.0762	50° 00′
10	.6450	8096	.7642	8832	.8441	9264	1.1847	0736	50
20	.6472	8111	.7623	8821	.8491	9289	1.1778	0711	40
30	.6494	8125	.7604	8810	.8541	9315	1.1708	0685	30
40	.6517	8140	.7585	8800	.8591	9341	1.1640	0659	20
50	.6539	8155	.7566	8789	.8642	9366	1.1571	0634	10
41° 00′	.6561	9.8169	.7547	9.8778	.8693	9.9392	1.1504	0.0608	49° 00′
10	.6583	8184	.7528	8767	.8744	9417	1.1436	0583	50
20	.6604	8198	.7509	8756	.8796	9443	1.1369	0557	40
30	.6626	8213	.7490	8745	.8847	9468	1.1303	0532	30
40	.6648	8227	.7470	8733	.8899	9494	1.1237	0506	20
50	.6670	8241	.7451	8722	.8952	9519	1.1171	0481	10
42° 00′	.6691	9.8255	.7431	9.8711	.9004	9.9544	1.1106	0.0456	48° 00′
10	.6713	8269	.7412	8699	.9057	9570	1.1041	0430	50
20	.6734	8283	.7392	8688	.9110	9595	1.0977	0405	40
30	.6756	8297	.7373	8676	.9163	9621	1.0913	0379	30
40	.6777	8311	.7353	8665	.9217	9646	1.0850	0354	20
50	.6799	8324	.7333	8653	.9271	9671	1.0786	0329	10
43° 00′	.6820	9.8338	.7314	9.8641	.9325	9.9697	1.0724	0.0303	47° 00′
10	.6841	8351	.7294	8629	.9380	9722	1.0661	0278	50
20	.6862	8365	.7274	8618	.9435	9747	1.0599	0253	40
30	.6884	8378	.7254	8606	.9490	9772	1.0538	0228	30
40	.6905	8391	.7234	8594	.9545	9798	1.0477	0202	20
50	.6926	8405	.7214	8582	.9601	9823	1.0416	0177	10
44° 00′	.6947	9.8418	.7193	9.8569	.9657	9.9848	1.0355	0.0152	46° 00′
10	.6967	8431	.7173	8557	.9713	9874	1.0295	0126	50
20	.6988	8444	.7153	8545	.9770	9899	1.0235	0101	40
30	.7009	8457	.7133	8532	.9827	9924	1.0176	0076	30
40	.7030	8469	.7112	8520	.9884	9949	1.0117	0051	20
50	.7050	8482	.7092	8507	.9942	9975	1.0058	0025	10
45° 00′	.7071	9.8495	.7071	9.8495	1.0000	0.0000	1.0000	0.0000	45° 00′
	Nat.	Log.	Nat.	Log.	Nat.	Log.	Nat.	Log.	
Angles	Cosines		Sines		Cotangents		Tangents		Angles

TABLE III. POWERS AND ROOTS

No.	Sq.	Sq. Root	Cube	Cube Root	No.	Sq.	Sq. Root	Cube	Cube Root
1	1	1.000	1	1.000	51	2,601	7.141	132,651	3.708
2	4	1.414	8	1.260	52	2,704	7.211	140,608	3.733
3	9	1.732	27	1.442	53	2,809	7.280	148,877	3.756
4	16	2.000	64	1.587	54	2,916	7.348	157,464	3.780
5	25	2.236	125	1.710	55	3,025	7.416	166,375	3.803
6	36	2.449	216	1.817	56	3,136	7.483	175,616	3.826
7	49	2.646	343	1.913	57	3,249	7.550	185,193	3.849
8	64	2.828	512	2.000	58	3,364	7.616	195,112	3.871
9	81	3.000	729	2.080	59	3,481	7.681	205,379	3.893
10	100	3.162	1,000	2.154	60	3,600	7.746	216,000	3.915
11	121	3.317	1,331	2.224	61	3,721	7.810	226,981	3.936
12	144	3.464	1,728	2.289	62	3,844	7.874	238,328	3.958
13	169	3.606	2,197	2.351	63	3,969	7.937	250,047	3.979
14	196	3.742	2,744	2.410	64	4,096	8.000	262,144	4.000
15	225	3.873	3,375	2.466	65	4,225	8.062	274,625	4.021
16	256	4.000	4,096	2.520	66	4,356	8.124	287,496	4.041
17	289	4.123	4,913	2.571	67	4,489	8.185	300,763	4.062
18	324	4.243	5,832	2.621	68	4,624	8.246	314.432	4.082
19	361	4.359	6,859	2.668	69	4,761	8.307	328,509	4.102
20	400	4.472	8,000	2.714	70	4,900	8.367	343,000	4.121
21	441	4.583	9,261	2.759	71	5,041	8.426	357,911	4.141
22	484	4.690	10,648	2.802	72	5,184	8.485	373,248	4.160
23	529	4.796	12,167	2.844	73	5,329	8.544	389,017	4.179
24	576	4.899	13,824	2.884	74	5,476	8.602	405,224	4.198
25	625	5.000	15,625	2.924	75	5,625	8.660	421,875	4.217
26	676	5.099	17,576	2.962	76	5,776	8.718	438,976	4.236
27	729	5.196	19,683	3.000	77	5,929	8.775	456,533	4.254
28	784	5.291	21,952	3.037	78	6,084	8.832	474,552	4.273
29	841	5.385	24,389	3.072	79	6,241	8.888	493,039	4.291
30	900	5.477	27,000	3.107	80	6,400	8.944	512,000	4.309
31	961	5.568	29,791	3.141	81	6,561	9.000	531,441	4.327
32	1,024	5.657	32,768	3.175	82	6,724	9.055	551,368	4.344
33	1,089	5.745	35,937	3.208	83	6,889	9.110	571,787	4.362
34	1,156	5.831	39,304	3.240	84	7,056	9.165	592,704	4.380
35	1,225	5.916	42,875	3.271	85	7,225	9.220	614,125	4.397
36	1,296	6.000	46,656	3.302	86	7,396	9.274	636,056	4.414
37	1,369	6.083	50,653	3.332	87	7,569	9.327	658,503	4.431
38	1,444	6.164	54,872	3.362	88	7,744	9.381	681,472	4.448
39	1,521	6.245	59,319	3.391	89	7,921	9.434	704,969	4.465
40	1,600	6.325	64,000	3.420	90	8,100	9.487	729,000	4.481
41	1,681	6.403	68,921	3.448	91	8,281	9.539	753,571	4.498
42	1,764	6.481	74,088	3.476	92	8,464	9.592	778,688	4.514
43	1,849	6.557	79,507	3.503	93	8,649	9.644	804,357	4.531
44	1,936	6.633	85,184	3.530	94	8,836	9.695	830,584	4.547
45	2,025	6.708	91,125	3.557	95	9,025	9.747	857,375	4.563
46	2,116	6.782	97,336	3.583	96	9,216	9.798	884,736	4.579
47	2,209	6.856	103,823	3.609	97	9,409	9.849	912,673	4.595
48	2,304	6.928	110,592	3.634	98	9,604	9.899	941,192	4.610
49	2,401	7.000	117,649	3.659	99	9,801	9.950	970,299	4.626
50	2,500	7.071	125,000	3.684	100	10,000	10.000	1,000,000	4.642

Table IV. Natural Logarithms

N	0	1	2	3	4	5	6	7	8	9
1.0	0.0 000	100	198	296	392	488	583	677	770	862
1.1	953	*044	*133	*222	*310	*398	*484	*570	*655	*740
1.2	0.1 823	906	989	*070	*151	*231	*311	*390	*469	*546
1.3	0.2 624	700	776	852	927	*001	*075	*148	*221	*293
1.4	0.3 365	436	507	577	646	716	784	853	920	988
1.5	0.4 055	121	187	253	318	383	447	511	574	637
1.6	700	762	824	886	947	*008	*068	*128	*188	*247
1.7	0.5 306	365	423	481	539	596	653	710	766	822
1.8	878	933	988	*043	*098	*152	*206	*259	*313	*366
1.9	0.6 419	471	523	575	627	678	729	780	831	881
2.0	931	981	*031	*080	*129	*178	*227	*275	*324	*372
2.1	0.7 419	467	514	561	608	655	701	747	793	839
2.2	885	930	975	*020	*065	*109	*154	*198	*242	*286
2.3	0.8 329	372	416	459	502	544	587	629	671	713
2.4	755	796	838	879	920	961	*002	*042	*083	*123
2.5	0.9 163	203	243	282	322	361	400	439	478	517
2.6	555	594	632	670	708	746	783	821	858	895
2.7	933	969	*006	*043	*080	*116	*152	*188	*225	*260
2.8	1.0 296	332	367	403	438	473	508	543	578	613
2.9	647	682	716	750	784	818	852	886	919	953
3.0	986	*019	*053	*086	*119	*151	*184	*217	*249	*282
3.1	1.1 314	346	378	410	442	474	506	537	569	600
3.2	632	663	694	725	756	787	817	848	878	909
3.3	939	969	*000	*030	*060	*090	*119	*149	*179	*208
3.4	1.2 238	267	296	326	355	384	413	442	470	499
3.5	528	556	585	613	641	669	698	726	754	782
3.6	809	837	865	892	920	947	975	*002	*029	*056
3.7	1.3 083	110	137	164	191	218	244	271	297	324
3.8	350	376	402	429	455	481	507	533	558	584
3.9	610	635	661	686	712	737	762	788	813	838
4.0	863	888	913	938	962	987	*012	*036	*061	*085
4.1	1.4 110	134	159	183	207	231	255	279	303	327
4.2	351	375	398	422	446	469	493	516	540	563
4.3	586	609	633	656	679	702	725	748	770	793
4.4	816	839	861	884	907	929	951	974	996	*019
4.5	1.5 041	063	085	107	129	151	173	195	217	239
4.6	261	282	304	326	347	369	390	412	433	454
4.7	476	497	518	539	560	581	602	623	644	665
4.8	686	707	728	748	769	790	810	831	851	872
4.9	892	913	933	953	974	994	*014	*034	*054	*074
5.0	1.6 094	114	134	154	174	194	214	233	253	273

If given number $n = N \times 10^m$, then $\log_e n = \log_e N + m \log_e 10$. Find $m \log_e 10$ from the following table:

Multiples of $\log_e$ 10

$\log_e 10 =$	2.3026	$-\ \log_e 10 = 7.6974 - 10$
$2 \log_e 10 =$	4.6052	$-2 \log_e 10 = 5.3948 - 10$
$3 \log_e 10 =$	6.9078	$-3 \log_e 10 = 3.0922 - 10$
$4 \log_e 10 =$	9.2103	$-4 \log_e 10 = 0.7897 - 10$
$5 \log_e 10 =$	11.5129	$-5 \log_e 10 = 9.4871 - 20$

Table IV. Natural Logarithms (Continued)

N	0	1	2	3	4	5	6	7	8	9
5.0	1.6 094	114	134	154	174	194	214	233	253	273
5.1	292	312	332	351	371	390	409	429	448	467
5.2	487	506	525	544	563	582	601	620	639	658
5.3	677	696	715	734	752	771	790	808	827	845
5.4	864	882	901	919	938	956	974	993	*011	*029
5.5	1.7 047	066	084	102	120	138	156	174	192	210
5.6	228	246	263	281	299	317	334	352	370	387
5.7	405	422	440	457	475	492	509	527	544	561
5.8	579	596	613	630	647	664	681	699	716	733
5.9	750	766	783	800	817	834	851	867	884	901
6.0	918	934	951	967	984	*001	*017	*034	*050	*066
6.1	1.8 083	099	116	132	148	165	181	197	213	229
6.2	245	262	278	294	310	326	342	358	374	390
6.3	405	421	437	453	469	485	500	516	532	547
6.4	563	579	594	610	625	641	656	672	687	703
6.5	718	733	749	764	779	795	810	825	840	856
6.6	871	886	901	916	931	946	961	976	991	*006
6.7	1.9 021	036	051	066	081	095	110	125	140	155
6.8	169	184	199	213	228	242	257	272	286	301
6.9	315	330	344	359	373	387	402	416	430	445
7.0	459	473	488	502	516	530	544	559	573	587
7.1	601	615	629	643	657	671	685	699	713	727
7.2	741	755	769	782	796	810	824	838	851	865
7.3	879	892	906	920	933	947	961	974	988	*001
7.4	2.0 015	028	042	055	069	082	096	109	122	136
7.5	149	162	176	189	202	215	229	242	255	268
7.6	281	295	308	321	334	347	360	373	386	399
7.7	412	425	438	451	464	477	490	503	516	528
7.8	541	554	567	580	592	605	618	631	643	656
7.9	669	681	694	707	719	732	744	757	769	782
8.0	794	807	819	832	844	857	869	882	894	906
8.1	919	931	943	956	968	980	992	*005	*017	*029
8.2	2.1 041	054	066	080	090	102	114	126	138	150
8.3	163	175	187	199	211	223	235	247	258	270
8.4	282	294	306	318	330	342	353	365	377	389
8.5	401	412	424	436	448	460	471	483	494	506
8.6	518	529	541	552	564	576	587	599	610	622
8.7	633	645	656	668	679	691	702	713	725	736
8.8	748	759	770	782	793	804	815	827	838	849
8.9	861	872	883	894	905	917	928	939	950	961
9.0	972	983	994	*006	*017	*028	*039	*050	*061	*072
9.1	2.2 083	094	105	116	127	137	148	159	170	181
9.2	192	203	214	225	235	246	257	268	279	289
9.3	300	311	322	332	343	354	364	375	386	396
9.4	407	418	428	439	450	460	471	481	492	502
9.5	513	523	534	544	555	565	576	586	597	607
9.6	618	628	638	649	659	670	680	690	701	711
9.7	721	732	742	752	762	773	783	793	803	814
9.8	824	834	844	854	865	875	885	895	905	915
9.9	925	935	946	956	966	976	986	996	*006	*016
10.	2.3 026	036	046	056	066	076	086	096	106	115

TABLE V. EXPONENTIAL AND HYPERBOLIC FUNCTIONS

x	e^x	e^{-x}	sinh x	cosh x	tanh x
.00	1.000	1.000	.000	1.000	.000
.01	1.010	.990	.010	1.000	.010
.02	1.020	.980	.020	1.000	.020
.03	1.030	.970	.030	1.000	.030
.04	1.041	.961	.040	1.001	.040
.05	1.051	.951	.050	1.001	.050
.06	1.062	.942	.060	1.002	.060
.07	1.073	.932	.070	1.002	.070
.08	1.083	.923	.080	1.003	.080
.09	1.094	.914	.090	1.004	.090
.1	1.105	.905	.100	1.005	.100
.2	1.221	.819	.201	1.020	.197
.3	1.350	.741	.305	1.045	.291
.4	1.492	.670	.411	1.081	.380
.5	1.649	.607	.521	1.128	.462
.6	1.822	.549	.637	1.185	.537
.7	2.014	.497	.759	1.255	.604
.8	2.226	.449	.888	1.337	.664
.9	2.460	.407	1.027	1.433	.716
1.0	2.718	.368	1.175	1.543	.762
1.1	3.004	.333	1.336	1.669	.800
1.2	3.320	.301	1.509	1.811	.834
1.3	3.669	.273	1.698	1.971	.862
1.4	4.055	.247	1.904	2.151	.885
1.5	4.482	.223	2.129	2.352	.905
1.6	4.953	.202	2.376	2.577	.922
1.7	5.474	.183	2.646	2.828	.935
1.8	6.050	.165	2.942	3.107	.947
1.9	6.686	.150	3.268	3.418	.956
2.0	7.389	.135	3.627	3.762	.964
2.1	8.166	.122	4.022	4.144	.970
2.2	9.025	.111	4.457	4.568	.976
2.3	9.974	.100	4.937	5.037	.980
2.4	11.023	.091	5.466	5.557	.984
2.5	12.182	.082	6.050	6.132	.987
2.6	13.464	.074	6.695	6.769	.989
2.7	14.880	.067	7.406	7.473	.991
2.8	16.445	.061	8.192	8.253	.993
2.9	18.174	.055	9.060	9.115	.994
3.0	20.086	.050	10.018	10.068	.995
3.1	22.20	.045	11.08	11.12	.996
3.2	24.53	.041	12.25	12.29	.997
3.3	27.11	.037	13.54	13.57	.997
3.4	29.96	.033	14.97	15.00	.998
3.5	33.12	.030	16.54	16.57	.998
3.6	36.60	.027	18.29	18.31	.999
3.7	40.45	.025	20.21	20.24	.999
3.8	44.70	.022	22.34	22.36	.999
3.9	49.40	.020	24.69	24.71	.999
4.0	54.60	.018	27.29	27.31	.999
4.1	60.34	.017	30.16	30.18	.999
4.2	66.69	.015	33.34	33.35	1.000
4.3	73.70	.014	36.84	36.86	1.000
4.4	81.45	.012	40.72	40.73	1.000
4.5	90.02	.011	45.00	45.01	1.000
4.6	99.48	.010	49.74	49.75	1.000
4.7	109.95	.0090	54.97	54.98	1.000
4.8	121.51	.0082	60.75	60.76	1.000
4.9	134.29	.0074	67.14	67.15	1.000
5.0	148.41	.0067	74.20	74.21	1.000
6.0	403.4	.0025	201.7		1.000
7.0	1096.6	.00091	548.3		1.000
8.0	2981.0	.00034	1490.5		1.000
9.0	8103.1	.00012	4051.5		1.000
10.0	22026.5	.000045	11013.2		1.000

ANSWERS

INTRODUCTION

Pages 7–8

1. 10.   **2.** -3.   **3.** 3.   **4.** $-5\frac{1}{2}$.

5. No solution.   **6.** No solution.   **7.** $6\frac{1}{3}$.   **8.** $\frac{1}{8}$.

9. $\frac{1}{3}(1 \pm \sqrt{5})$.   **10.** $\frac{1}{5}(3 \pm \sqrt{3})$.   **11.** 14, 1.9.

12. $-3, \frac{16}{3}$.   **13.** $-9, -3$.   **14.** 5, 3.

15. $\frac{9}{2}$.   **16.** $-\frac{8}{3}$.   **17.** No solution.   **18.** 14.

19. $2 \pm i$.   **20.** $2, -\frac{3}{2}$.   **21.** $2, -1 \pm \sqrt{3}\, i$.   **22.** -13.

23. 5.   **24.** $-\frac{3}{2}$.   **25.** 28.   **26.** -14.

27. 60.   **28.** $x = 4, y = -1$.   **29.** $x = \frac{12}{11}, y = \frac{1}{11}$.

30. $x = -2, y = 1, z = 5$.   **31.** $x = 4, y = -3, z = 2$.

32. $x = -4, y = -2, z = 3$.   **33.** $x = 3, y = \frac{3}{2}, z = -2$.

Pages 14–15

1. (a) $\frac{7}{4}\pi$; (c) $\frac{25}{6}\pi$; (e) 1.187; (g) 4.363.

2. (a) $225°$; (c) $220°0'57''$; (e) $540°$; (g) $436°35'38''$.

3. (a) $\frac{1}{2}\sqrt{3}$; (c) 0.   **4.** 2.25.   **5.** $2 - \sqrt{2}$.

6. -7.   **7.** 7.   **8.** $\frac{1}{2}$.   **9.** 0.4067; -0.9397; 0.1763.

14. $\frac{24}{25}; \frac{7}{25}; \frac{1}{3}$.   **15.** $-\frac{120}{169}; \frac{119}{169}; -\frac{120}{119}$.

16. $-\frac{63}{65}; \frac{16}{65}$.   **17.** $\frac{3}{5}; \frac{4}{5}$.   **18.** $\frac{2}{\sqrt{5}}; \frac{1}{\sqrt{5}}$.

19. $\cos\theta$.   **20.** $\cos\theta$.   **21.** $2\csc\theta$.

22. $\cot\theta$.   **23.** $\frac{1}{2}\pi; \frac{3}{2}\pi; \frac{1}{6}\pi; \frac{5}{6}\pi$.

24. $\frac{2}{3}\pi; \frac{4}{3}\pi$.   **25.** $\frac{1}{6}\pi; \frac{5}{6}\pi$.   **26.** $\frac{3}{4}\pi; \frac{7}{4}\pi$; arctan 3.

27. $0, \pi, \frac{2}{3}\pi, \frac{4}{3}\pi$.   **28.** $0, \frac{2}{3}\pi, \pi, \frac{4}{3}\pi$.   **29.** $36°52'$.   **30.** $\frac{3}{4}\pi, \frac{7}{4}\pi$.

CHAPTER 1

Pages 22–23

1. $54(2^{2/3})$.   **2.** $200\sqrt{2}$.   **3.** $4(36\pi - 27\sqrt{3})$.

11. -5 and 5; -2 and 8.   **12.** -3 and 3; -5 and 1.

13. -10 and 10; -4.5 and 5.5.   **14.** $|x - 1| < 4$.

15. 4 and 6.5.   **16.** $x \geqq 5; x \leqq 5$.   **17.** $x \geqq 3.5; x \leqq 3.5$. **18.** $x \leqq 1.5; x \geqq 1.5$.

19. $x \geqq -4.5; x \leqq -4.5$.   **20.** $3x + 2y$.

21. $3x + 1$.   **22.** $3; 2x + 3$.

Pages 29–30

1. (a) 2, 2; $-6, 4; 4, 7$.   (c) $-6, -1; 3, 2; 2, 1$.

2. (a) $3; -3; -8$.   (c) $6; -6; -6$.

3. (a) $7; -6; 6.$ (c) $8; 4; -5.$

5. $5 - y.$ **6.** $x - 4.$ **14.** $(-8\frac{5}{6}, -3).$

15. $(5 + 5\sqrt{3}, 1 + 5\sqrt{3});$ $(5 - 5\sqrt{3}, 1 - 5\sqrt{3}).$

16. $(4\frac{1}{9}, 0).$ **17.** $(-2, -2).$ **18.** $(-\frac{17}{4}, 5).$

19. $(2, -2);$ $(-6, -2).$ **20.** $(5.8, 11.6).$

21. $(20, 24).$ **23.** $|x + 3|$ or $\sqrt{(x + 3)^2};$ $x + 3.$

24. $(\frac{11}{5}, \frac{27}{5}).$ **25.** $\pm 4.8.$

Pages 34–36

1. (a) $(6.5, 8);$ (c) $(-7, -4);$ (e) $(2, 4).$

2. (a) $(1, -4);$ (c) $(9, 2);$ (e) $(-4.5, 0).$

3. (a) $(5, 7);$ (c) $(-6.5, -9.5);$ (e) $(-\frac{2}{3}, -18).$

4. $(-3, -\frac{5}{3});$ $(0, -\frac{1}{3}).$ **5.** $(\frac{11}{2}, -\frac{3}{4});$ $(3, \frac{3}{2});$ $(\frac{1}{2}, \frac{15}{4}).$

6. $(2, \frac{2}{3}).$ **7.** $(-\frac{4}{3}, 0).$ **10.** (a) $23,$ (c) $40,$ (e) $29.$

11. (a) $38,$ (c) $14.$ **12.** (a) $60,$ (c) $36.5.$

15. $\frac{148}{13}.$ **16.** $11.4.$ **17.** $\frac{60}{13}.$ **18.** $0.6.$

19. $\frac{11}{8}.$

Pages 40–41

1. $-\sqrt{3}.$ **2.** $135°.$ **3.** $\sqrt{3};\ -\dfrac{1}{\sqrt{3}}.$

4. $\frac{2}{3};\ -\frac{3}{2}.$ **5.** $-\frac{5}{2}.$ **6.** $3.$

8. $-\frac{13}{4}, \frac{1}{5}, \frac{5}{2};\ -\frac{16}{17}, -\frac{1}{14}, \frac{14}{11}.$ **13.** $\frac{56}{33};\ -\frac{12}{5}.$

14. (a) $\tan \theta = \frac{29}{15};$ (c) $\tan \theta = \frac{11}{7}.$ **15.** $\frac{31}{24};\ \frac{41}{42}.$

16. (a) $\tan A = \frac{3}{5};$ $B = 90°;$ $\tan C = \frac{5}{3}.$

(c) $\tan L = \frac{22}{19};$ $\tan M = \frac{22}{7};$ $\tan N = \frac{44}{27}.$

17. $0.2.$ **18.** $0.8.$ **19.** $\frac{38}{9}.$ **20.** $\frac{19}{13}.$

Pages 44–45

15. $5; -5.$ **16.** $(0, -\frac{20}{9}).$ **17.** $7; -3\frac{2}{3}.$

18. $(3, 9);$ $\sqrt{106}.$ **19.** $m_2 = \dfrac{m_1 - 1}{m_1 + 1},\ m_1 \neq -1.$

20. $3\sqrt{2}.$ **21.** $(-39, 39).$ **22.** $\frac{127}{78}.$

23. $10.$ **24.** $(4, \pm 6.4).$ **25.** $(0, 10.5).$

CHAPTER 2

Pages 51–52

2. $x + 3 = 0.$ **3.** $y = 5.$ **4.** $x + y = 0.$

33. $V = \left(\dfrac{S}{6}\right)^{\frac{3}{2}}.$ **34.** $V = \dfrac{S\sqrt{S}}{6\sqrt{\pi}}.$ **35.** $L = \dfrac{gT^2}{4\pi^2}.$

36. $L = 2\sqrt{144 - x^2}.$ **37.** $D = \sqrt{(x - 2)^2 + 64}.$ **38.** $AP = x + 3.$

Pages 56–58

19. $V = 4x(9 - x)(6 - x).$ **20.** $C = 4\pi x^2 + \dfrac{1,200}{x}$ cents. **21.** $A = \frac{5}{6}(12y - y^2).$

22. $L = 2\sqrt{36 - x^2}.$ **23.** $V = 2\pi x^2(6 - x).$ **24.** $A = x\sqrt{144 - x^2}.$

Pages 61–63

1. $(x + 3)^2 + (y + 1)^2 = 9.$
3. $(x + 5)^2 + (y - 5)^2 = 50.$
5. $3x - 4y = 7.$
7. $y^2 = 8x - 16.$
10. $y^2 = 16x.$
13. $y = x \, (x \neq 1).$
15. $2xy + x - 3y = 0 \, (x \neq 0 \text{ or } 1).$
17. (a) $x^2 + y^2 = 36$; (c) $x^2 + y^2 - 2x - 4y = 8.$
18. $16x^2 + 25y^2 = 400.$
20. $5x^2 + 9y^2 - 40x - 100 = 0.$

2. $(x - 6)^2 + (y + 2)^2 = 16.$
4. $12x + 10y + 23 = 0.$
6. (a) $7x - 3y = 7$; (c) $14x + 8y = 27.$
8. $x^2 - 6x - 8y + 25 = 0.$ **9.** $x^2 + 8y = 16.$
11. $x^2 + y^2 + 8x - 48 = 0.$ **12.** $x^2 + y^2 = 16x.$
14. $y(x - 12) = 0.$
16. $4x^2 + 3y^2 - 32y + 64 = 0.$
19. $9x^2 - 16y^2 = 144 \, (x \geqq 4).$

CHAPTER 3

Pages 67–69

1. (a) $2x - 3y + 19 = 0$; (c) $2x + y = 13$; (e) $3x - 10y = 41.$
2. (a) $5x + 4y = 22$; (c) $x + y = 1$; (e) $9x + 7y = 12.$
3. (a) $y = \frac{2}{3}x - 4$; (c) $y = -\frac{5}{2}x - 8$; (e) $7x + 10y + 35 = 0.$
4. Sides: $y = 0$; $y = -6$; $x = 0$; $x = -8.$
   Diagonals: $y = \frac{3}{4}x$; $3x + 4y + 24 = 0.$
5. $x - 11y + 64 = 0$; $11x + y = 28.$ **6.** (a) $3x - 2y + 1 = 0$; (c) $3x + 2y = 5.$
7. (a) $3x - 2y = 8$; (c) $x - 3y + 17 = 0.$
8. $3x + 2y = 18.$ **9.** $10x + 3y = 0.$ **10.** $3x + y = 6.$
11. (a) $2x + 13y = 16.$ (c) $2x - 13y = 19.$
12. $(12, -2).$ **13.** $\left(\frac{17}{28}, \frac{27}{14}\right).$ **14.** $(5.8, -0.65).$ **15.** $(0,1).$
16. $(5, -3).$ **18.** (a) $x - 3y + 12 = 0$; (c) $3x + 4y = 0.$
19. 30. **20.** 75.

Pages 74–76

1. (a) $m = \frac{3}{4}$; $b = -\frac{9}{2}$; $y = \frac{3}{4}x - \frac{9}{2}.$
   (c) $m = \frac{2}{3}$; $b = \frac{4}{3}$; $y = \frac{2}{3}x + \frac{4}{3}.$
   (e) $m = -\frac{4}{3}$; $b = 2$; $y = -\frac{4}{3}x + 2.$

2. (a) $a = 8$; $b = 6$; $\dfrac{x}{8} + \dfrac{y}{6} = 1.$

   (c) $a = 9$; $b = -6$; $\dfrac{x}{9} + \dfrac{y}{-6} = 1.$

   (e) $a = -\frac{7}{5}$; $b = -\frac{7}{2}$; $\dfrac{x}{-\frac{7}{5}} + \dfrac{y}{-\frac{7}{2}} = 1.$

3. (a) $A = -\frac{2}{3}$; $A = 6.$ (c) $B = 15$; $B = -\frac{5}{3}.$
4. (a) $3x + 2y + 1 = 0$; $2x - 3y - 21 = 0.$
   (c) $3x - 5y + 2 = 0$; $5x + 3y = 42.$
5. $3x + 2y = 12$; $x - 3y = 15.$ **6.** (a) $\frac{9}{13}$; (c) $\frac{11}{2}.$
7. $\arctan \frac{3}{2}.$ **8.** 9.25. **9.** 13. **10.** (a) $\sqrt{10}.$ (c) 4.
11. (a) 3. (c) $\frac{33}{13}.$ **12.** $3x - 4y = \pm 15.$ **13.** $5x - 12y = \pm 65.$
14. $25\frac{1}{2}.$ **15.** 30. **16.** $3\sqrt{5}.$ **19.** 10; $-\frac{2}{5}.$
20. $\frac{2}{3}$; $-6.$ **22.** $-\frac{1}{2}\sqrt{2}\,x + \frac{1}{2}\sqrt{2}\,y = 8.$
23. $y = 3.$ **24.** $-\frac{1}{2}x - \frac{1}{2}\sqrt{3}\,y = 6.$ **25.** $-x = 5.$

Pages 80–82

2. $y = -\frac{4}{3}x + b$; $y = -\frac{4}{3}x + 4$.   **3.** $y - 4 = m(x - 6)$; $9x - 4y = 38$.

4. $y - 6 = m(x + 3)$; $x + 2y = 9$.   **5.** $x - y = a$; $x - y = \pm 10$.

6. $\dfrac{x}{-6} + \dfrac{y}{b} = 1$; $3x - 2y + 18 = 0$.

7. $y + 5 = m(x - 6)$; $5x + 2y = 20$; $5x + 18y + 60 = 0$.

8. $y - 4 = m(x - 6)$; $x + y = 10$; $2x + 3y = 24$.

9. $y = mx - 4$; $y = \pm 4x - 4$.   **10.** $y = -2x + b$; $2x + y = 9$.

12. $3x + 4y - 6 + k(x - 2y + 10) = 0$; $13x + 4y + 22 = 0$.

13. $x + 2y + 2 = 0$.   **28.** $L = 30 + 0.000195(t - 50)$.

CHAPTER 4

Pages 88–89

3. ± 8.   **4.** 1.8.   **22.** 150 by 225 ft.

23. 45 by 90 ft.   **24.** 50 ft.   **25.** $80\sqrt{2}$ ft. per second.

26. $V = \frac{5}{3}x^2(9 - x)$; $x = 6$ in.   **27.** $V = \frac{1}{4}\pi y(144 - y^2)$; about 7 in.

CHAPTER 5

Pages 97–98

26. $V = 12\pi \dfrac{y^2}{y - 12}$.   **27.** $C = 6\left(x^2 + \dfrac{432}{x}\right)$; about 6 ft.

CHAPTER 6

Pages 103–104

1. $2y' = x'$.   **2.** $x' - y' = 3$.   **3.** $2x' + 3y' = 0$.

4. $y' = \frac{2}{3}x'$.   **5.** $y' = -x'^2$.   **6.** $y' = 2x'^2 + 13x'$.

7. $y' = -x'^2$.   **8.** $y' = \frac{1}{2}(x'^2 - 16)$.   **9.** $y' = x'^3$.

10. $y' = x'^3 - 4x'$.   **11.** $y' = x'^4 - 4x'^2$.   **12.** $y' = \dfrac{3}{x'}$.

13. $y' = \dfrac{8}{x'^2 + 4}$.   **14.** $y' = \dfrac{x'}{x'^2 + 1}$.   **15.** $y' = \dfrac{5x'}{x'^2 + 1}$.

17. $A(4\sqrt{3} - 3, -3\sqrt{3} - 4)$; $B(-2\sqrt{3} - 2, 2 - 2\sqrt{3})$; $C(5, 5\sqrt{3})$.

18. $A(7\sqrt{2}, \sqrt{2})$; $B(0, -4\sqrt{2})$; $C(-5\sqrt{2}, 5\sqrt{2})$.

19. $A(-6, -8)$; $B(-4, 4)$; $C(10, 0)$.

20. $x' = \dfrac{4}{\sqrt{5}}$.   **21.** $y' + 4 = 0$.

22. $x'^2 - 2x'y' + y'^2 - x' - y' = 0$.   **23.** $x'^2 - y'^2 = 2$.

24. $x' = x\cos\theta + y\sin\theta$; $y' = y\cos\theta - x\sin\theta$.

CHAPTER 7

Pages 109–111

1. (a) $(x - 4)^2 + (y + 2)^2 = 9$; $x^2 + y^2 - 8x + 4y + 11 = 0$.

    (c) $x^2 + (y + 5)^2 = 25$; $x^2 + y^2 + 10y = 0$.

    (e) $(x - 4)^2 + (y - 1)^2 = 16$; $x^2 + y^2 - 8x - 2y + 1 = 0$.

2. (a) $C(2,-3)$; $r = 5$.

(c) $C(\frac{3}{2},-\frac{5}{2})$; $r = \frac{1}{2}\sqrt{6}$.

(e) $C(-1,\frac{5}{4})$; $r = \frac{5}{4}$.

3. $x^2 + y^2 = 2ry$.

6. (a) $(x - 2)^2 + y^2 = 32$.

(c) $(x - 6)^2 + (y - 6)^2 = 36$; $(x + 2)^2 + (y - 2)^2 = 4$.

(e) $(x - 8)^2 + (y - 4)^2 = 20$.

7. $x^2 + y^2 - 32x + 192 = 0$.　　　　**8.** $(x - 9)^2 + (y - 8)^2 = 52$.

9. $x^2 + y^2 - 19x - 13y + 110 = 0$.　　**10.** $x^2 + y^2 = cx$.

11. $x^2 + y^2 - cx - cy = 0$.　　　　**12.** $(x + c)^2 + (y - c)^2 = c^2$.

13. $(x - h)^2 + (y - 2h)^2 = 5h^2$; $x^2 + y^2 - 4x - 8y = 0$.

14. $x^2 + y^2 = 32$.　　　　　　　　**15.** Two points.

16. (a) $(x - 7)^2 + (y - 3)^2 = 50$; (c) $x^2 + y^2 + 11x - 5y + 4 = 0$.

17. $(x - 5)^2 + (y + 3)^2 = 9$.　　　**18.** $x^2 + (y + 6)^2 = 68$.

19. $(x - 3)^2 + (y + 5)^2 = 25$.　　**20.** $(x - 7)^2 + (y - 1)^2 = 5$.

21. $(x + 2)^2 + (y + 1)^2 = 5$; $(x - 10)^2 + (y + 5)^2 = 125$.

22. $2x - y = 2$.

CHAPTER 8

Pages 117–119

1. (a) $F(\frac{3}{2},0)$; $x = -\frac{3}{2}$.　(c) $F(0,-2)$; $y = 2$.

(e) $F(\frac{5}{12},0)$; $x = -\frac{5}{12}$.　(g) $F(\frac{1}{16},0)$; $x = -\frac{1}{16}$.

(i) $F(0,\frac{9}{16})$; $y = -\frac{9}{16}$.

2. (a) $y^2 = 12x$.　(c) $y^2 = -\frac{16}{3}x$.

3. (a) $(y - 2)^2 = \frac{25}{4}(x - 4)$.　(c) $x^2 = \frac{32}{3}(y + 6)$.

4. $(x - 3)^2 = 24(y + 2)$.

6. (a) $y = x^2 - 3x + 5$.　(c) $3y = 5x^2 - 6x - 14$.

7. (a) $y^2 + 6y - 2x - 4 = 0$.　(c) $3x = y^2 - 12$.

8. $2\frac{1}{4}$ in. from vertex.　　**9.** $10\frac{2}{3}$ in.　　　**10.** $x^2 + 25y + 100 = 0$.

15. c.　　　　　**16.** $\left(-\dfrac{b}{2a}, -\dfrac{b^2 - 4ac}{4a}\right)$; $p = \dfrac{1}{2a}$.

17. (a) $(y - 4)^2 = 3(x - 2)$.　(c) $(x + 1)^2 = 4(y + 3)$.

(e) $(x - 6)^2 = -1(y - 36)$.　(g) $(y - \frac{3}{2})^2 = 3(x - 2)$.

18. $A = 50x - x^2$.　　　**19.** 120 by 300 ft.　　　**20.** 288 ft.; 72 ft.

Pages 124–126

1. (a) $F(0,\pm 4)$; $e = \frac{4}{5}$.　(c) $F(0,\pm\sqrt{3})$; $e = \frac{1}{2}$.

(e) $F(\pm 2\sqrt{5},0)$; $e = \frac{1}{3}\sqrt{5}$.

2. (a) $\dfrac{x^2}{108} + \dfrac{y^2}{144} = 1$.　(c) $\dfrac{x^2}{25} + \dfrac{y^2}{16} = 1$.

3. (a) $\dfrac{(x - 6)^2}{16} + \dfrac{(y + 4)^2}{12} = 1$.　(c) $\dfrac{(x - 4)^2}{16} + \dfrac{(y + 4)^2}{32} = 1$.

4. $\frac{1}{2}\sqrt{3}$ or 0.866; $\frac{3}{10}\sqrt{11}$ or 0.995.

8. $\dfrac{x^2}{16} + \dfrac{(y + 6)^2}{25} = 1$.　　　**9.** $\dfrac{(x - 3)^2}{36} + \dfrac{y^2}{27} = 1$.

10. $\dfrac{x^2}{12} + \dfrac{(y+4)^2}{16} = 1.$

11. $5x^2 + 9y^2 - 108x + 324 = 0.$

12. 5.9, 5.5, 4.8, 3.6, 2.6.

13. $\dfrac{x^2}{256} + \dfrac{y^2}{64} = 1.$

14. 94.5 and 91.3 million miles.

15. $\dfrac{(x-3)^2}{4} + \dfrac{(y+1)^2}{9} = 1.$

16. $\dfrac{(x+3)^2}{9} + \dfrac{(y-2)^2}{4} = 1.$

17. $\dfrac{x^2}{16} + \dfrac{(y-4)^2}{4} = 1.$

18. $\dfrac{(x-2)^2}{4} + \dfrac{y^2}{16} = 1.$

19. $(x + \tfrac{3}{2})^2 + (y-2)^2 = \tfrac{25}{4}.$

20. $\dfrac{(x+2)^2}{\frac{17}{2}} + \dfrac{(y+\frac{3}{2})^2}{\frac{17}{4}} = 1.$

21. $\dfrac{(x-2)^2}{3} + \dfrac{(y-3)^2}{2} = 1.$

22. $9(x+2)^2 + 4(y+3)^2 = 0.$

23. $(3,2.4); (-4,-1.8).$ **24.** $(8,2.4); (5,-3).$ **25.** $(-1,\sqrt{3}); (-1,-\sqrt{3}).$

Pages 130–132

1. (a) $V(\pm 10,0); F(\pm 5\sqrt{5},0).$ (c) $V(\pm 3,0); F(\pm 5,0).$ (e) $V(\pm 6,0); F(\pm 3\sqrt{5},0).$

2. $\sqrt{2}.$ **4.** $xy = -2.$

7. (a) $\dfrac{x^2}{36} - \dfrac{y^2}{28} = 1.$ (c) $\dfrac{y^2}{16} - \dfrac{x^2}{20} = 1.$

8. (a) $\dfrac{(y-2)^2}{9} - \dfrac{(x-4)^2}{16} = 1.$ (c) $\dfrac{(y+2)^2}{9} - \dfrac{(x+1)^2}{27} = 1.$

9. $\dfrac{(x-5)^2}{9} - \dfrac{y^2}{16} = 1.$ **14.** (a) $\dfrac{(x-1)^2}{1} - \dfrac{(y+2)^2}{4} = 1.$

(c) $\dfrac{(x+3)^2}{4} - \dfrac{(y+1)^2}{12} = 1.$ (e) $4(x-1)^2 - 3(y-2)^2 = 0.$

(g) $4(x-4)^2 - 9(y-3)^2 = 0.$

Pages 137–138

1. (a) Circle. (c) Hyperbola. (e) Ellipse.

3. (a) Ellipse; $\sin\theta = \dfrac{2}{\sqrt{5}}; \cos\theta = \dfrac{1}{\sqrt{5}}.$ (c) Hyperbola; $\sin\theta = \tfrac{3}{5}; \cos\theta = \tfrac{4}{5}.$

(e) Hyperbola; $\sin\theta = \dfrac{1}{\sqrt{17}}; \cos\theta = \dfrac{4}{\sqrt{17}}.$

4. (a) $4x'^2 - y'^2 = 4.$ (c) $y'^2 = 6x'.$ (e) $x'^2 - 4y'^2 = 16.$ (g) $9x'^2 + y'^2 = 25.$

7. (a) Two intersecting lines. (c) Two intersecting lines. (e) Two intersecting lines.

8. $\dfrac{(x-8)^2}{36} + \dfrac{y^2}{27} = 1.$ **9.** $\dfrac{(x-4)^2}{4} + \dfrac{y^2}{3} = 1.$

10. $\dfrac{(y+4)^2}{36} - \dfrac{x^2}{45} = 1.$ **11.** $\dfrac{(y+2)^2}{16} - \dfrac{x^2}{48} = 1.$

14. $\left(\dfrac{1}{4}, \pm \dfrac{1}{\sqrt{2}}\right).$ **15.** $9y^2 - 7x^2 - 72x + 144 = 0.$

CHAPTER 10

Pages 154–156

5. 3.827; 10; 3.827; -7.071; 0.   **6.** -2.5; 2.5; 3.536; 4.330; 4.330.

7. 0; 1.308; 2.473; 3.464; 3.888; 3.637; 3.464; 4, when $t = \frac{3}{4}\pi$.

8. 9; -1; $t = 0$; $t = 3$.   **9.** 9.5; 4.5; $x = \frac{3}{4}\pi$; $x = \frac{1}{4}\pi$.

10. 0.473; 3.700.   **22.** 120π.   **25.** 12 sec.   **27.** 4; 12.

Pages 161–162

23. $\pm \sqrt{13}$; 8 sec.   **24.** 9, -1; 20 sec.

35. $(0,0)$, $(\frac{1}{3}\pi, \frac{1}{2}\sqrt{3})$, $(\pi, 0)$, $(\frac{5}{3}\pi, -\frac{1}{2}\sqrt{3})$.

36. $(\frac{1}{6}\pi, \frac{1}{2}\sqrt{3})$, $(\frac{1}{2}\pi, 0)$, $(\frac{5}{6}\pi, -\frac{1}{2}\sqrt{3})$, $(\frac{3}{2}\pi, 0)$.

37. $(0,0)$, $(\frac{2}{3}\pi, \sqrt{3})$, $(\frac{10}{3}\pi, -\sqrt{3})$, $(4\pi, 0)$.   **38.** $(\frac{1}{12}\pi, \sqrt{3})$, $(\frac{1}{4}\pi, 0)$, $(\frac{5}{12}\pi, -\sqrt{3})$.

39. $(\frac{2}{3}, \frac{1}{2}\sqrt{3})$, $(2,0)$, $(\frac{10}{3}, -\frac{1}{2}\sqrt{3})$, $(6,0)$.

Pages 166–167

1. $\frac{3}{5}$.   **2.** $\dfrac{3}{\sqrt{91}}$.   **3.** $\frac{1}{2}\sqrt{3}$.   **4.** $\frac{1}{2}\sqrt{2}$.   **5.** $\frac{5}{4}$.

6. $\frac{3}{2}$.   **7.** $\frac{12}{13}$.   **8.** 5.   **9.** 0.   **10.** 1.

11. $\frac{14}{7}$.   **12.** $\frac{2}{3}$.   **13.** $2\sqrt{5}$.   **14.** 2.25.   **15.** $-\frac{13}{40}$.

16. $\frac{24}{7}$.   **17.** $\frac{4}{5}$.   **18.** $\frac{1}{9}$.   **19.** $\frac{20}{21}$.   **20.** $\frac{1}{3}$.

21. $\frac{1}{2}\sqrt{2 - \sqrt{3}}$.   **22.** $\dfrac{2}{\sqrt{2} + 1}$.   **23.** $2\sqrt{3}$.   **24.** $\frac{4}{5}$.

25. $\frac{1}{3}$.   **26.** $-\frac{56}{65}$.   **27.** $-\frac{3}{5}$.   **28.** $-\frac{4}{5}$.   **29.** $\dfrac{3}{\sqrt{130}}$.

32. $\frac{1}{2}$.   **33.** $\frac{1}{6}$.   **34.** $\frac{3}{4}$.   **35.** $\frac{2}{5}$.

36. $\theta = 2 \arctan \dfrac{4}{3 + 0.2t}$.   **37.** $\theta = \arctan \dfrac{5}{x} - \arctan \dfrac{3}{x}$.

CHAPTER 11

Pages 175–176

3. $\frac{3}{4}$.   **4.** $\frac{3}{8}$.   **5.** $4\frac{1}{2}$.   **6.** $\frac{64}{27}$.   **33.** $e^{4.27x}$.

34. $e^{-0.268x}$.   **35.** $e^{2.75x}$.   **36.** $\log_e 10$.   **37.** $\$944.90$.   **38.** $\$546.60$.

39. (a) 3.9627; (c) 6.5837; (e) $7.4229 - 10$.   **40.** (a) 11.32; (c) 0.02385.

Pages 180–181

35. $x = \log_e (y + \sqrt{y^2 + 1})$.   **36.** $x = \log_e (y + \sqrt{y^2 - 1})$.

37. $x = \dfrac{1}{2} \log_e \dfrac{1 + y}{1 - y}$.

CHAPTER 12

Pages 187–188

1. $y = 4x - x^2$.   **2.** $2y = x^2 + 6x$.   **3.** $4y = x^3 - 4x^2$.

4. $y = 1 - x^2$.   **5.** $y = (x - 2)^2$.   **6.** $4y = 3x^2 - 12x + 4$.

7. $x^4 + y^4 = 256.$ **8.** $y = \dfrac{4x}{x^2 + 4}.$ **9.** $y^2 = \dfrac{6x^2}{x^4 + 1}.$

10. $y = \dfrac{64}{x^2 + 16}.$ **22.** 99 ft.   **23.** 113 ft./sec.

24. $x = 248$ ft., $y = -59.5$ ft.

Pages 191–193

3. $(x - 1)^2 + (y - 2)^2 = 1.$ **4.** $(x - 3)^2 + (y - 4)^2 = 25.$

5. $x^2 + (y - 2)^2 = 4.$ **6.** $(x - 3)^2 + y^2 = 9.$

7. $\dfrac{(x + 2)^2}{9} + \dfrac{(y - 2)^2}{25} = 1.$ **8.** $\dfrac{(x - 8)^2}{16} + \dfrac{y^2}{4} = 1.$

9. $\dfrac{x^2}{9} + (y - 1)^2 = 1.$ **10.** $\dfrac{(x - 6)^2}{36} + \dfrac{y^2}{9} = 1.$

11. $\dfrac{(x - 1)^2}{4} + (y + 2)^2 = 1.$ **12.** $\dfrac{(x - 5)^2}{25} + \dfrac{(y - 2)^2}{4} = 1.$

15. $x = a(\theta - \pi - \sin \theta);\ y = -a(1 + \cos \theta)$ or
$x = a(\theta' + \sin \theta');\ y = -a(1 - \cos \theta').\quad \theta = \theta' + \pi.$

CHAPTER 13

Pages 199–200

1. $A(0,2);\ B(-5,0);\ C(-3,3).$ **2.** $A(-3,0);\ B(-2\sqrt{2},2\sqrt{2});\ C(0,-2).$

3. $A(0,5);\ B(4,0);\ C(-2,-2).$ **4.** $A(-4,0);\ B(2,0);\ C(-3\sqrt{3},3).$

5. $A(-2,-2\sqrt{3});\ B(0,6);\ C(-5,5).$ **6.** $A(-3,0);\ B(-2,2\sqrt{3});\ C(\frac{5}{2},-\frac{5}{2}\sqrt{3})$

Pages 207–208

1. $x + y = 3.$ **2.** $2x + 3y = 8.$ **3.** $2x - 3y = 12.$

4. $y - 2x = 5.$ **5.** $x + 4 = 0.$ **6.** $y + 2 = 0.$

7. $x - 3y = 6.$ **8.** $4x + 5y + 20 = 0.$ **9.** $x^2 + y^2 = 4x.$

10. $x^2 + y^2 = 5y.$ **11.** $x^2 + y^2 + 3y = 0.$ **12.** $x^2 + y^2 + 2x = 0.$

13. $x^2 + y^2 - 6x + 4y = 48.$ **14.** $x^2 + y^2 - 8x - 6y = 0.$

15. $x^2 + y^2 + 2x - 3y = 0$ **16.** $x^2 + y^2 - 8x + 4y + 11 = 0.$

17. $x^2 + y^2 - 6y - 16 = 0.$ **18.** $x^2 + y^2 - 4y - 12 = 0.$

19. $x^2 + y^2 = \dfrac{5}{\sqrt{2}}(x + y).$ **20.** $x^2 + y^2 + 1.4(\sqrt{3}y + x) = 0.$

21. $4x^2 + 3y^2 + 16y = 64.$ **22.** $5x^2 + 9y^2 + 48x = 144.$

23. $7x^2 + 16y^2 + 72x = 144.$ **24.** $4x^2 + 3y^2 - 12y = 36.$

25. $16x^2 - 9y^2 + 150y = 225.$ **26.** $7x^2 + 16y^2 + 42x = 49.$

27. $12x^2 + 16y^2 + 36x = 81.$ **28.** $36x^2 + 20y^2 - 72y = 81.$

29. $x^2 = -8(y - 2).$ **30.** $4y^2 = 49 - 28x.$ **31.** $9y^2 = 64 - 48x.$

32. $4x^2 = 81 + 36y.$ **33.** $9x^2 = 64 - 48y.$ **34.** $4y^2 = 81 - 36x.$

35. $5x^2 - 4y^2 + 36x + 36 = 0.$ **36.** $16x^2 + 7y^2 + 48y = 64.$

37. $9x^2 - 16y^2 - 240x + 576 = 0$ **38.** $9x^2 - 27y^2 + 192y - 256 = 0.$

39. $x^2 - 3y^2 - 52y - 169 = 0.$ **40.** $5x^2 - 4y^2 + 48x + 64 = 0.$

41. $y^2 = 6x.$ **42.** $y(y - 4) = 0.$

43. $9x^2 + 16y^2 = 144.$ **44.** $4x^2 - 9y^2 = 36.$

Pages 214–215

32. $(\frac{12}{5},\arctan \frac{3}{4})$; origin.   **33.** $(6,\frac{1}{6}\pi);\ (6,\frac{5}{6}\pi).$ **34.** $(2\sqrt{2},\frac{1}{4}\pi);\ (2\sqrt{2},\frac{3}{4}\pi).$

35. $(3,\frac{1}{3}\pi)$; $(3,\frac{5}{3}\pi)$; origin.

36. Assuming $\rho \geqq 0$: $(2,\frac{1}{2}\pi)$; origin. **37.** Assuming $\rho \geqq 0$: $(\frac{1}{2}\sqrt{3},\frac{1}{3}\pi)$; origin.

38. Assuming $\rho \geqq 0$: $(1,0)$; $(1,\pi)$: $(\frac{1}{2},\frac{7}{6}\pi)$; $(\frac{1}{2},\frac{11}{6}\pi)$; origin.

39. $(\frac{3}{2},\frac{1}{3}\pi)$; $(\frac{3}{2},\frac{5}{3}\pi)$; origin. **40.** $\left(\frac{2}{\sqrt{5}}, \arctan 2\right)$; origin.

43. $2\rho \sin^3 \theta = (1 - 3 \sin \theta)(1 + 3 \sin \theta)$. **44.** $\rho \cos^4 \theta = \sin^2 \theta(3 \cos \theta - 2 \sin \theta)$.

CHAPTER 14

Pages 221–223

1. $y = 0.431x + 5.49$. **3.** $y = 0.584x - 1.88$.

5. $L = 0.2800P + 10.12$; 16.28 lb. **7.** $y = 0.185x^2 + 0.460x - 5.64$.

Pages 228–230

1. $y = 0.522x^{1.4833}$. **3.** $y = 25.63x^{-1.4396}$.

5. $y = (40.67)10^{-0.1952x} = (40.67)e^{-0.4495x}$. **7.** $t = 0.2532s^{0.5178}$.

9. $R = 0.07495V^{2.011}$. **11.** $P = 365.5v^{-1.401}$.

Pages 233–234

1. $y = 1.303x - 4.161$. **3.** $y = 0.5895x + 2.3286$. **5.** $y = 2.483x^{1.6513}$.

7. $y = (2.605)10^{0.1806}$.

CHAPTER 15

Pages 242–244

1. (a) $\cos \alpha = \cos \beta = \frac{1}{6}\sqrt{6}$; $\cos \gamma = \frac{1}{3}\sqrt{6}$. (c) $\cos \alpha = \frac{2}{13}\sqrt{26}$;

$\cos \beta = -\frac{3}{26}\sqrt{26}$; $\cos \gamma = \frac{1}{26}\sqrt{26}$. (e) $\cos \alpha = \frac{-3}{7}$; $\cos \beta = \frac{2}{7}$; $\cos \gamma = \frac{-6}{7}$.

2. $\pm\frac{2}{3}$. **3.** $\frac{1}{3}\sqrt{3}$.

5. (a) $(-x,-y,-z)$; (c) $(x,-y,-z)$. **6.** (a) 9; (c) 12.

7. (a) $\sqrt{41}$, $\sqrt{50}$, $\sqrt{141}$. **10.** $(4,4,\frac{7}{3})$; $(6,1,\frac{11}{3})$.

11. $x^2 + y^2 + z^2 = 25$. **12.** $(x - 3)^2 + (y - 2)^2 + (z - 5)^2 = 25$.

13. $y^2 + z^2 - 8x + 16 = 0$. **14.** $12x - 8y + 10z = 71$.

15. $9x^2 + 25y^2 + 25z^2 = 225$. **16.** $(-\frac{3}{2},0,0)$.

17. (a) $F_x = F_y = 66\frac{2}{3}$ lb.; $F_z = 33\frac{1}{3}$ lb. (c) $F_x = 36$ lb.; $F_y = 0$; $F_z = -48$ lb.

18. $F_x = -3$ lb.; $F_y = -2$ lb.; $F_z = 51$ lb. $F = \sqrt{9 + 4 + 2{,}601} = \sqrt{2{,}614}$.

$\cos \alpha = \frac{-3}{\sqrt{2{,}614}}$; $\cos \beta = \frac{-2}{\sqrt{2{,}614}}$; $\cos \gamma = \frac{51}{\sqrt{2{,}614}}$.

19. $F_x = 20$ lb.; $F_y = 36$ lb.; $F_z = 8$ lb. **20.** $F_x = 24$ lb.; $F_y = 31$ lb.; $F_z = -14$ lb.

Pages 250–252

1. (a) $4:5:3$; $\cos \alpha = \frac{4}{\sqrt{50}}$; $\cos \beta = \frac{5}{\sqrt{50}}$; $\cos \gamma = \frac{3}{\sqrt{50}}$.

(c) $0:4:3$; $\cos \alpha = 0$; $\cos \beta = \frac{4}{5}$; $\cos \gamma = \frac{3}{5}$.

(e) $2:-2:1$; $\cos \alpha = \frac{2}{3}$; $\cos \beta = -\frac{2}{3}$; $\cos \gamma = \frac{1}{3}$.

3. 1, 0, 0; 0, 1, 0; 0, 0, 1. **4.** $\frac{1}{\sqrt{2}}$, $\frac{1}{2}$, $\frac{1}{2}$. **5.** $(0,2,3)$; $(2,0,4)$.

6. $(13,8,0)$; $(1,0,4)$. **7.** $(2,5,0)$; $(-3,0,-5)$; $(0,3,-2)$.

8. (a) $\pm\frac{4}{21}$.   (c) ± 0.1.   **9.** (a) $\frac{5}{14}\sqrt{7}$.   (c) $\frac{1}{2}\sqrt{2}$.

10. $\cos\theta = \pm\frac{1}{3}\sqrt{3}$.   **12.** 26.6 lb.   **13.** 34.6 lb.

15. $-2:1:2$.   **16.** (a) $3:2:3$, (c) $5:8:5$.   **17.** $5:7:5$.

CHAPTER 16

Pages 258–259

1. (a) $x + \sqrt{2}\,y + z = 8$; (c) $y - \sqrt{3}\,z + 12 = 0$.

2. (a) $x + 2y + z = 12$; (c) $4x + 3y + 25 = 0$; (e) $x + y - z = 6$.

3. (a) $-\frac{2}{7}x - \frac{3}{7}y - \frac{6}{7}z = 3$.   (c) $\frac{8}{9}x + \frac{4}{9}y - \frac{1}{9}z = 3$.

5. (a) $3x + 2y + z = 10$; (c) $x - 2y + z = 0$.

6. $2x - y + z = 4$.   **7.** $3x + 2y + z = 22$.   **8.** $5x + y + 3z = 15$.

9. $(0,\frac{14}{5},0)$.   **10.** $(4,3,1)$; $r = 9$.   **12.** (a) 3; (c) $\dfrac{14\sqrt{2}}{5}$

14. $y + z = 5$.   **15.** $11x - 6y + 5z + 4 = 0$.

Pages 263–264

1. (a) $x + y + 2z = 12$.   (c) $2x + 3y - 2z = 12$.

2. $x - 6y + 3z = 18$.   **3.** $2x - 5y + 3z = 20$.   **4.** $3x - y + 7z = 14$.

5. $6x - 7y - 4z + 24 = 0$.   **6.** (a) $45°$; (c) $44°19'$.   **7.** $49°2'$.

8. $85°36'$.   **9.** $55°33'$.   **10.** $3x + y - 2z + 20 = 0$.

11. $k = 2$.   **12.** (a) $38°57$; (c) 0.   **13.** $(0,0,12)$.

Pages 269–271

2. (a) $(4,6,0)$, $(1,0,4)$; (c) $(1,5\frac{1}{2},0)$, $(7,0,-3\frac{1}{2})$.

3. $\frac{6}{7}, \frac{2}{7}, \frac{3}{7}$.

4. (a) $\dfrac{x-2}{4} = \dfrac{y-1}{3} = \dfrac{z-6}{-2}$; $3x - 4y = 2$, $x + 2z = 14$.

     (c) $\dfrac{x+2}{3} = \dfrac{y+5}{2} = \dfrac{z+2}{2}$; $2x - 3y = 11$, $2x - 3z = 2$.

5. (a) $x - 8 = y - 10 = \frac{1}{2}(z - 8)$.   **6.** $19°28'$.

8. $(0,0,\frac{16}{5})$.   **9.** $19°28'$ or $160°32'$.   **10.** $(1\frac{1}{2},2,1)$.

11. $4x + 3y - 11 = 0$, $x - 3z + 16 = 0$.   **12.** $(5,5,2)$.

13. 3.86.   **14.** 6.79.   **15.** 53.9 lb.

16. $4x - y + 2z + 20 = 0$.   **17.** $3x - 2y - 3z = 0$.   **18.** $6x - 8y + z = 0$.

19. $3x - 7y + 2z = 5$.   **20.** $x + 2y + z + 5 = 0$.

CHAPTER 17

Pages 275–276

1. (c) $x^2 + (y-3)^2 + (z-4)^2 = 29$.   **3.** $6x + 2y + 3z = 61$.

4. $7x - 4y + 4z = 65$; $4x + 7y = 28$, $4x - 7z = 0$.

6. $x^2 + y^2 = 4z$.   **7.** $x^2 + y^2 + z^2 = a^2$.   **9.** $4x^2 + 4z^2 - y^2 = 0$.

11. $9x^2 + 9y^2 + 25z^2 = 225$.   **13.** $x^2 + y^2 + \log_e z = 0$.

Page 284

13. $r^2 = 6$, $\rho^2 \sin^2\phi = 6$.   **15.** $r^2 \sin 2\theta = 4$, $\rho^2 \sin^2\phi \sin 2\theta = 4$.

17. $r^2 + z^2 = 16$; $\rho = 4$.

19. $r^2 \cos 2\theta - 2z^2 = 4$; $\rho^2(\sin^2\phi \cos 2\theta - 2\cos^2\phi) = 4$.

INDEX

307

901

Cн.

4.00